HELLO

You've probably picked this thing up, read the blurb on t
times, put it back down again etc. etc. ... so now it's tim ... rea!

But first, a few housekeeping rules about how to use this guide:

 Make sure you have the correct equipment. You will need the usual maths stuff and we also recommend you use a notebook/paper alongside this workbook to make notes and for more working out if needed.

 Remind yourself of the key skills on the pages titled 'Key Skills' ... clever title for these pages huh? Make sure you identify any that you need to revise. Don't just ignore them ... do something about it!

 Look through the command word glossary on the 'Command Word' page. These words are the key words that can appear in a question and will instruct you on how to tackle the problem.

 Work through the 'Ready' section of a double page, making notes if needed. Then have a go at the 'Set' and 'Go' questions (no cheating with the answers at the back ... they're for when you've finished).

 Return to the same double page a couple of days later and check you still remember the content. Then and only then are you allowed to tick the checklist and rip off the corner of the page*.

* if it's not your workbook ... check with the owner!

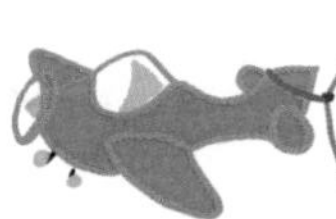

Also included ... a set of cut-out flashcards to help you remember the stuff you need to know (you can always make more)

On each double-page there are three sections for you to work through:

Read the key information and work carefully through the examples. Sometimes highlighting is used to give extra guidance and look out for the maths police who point out common misconceptions!

SET? Dive right in and have a go at these questions. They are closely linked to the worked examples (no curveballs yet). Check your answers.

Here we go ... some more questions, but this time exam-style (curveballs included). Again, don't forget to check your answers.

You CAN do this ... now let's get started!

You're almost ready to get started ... but first you must decide where you will work:

In bed under a duvet	
On a sofa in front of the TV	
At a well-lit desk with a proper chair	

Turn to page ...		READY?	SET?	GO!
Two-Way Tables	10	✓		
Frequency Trees	12	✓		
Rounding	14	✓		
Error Intervals	16	✓		
Estimation	18	✓		
Use of Calculator	20	✓		
Product of Prime Factors	22	✓		
HCF & LCM	24	✓		
Real Life Multiples	26	✓		
Fractions 1	28	✓		
Fractions 2	30	✓		
Ratio 1	32	✓		
Ratio 2	34	✓		
Direct Proportion	36			
Proportion: Best Value	38			
Proportion: Recipes	40	✓		
Proportion: Exchange Rates	42			
Inverse Proportion	44			
Percentages 1	46	✓		
Percentages 2	48	✓		

Turn to page ...		READY?	SET?	GO!
Interest and Growth	50			
Depreciation and Decay	52			
Reverse Percentages	54			
Index Laws	56	✓		
Expand and Simplify	58	✓		
Sequences	60	✓		
Solving Equations	62	✓		
Forming and Solving	64	✓		
Inequalities	66			
Factorising 1	68	✓		
Factorising 2	70	✓		
Changing the Subject	72	✓		
Standard Form 1	74	✓		
Standard Form 2	76	✓		
Alternate/Corresponding Angles	78			
Interior and Exterior Angles	80			
Plans and Elevations	82			
Constructions	84			
Bearings	86			
Pythagoras' Theorem 1	88	✓		

Make the learning visible ...

... and tick the checklist above when you've nailed each section.

Check ... is it still nailed a few days later?

Ace!

Now ... tear off the corner thingy

And now for a couple of non-sticky notes about this book:

1) Try to do as much as possible without a calculator ... unless it's clear you need to use one.
2) Diagrams are only drawn to scale when it says so.
3) Some questions refer to students' workings, shown in blue font.

Checklist & Contents

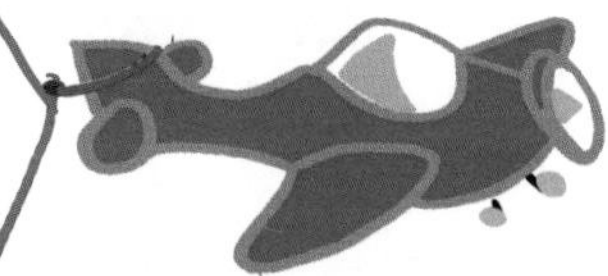

Always check your answers ... page 172 onwards

Know the formulae you need to remember (cut out the flashcards)

Seriously ... who has this many different colour sticky notes?!

Make sure you have all the correct equipment

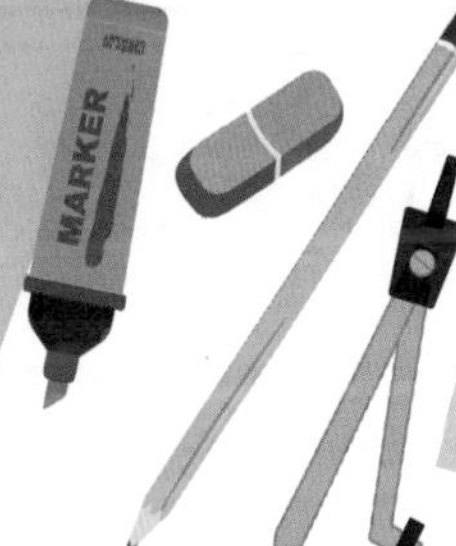

This is tracing paper!

MULDOWNEY justaroo.co.uk

Turn to page ...		READY?	SET?	GO!
Pythagoras' Theorem 2	90	✓		
Trigonometry 1	92	✓		
Trigonometry 2	94	✓		
Trigonometry 3	96	✓		
Pythagoras with Trigonometry	98			
Circles 1	100			
Circles 2	102			
Arcs and Sectors	104			
Surface Area and Volume 1	106			
Surface Area and Volume 2	108			
Sampling	110			
Averages	112			
Averages from a Table	114			
Averages from Grouped Data	116			
Frequency Diagrams	118			
Scatter Graphs	120			
Time Series	122			
Pie Charts	124			
Coordinates	126			
Straight Line Graphs 1	128			

Turn to page ...		READY?	SET?	GO!
Straight Line Graphs 2	130			
Straight Line Graphs 3	132			
Non-Linear Graphs	134			
Speed, Distance, Time	136			
Compound Measures	138			
Real Life Graphs	140			
Congruence	142			
Similar Shapes	144			
Reflections	146			
Rotations	148			
Translations	150			
Enlargements	152			
Combined Transformations	154			
Vectors	156			
Probability	158			
Probability Tree Diagrams 1	160			
Probability Tree Diagrams 2	162			
Venn Diagrams	164			
Simultaneous Equations 1	166			
Simultaneous Equations 2	168			

It's no good just owning a revision workbook ...

use it!

Number line

GETTING LARGER

-9	-8	-7	-6	-5	-4	-3	-2	-1	0	1	2	3	4	5	6	7	8	9

Need to revise ☐ Nailed it! ☐

Number properties

Factors divide into another number without a remainder, e.g. factors of 12 are 1, 2, 3, 4, 6 and 12

Multiples: The result of multiplying a number by an integer, e.g. multiples of 6 are 6, 12, 18, 24, ...

Prime numbers: A number with exactly two factors 2, 3, 5, 7, 11, 13, 17, 19, etc.

Integer: A positive or negative whole number or zero, e.g. -3, 0 or 5

Even: Numbers that can be divided exactly by 2 e.g. multiples of 2 are 2, 4, 6, 8, etc.

Square number: The result of multiplying a whole number by itself e.g. 3 × 3 = 9

Cube number: The result of multiplying a whole number by itself, then by itself again e.g. 4 × 4 × 4 = 64

Need to revise ☐ Nailed it! ☐

Useful FDP conversions

1 = 1	100%
0.5 = $\frac{1}{2}$	50%
0.33... = $\frac{1}{3}$	33.3...%
0.25 = $\frac{1}{4}$	25%
0.2 = $\frac{1}{5}$	20%
0.1 = $\frac{1}{10}$	10%

1% = $\frac{1}{100}$ = 0.01

3% = $\frac{3}{100}$ = 0.03

30% = $\frac{3}{10}$ = 0.3

Need to revise ☐ Nailed it! ☐

Place value

Ten millions	Millions	Hundred thousands	Ten thousands	Thousands	Hundreds	Tens	Ones	.	Tenths	Hundredths	Thousandths

The number 1,023,456 is one million, twenty three thousand, four hundred and fifty six

Need to revise ☐ Nailed it! ☐

Times tables

If you know your 1×, 2×, 5× and 10× facts and remember that multiplication works both ways e.g. 7 × 6 = 6 × 7 then the colour shows the rest we need to learn...

1 × 3 = 3	1 × 4 = 4	1 × 6 = 6	1 × 7 = 7	1 × 8 = 8	1 × 9 = 9	1 × 11 = 11	1 × 12 = 12
2 × 3 = 6	2 × 4 = 8	2 × 6 = 12	2 × 7 = 14	2 × 8 = 16	2 × 9 = 18	2 × 11 = 22	2 × 12 = 24
3 × 3 = 9	3 × 4 = 12	3 × 6 = 18	3 × 7 = 21	3 × 8 = 24	3 × 9 = 27	3 × 11 = 33	3 × 12 = 36
4 × 3 = 12	4 × 4 = 16	4 × 6 = 24	4 × 7 = 28	4 × 8 = 32	4 × 9 = 36	4 × 11 = 44	4 × 12 = 48
5 × 3 = 15	5 × 4 = 20	5 × 6 = 30	5 × 7 = 35	5 × 8 = 40	5 × 9 = 45	5 × 11 = 55	5 × 12 = 60
6 × 3 = 18	6 × 4 = 24	6 × 6 = 36	6 × 7 = 42	6 × 8 = 48	6 × 9 = 54	6 × 11 = 66	6 × 12 = 72
7 × 3 = 21	7 × 4 = 28	7 × 6 = 42	7 × 7 = 49	7 × 8 = 56	7 × 9 = 63	7 × 11 = 77	7 × 12 = 84
8 × 3 = 24	8 × 4 = 32	8 × 6 = 48	8 × 7 = 56	8 × 8 = 64	8 × 9 = 72	8 × 11 = 88	8 × 12 = 96
9 × 3 = 27	9 × 4 = 36	9 × 6 = 54	9 × 7 = 63	9 × 8 = 72	9 × 9 = 81	9 × 11 = 99	9 × 12 = 108
10 × 3 = 30	10 × 4 = 40	10 × 6 = 60	10 × 7 = 70	10 × 8 = 80	10 × 9 = 90	10 × 11 = 110	10 × 12 = 120
11 × 3 = 33	11 × 4 = 44	11 × 6 = 66	11 × 7 = 77	11 × 8 = 88	11 × 9 = 99	11 × 11 = 121	11 × 12 = 132
12 × 3 = 36	12 × 4 = 48	12 × 6 = 72	12 × 7 = 84	12 × 8 = 96	12 × 9 = 108	12 × 11 = 132	12 × 12 = 144

Need to revise ☐ Nailed it! ☐

Time

Twenty five past one or 1:25 a.m. or 01:25 or 1:25 p.m. or 13:25

Need to revise ☐ Nailed it! ☐

1 year = 365 days

1 week = 7 days

1 day = 24 hours

1 hour = 60 minutes

1 minute = 60 seconds

A leap year has 366 days

January - 31 days
February - 28 or 29 days
March - 31 days
April - 30 days
May - 31 days
June - 30 days

July - 31 days
August - 31 days
September - 30 days
October - 31 days
November - 30 days
December - 31 days

Metric units

Need to revise ☐ Nailed it! ☐

10 mm = 1 cm

100 cm = 1 m

1000 m = 1 km

1000 ml = 1 litre

1000 cm³ = 1 litre

1000 g = 1 kg

Fraction of an amount

Finding $\frac{1}{3}$ of 24

$\frac{1}{3}$ = 1 of 3 equal parts

24

8	8	8

The whole is 24

24 ÷ 3 = 8

Finding $\frac{3}{5}$ of 30

6	6	6		

The value of one part = 30 ÷ 5 = 6

30

$\frac{1}{5}$ of 30 = 6 so $\frac{3}{5}$ of 30 = 3 × 6 = 18

Need to revise ☐ Nailed it! ☐

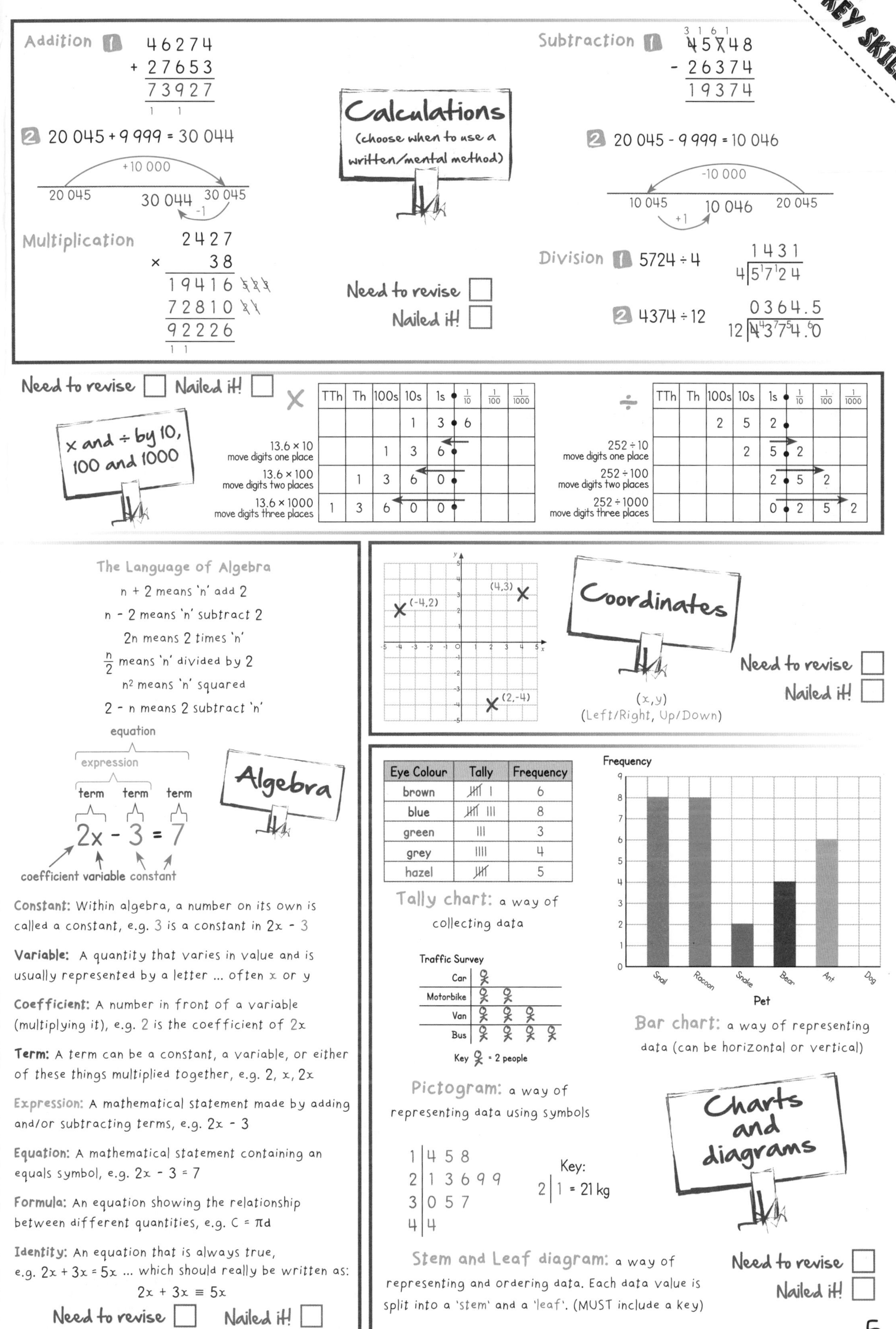

Calculations
(choose when to use a written/mental method)

Addition

1.

```
  46274
+ 27653
  73927
  1  1
```

2. 20 045 + 9 999 = 30 044

(Number line: 20 045 → +10 000 → 30 045, −1 → 30 044)

Subtraction

1.

```
  3 1 6 1
  45X48
- 26374
  19374
```

2. 20 045 − 9 999 = 10 046

(Number line: 20 045 → −10 000 → 10 045, +1 → 10 046)

Multiplication

```
   2427
 ×   38
  19416
  72810
  92226
   1 1
```

Division

1. 5724 ÷ 4

```
   1 4 3 1
 4|5 ¹7 ¹2 4
```

2. 4374 ÷ 12

```
    0 3 6 4 . 5
 12|4 ⁴3 ⁷7 ⁵4 . ⁶0
```

Need to revise ☐ Nailed it! ☐

x and ÷ by 10, 100 and 1000

Need to revise ☐ Nailed it! ☐

×

	TTh	Th	100s	10s	1s	$\frac{1}{10}$	$\frac{1}{100}$	$\frac{1}{1000}$
				1	3	6		
13.6 × 10 move digits one place			1	3	6			
13.6 × 100 move digits two places		1	3	6	0			
13.6 × 1000 move digits three places	1	3	6	0	0			

÷

	TTh	Th	100s	10s	1s	$\frac{1}{10}$	$\frac{1}{100}$	$\frac{1}{1000}$
			2	5	2			
252 ÷ 10 move digits one place				2	5	2		
252 ÷ 100 move digits two places					2	5	2	
252 ÷ 1000 move digits three places					0	2	5	2

Algebra

The Language of Algebra

n + 2 means 'n' add 2

n − 2 means 'n' subtract 2

2n means 2 times 'n'

$\frac{n}{2}$ means 'n' divided by 2

n^2 means 'n' squared

2 − n means 2 subtract 'n'

$2x - 3 = 7$ (equation; expression: $2x - 3$; terms: $2x$, 3, 7; coefficient, variable, constant)

Constant: Within algebra, a number on its own is called a constant, e.g. 3 is a constant in 2x − 3

Variable: A quantity that varies in value and is usually represented by a letter ... often x or y

Coefficient: A number in front of a variable (multiplying it), e.g. 2 is the coefficient of 2x

Term: A term can be a constant, a variable, or either of these things multiplied together, e.g. 2, x, 2x

Expression: A mathematical statement made by adding and/or subtracting terms, e.g. 2x − 3

Equation: A mathematical statement containing an equals symbol, e.g. 2x − 3 = 7

Formula: An equation showing the relationship between different quantities, e.g. $C = \pi d$

Identity: An equation that is always true, e.g. 2x + 3x = 5x ... which should really be written as:

$$2x + 3x \equiv 5x$$

Need to revise ☐ Nailed it! ☐

Coordinates

(x,y)
(Left/Right, Up/Down)

Need to revise ☐ Nailed it! ☐

Charts and diagrams

Eye Colour	Tally	Frequency
brown	𝍸 I	6
blue	𝍸 III	8
green	III	3
grey	IIII	4
hazel	𝍸	5

Tally chart: a way of collecting data

Pictogram: a way of representing data using symbols

Bar chart: a way of representing data (can be horizontal or vertical)

```
1 | 4 5 8
2 | 1 3 6 9 9
3 | 0 5 7
4 | 4
```

Key: 2 | 1 = 21 kg

Stem and Leaf diagram: a way of representing and ordering data. Each data value is split into a 'stem' and a 'leaf'. (MUST include a key)

Need to revise ☐ Nailed it! ☐

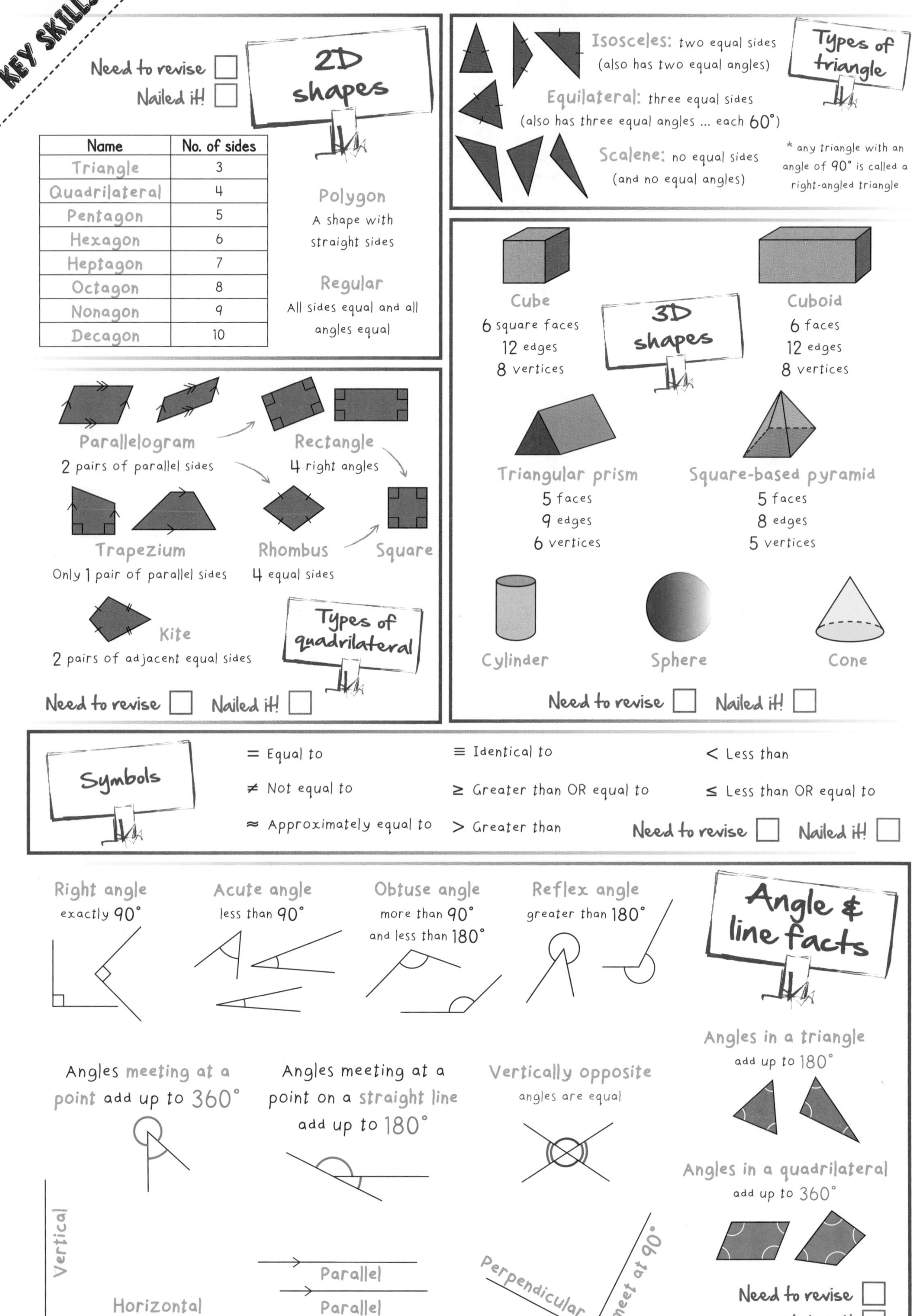

2D shapes

Need to revise ☐ Nailed it! ☐

Name	No. of sides
Triangle	3
Quadrilateral	4
Pentagon	5
Hexagon	6
Heptagon	7
Octagon	8
Nonagon	9
Decagon	10

Polygon
A shape with straight sides

Regular
All sides equal and all angles equal

Types of triangle

Isosceles: two equal sides (also has two equal angles)

Equilateral: three equal sides (also has three equal angles ... each 60°)

Scalene: no equal sides (and no equal angles)

* any triangle with an angle of 90° is called a right-angled triangle

Types of quadrilateral

Parallelogram
2 pairs of parallel sides

Rectangle
4 right angles

Trapezium
Only 1 pair of parallel sides

Rhombus
4 equal sides

Square

Kite
2 pairs of adjacent equal sides

Need to revise ☐ Nailed it! ☐

3D shapes

Cube
6 square faces
12 edges
8 vertices

Cuboid
6 faces
12 edges
8 vertices

Triangular prism
5 faces
9 edges
6 vertices

Square-based pyramid
5 faces
8 edges
5 vertices

Cylinder **Sphere** **Cone**

Need to revise ☐ Nailed it! ☐

Symbols

= Equal to
≠ Not equal to
≈ Approximately equal to
≡ Identical to
≥ Greater than OR equal to
> Greater than
< Less than
≤ Less than OR equal to

Need to revise ☐ Nailed it! ☐

Angle & line facts

Right angle
exactly 90°

Acute angle
less than 90°

Obtuse angle
more than 90° and less than 180°

Reflex angle
greater than 180°

Angles **meeting at a point** add up to 360°

Angles meeting at a point on a **straight line** add up to 180°

Vertically opposite angles are equal

Angles in a triangle add up to 180°

Angles in a quadrilateral add up to 360°

Vertical

Horizontal

Parallel

Parallel

Perpendicular

meet at 90°

Need to revise ☐ Nailed it! ☐

Flashcards to cut out

Prime number	Volume of a cuboid
Square number	Volume of a prism
Cube number	Volume of a cylinder
Percentage change	Pythagoras' theorem
Area of a rectangle	sin θ
Area of a triangle	cos θ
Area of a parallelogram	tan θ
Area of a trapezium	Exact values of sin θ
Area of a circle	Exact values of cos θ
Circumference of a circle	Exact values of tan θ
Speed	Metric conversions: length
Density	Metric conversions: mass
Pressure	Metric conversions: capacity

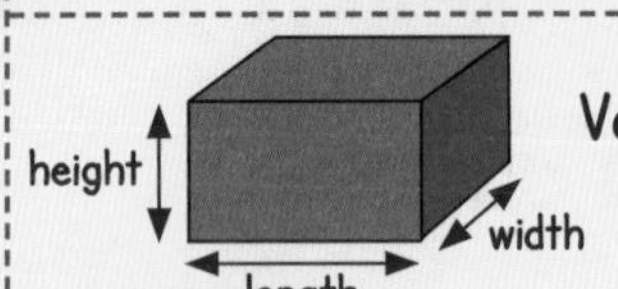

Volume = length × width × height

$V = lwh$

has exactly two factors

2, 3, 5, 7, 11, 13, 17, 19, 23, 29, ...

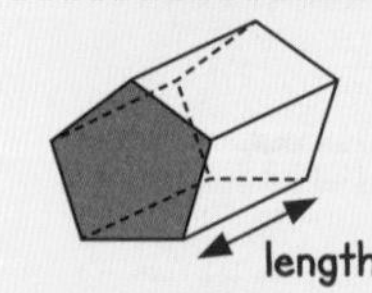
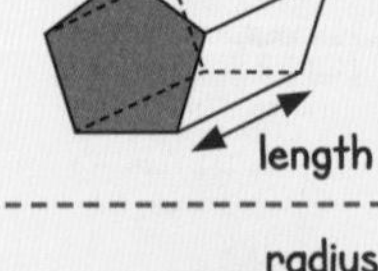

Volume = area of cross-section × length

the result of multiplying a whole number by itself

1, 4, 9, 16, 25, 36, 49, ...

1 × 1 2 × 2 3 × 3 4 × 4 5 × 5 6 × 6 7 × 7 ...

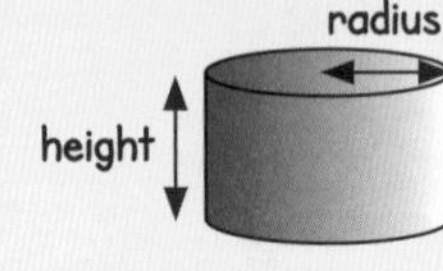

Volume = area of circular cross-section × height

$V = \pi r^2 h$

the result of multiplying a whole number by itself, then by itself again

1, 8, 27, 64, 125, ...

1 × 1 × 1 2 × 2 × 2 3 × 3 × 3 4 × 4 × 4 5 × 5 × 5 ...

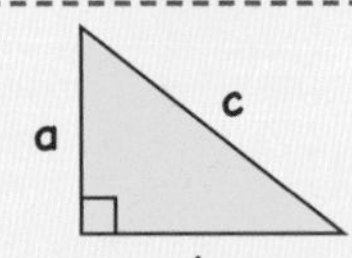

$a^2 + b^2 = c^2$

$$\frac{\text{actual change}}{\text{original amount}} \times 100\%$$

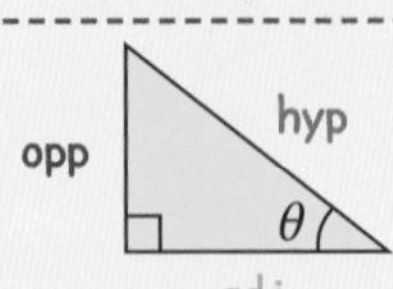

$$\sin\theta = \frac{\text{opposite}}{\text{hypotenuse}}$$

length
width

Area = length × width

$A = lw$

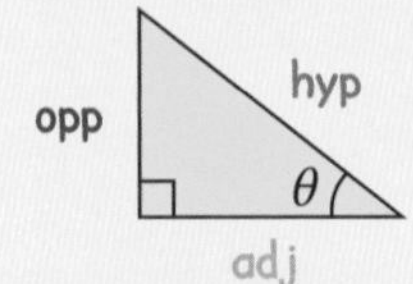

$$\cos\theta = \frac{\text{adjacent}}{\text{hypotenuse}}$$

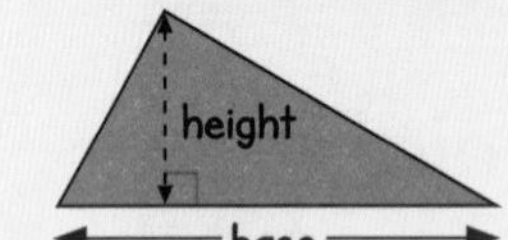

Area = base × height ÷ 2

$$A = \frac{bh}{2}$$

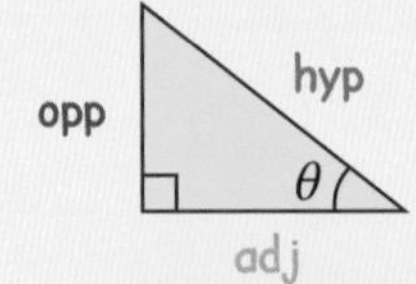

$$\tan\theta = \frac{\text{opposite}}{\text{adjacent}}$$

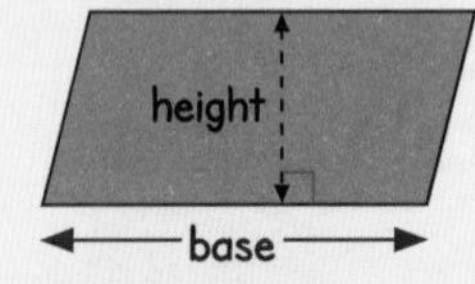

Area = base × height

$A = bh$

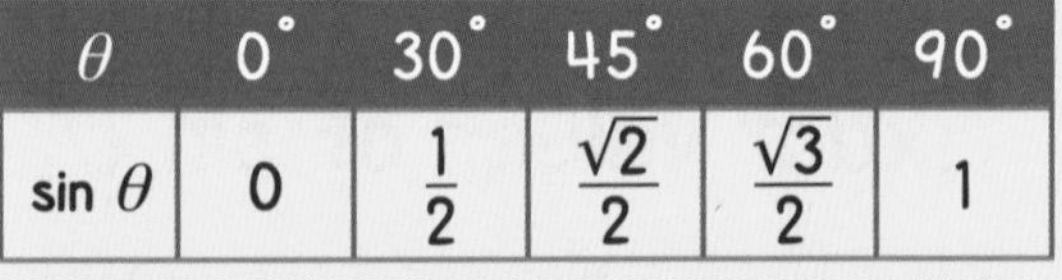

θ	0°	30°	45°	60°	90°
$\sin\theta$	0	$\frac{1}{2}$	$\frac{\sqrt{2}}{2}$	$\frac{\sqrt{3}}{2}$	1

a
height (h)
b

Area = half the sum of the parallel sides × height

$$A = \frac{a+b}{2} \times h$$

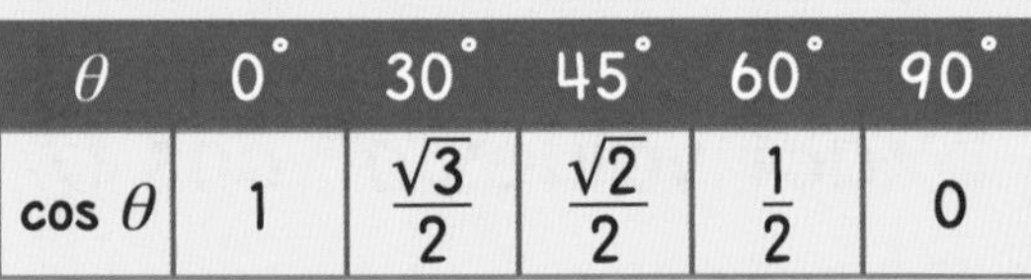

θ	0°	30°	45°	60°	90°
$\cos\theta$	1	$\frac{\sqrt{3}}{2}$	$\frac{\sqrt{2}}{2}$	$\frac{1}{2}$	0

radius

Area = π × radius × radius

$A = \pi r^2$

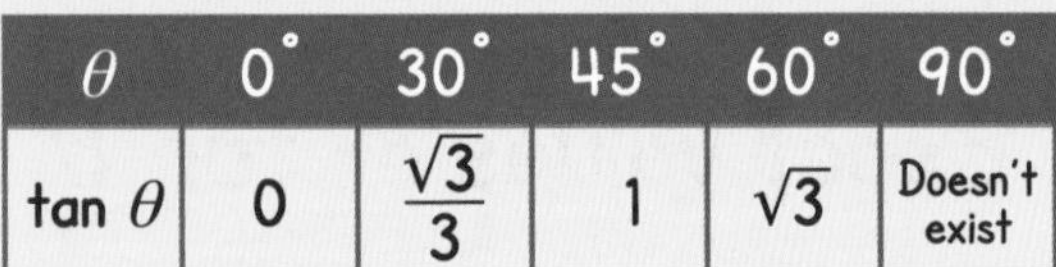

θ	0°	30°	45°	60°	90°
$\tan\theta$	0	$\frac{\sqrt{3}}{3}$	1	$\sqrt{3}$	Doesn't exist

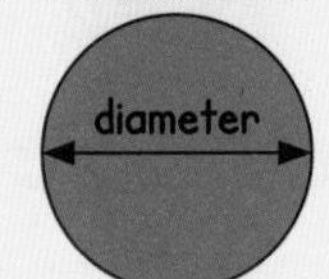

Circumference = π × diameter

$C = \pi d$

1 kilometre = 1000 metres

1 metre = 100 centimetres

1 centimetre = 10 millimetres

$$\text{Speed} = \frac{\text{distance}}{\text{time}}$$

1 tonne = 1000 kilograms

1 kilogram = 1000 grams

1 gram = 1000 milligrams

M
D V

$$\text{Density} = \frac{\text{mass}}{\text{volume}}$$

1 litre = 1000 millilitres

1 litre = 100 centilitres

1 centilitre = 10 millilitres

F
P A

$$\text{Pressure} = \frac{\text{force}}{\text{area}}$$

COMMAND WORDS

Command words are words that tell you to 'do something'

EXPAND
Remove brackets from an algebraic expression

$5(2x + 3) = 10x + 15$

In maths, Expand does not mean E x p a n d

EVALUATE
Find the VALUE

Evaluate 4^3:

$4 \times 4 \times 4 = 64$

ORDER
Use a rule to arrange

Order from smallest to largest

5, -2, 0.24

-2, 0.24, 5

SIMPLIFY
Make an algebraic expression simpler by collecting like terms:

$3x + 4 + 2x = 5x + 4$

Make a fraction simpler by cancelling common factors:

$\frac{12}{16} = \frac{3}{4}$

WRITE
Give the answer without needing to show working out

Write $\frac{3}{4}$ as a decimal:

0.75

SOLVE
Find the answer to a problem

Solve: $2x + 13 = 35$

$x = 11$

ROUND
Make a number simpler but keep its value close to what it was

74.26 rounded to ...

2 significant figures is 74

1 decimal place is 74.3

FACTORISE
Put brackets into an algebraic expression

$x^2 + 6x + 8 = (x + 2)(x + 4)$

$15y + 12 = 3(5y + 4)$

CALCULATE or WORK OUT
Perform one or more steps to get an answer

Calculate 15% of £40:

10% → £4 so 5% → £2

15% → £6

Calculate doesn't always mean you have to use a calculator

EXPLAIN
Give reasons to support the decision or the answer

ESTIMATE
Give a sensible approximate answer using rounding

Estimate 21.7×6.3:

$20 \times 6 = 120$

CONSTRUCT
Create an accurate drawing using the correct maths equipment

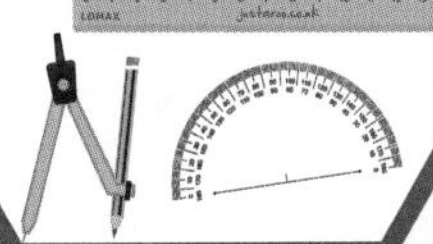

DRAW
Create a neat drawing that shows key features

Draw a plan of the 3D solid:

MEASURE
Find the length or size of an angle using ... a ruler or protractor

SKETCH
Create a rough drawing that shows key features

Sketch a cylinder:

No need to use a ruler or a pair of compasses

LABEL
Attach the correct name

Diameter

DESCRIBE
Use correct maths vocabulary to explain key features

Rotation 180° centre (0,0)

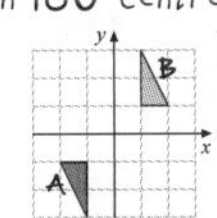

PLOT
Mark a point on a graph using a cross

Plot the point (1,2):

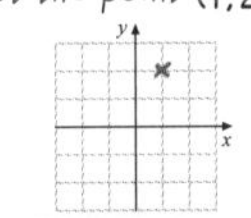

GIVE or JUSTIFY
Use reasons to explain thinking, such as

'the angles on a straight line add up to 180°'

FIND
Work out an answer to a problem

Find the mode of 6, 3, 9, 5, 3:

Mode = 3

REPRESENT
Display information in a chart or graph, such as a scatter graph

COMPLETE
Fill in missing values in a table such as

$y = 2x + 1$

x	-2	-1	0	1	2
y				3	

... and on a diagram such as

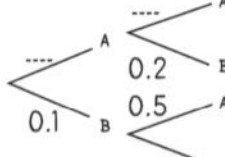

SHOW
Give all working to get to the answer

CONVERT
Change from one form to another

READY?

A two-way table is a really useful way of organising information that includes two (or more) categories.

e.g. 1 The two-way table shows some information about whether students in a class are left or right-handed. Complete the table.

	Left	Right	Total
Male	8		43
Female		17	
Total			80

Look for any row or column with only one missing piece of information

	Left	Right	Total
Male	8	35	43
Female		17	37
Total			80

1 Which numbers can be calculated?

80 – 43 = 37
and
43 – 8 = 35

2 Which numbers can now be calculated?

37 – 17 = 20
and
35 + 17 = 52

	Left	Right	Total
Male	8	35	43
Female	20	17	37
Total		52	80

	Left	Right	Total
Male	8	35	43
Female	20	17	37
Total	28	52	80

3 Calculate the final number

8 + 20 = 28
or
80 – 52 = 28

Do both ways to check

Sometimes we need to create the table.

e.g. 2 30 students were asked how they travel to school. All students either walk, ride a bike or travel by car.

- 13 of the students are girls
- 4 of the boys walk
- 7 girls ride a bike
- 3 of the 5 students who travel by car are boys

How many students walk to school?

1 Decide on row and column titles

2 Fill in the given information

3 Calculate the missing values

	Walk	Bike	Car	Total
Girls	4	7	2	13
Boys	4	10	3	17
Total	8	17	5	30

'3 out of 5' gives you two values for the table

Don't forget to answer the question

8 students walk to school

A. Complete the table:

	Finance	Sales	Ops	Total
Male		17		
Female	8		25	44
Total			32	90

B. This table shows the languages that a group of students study at school.

	French	Spanish	Other	Total
Girls		9	16	
Boys	6			32
Total			21	100

(i) How many girls study French?

(ii) How many students study Spanish?

C. Kelly asks 100 students if they like biology or chemistry or physics best.

38 of the students are girls.
21 of these girls like biology best.
18 boys like physics best.

7 out of the 23 students who like chemistry best are girls.

Work out the number of students who like biology best.

Highlight the key information like in e.g. 2

TWO-WAY TABLES

Exceptional!

1. 50 students were asked to choose an activity from netball, tennis or rounders.

15 chose rounders
28 of the students were female
9 of the females chose netball
No males chose netball
14 males chose tennis

Marcus has completed the two-way table using this information. Do you agree with Marcus? Explain why.

	Netball	Tennis	Rounders	Total
Female	9	12	1	22
Male	0	14	14	28
Total	9	26	15	50

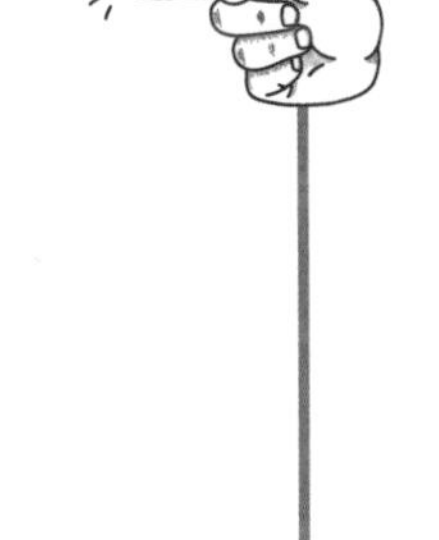

2. Students were asked to choose an activity from origami, metalwork or pottery.

There were 257 students
84 chose pottery
154 of the students were girls
79 of the girls chose origami
No boys chose origami
Equal numbers of boys and girls chose metalwork

Work out the difference between the number of boys who chose metalwork and the number of boys who chose pottery.

3. Orange cordial is sold in various size bottles:

Demi (375 ml)
Standard (750 ml)
Magnum (1.5 litres)

One weekend a shop sold 123 bottles of cordial.

84 of the bottles were sold on Sunday
19 of the bottles sold on Sunday were 1.5 litres
17 of the bottles sold on Saturday were Demi bottles
29 of the bottles sold were Magnum bottles
36 of the bottles sold were Standard size bottles

How many Demi size bottles were sold on Sunday?

READY?

Frequency trees are a really useful way of organising information and recording all the possible outcomes of two or more events.

There is one **GOLDEN** rule: Each "node" (circle) is equal to the sum of the other circles that branch off from it.

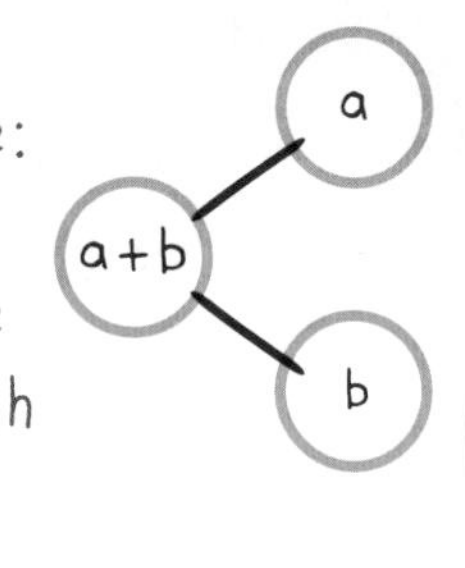

e.g. 1 30 students were asked if they had a pet. ✓

10 of the students were girls. ✓

6 girls had a pet. ✓

12 boys did not have a pet. ✓

Ticking off the information as you use it helps to keep organised

a) Complete the frequency tree.

1 Fill in the given information

2 Calculate the missing values

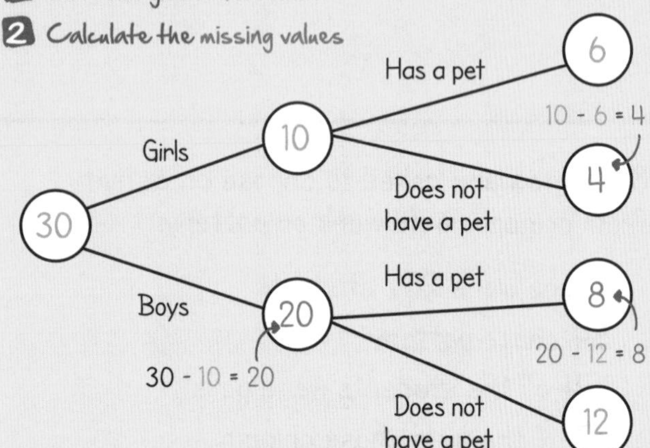

b) How many students have a pet?

6 + 8 = 14 students have a pet

e.g. 2 Amelie asks 80 students how they travel to school. $\frac{2}{5}$ of the students are girls. 19 of these girls walk to school. 18 boys travel by car. 3 out of the 17 students who travel by bus are girls.

Use a frequency tree to work out the total number of students who travel to school by car.

1 Decide on the first and second branches

2 Draw the tree and fill in the given information

3 Calculate the missing values

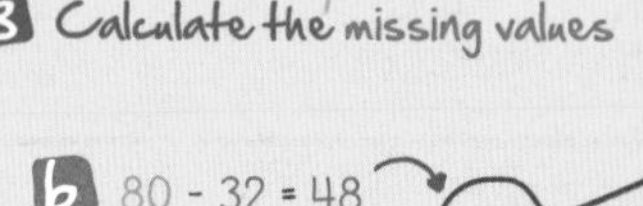

d 18 + 14 = 32; 48 - 32 = 16

b 80 - 32 = 48

80 → Boys 48 → Walk 16, Car 18, Bus 14

80 → Girls 32 → Walk 19, Car 10, Bus 3

c 19 + 3 = 22 → 32 - 22 = 10

'3 out of 17' means you can work this out too: 17 - 3 = 14

a $\frac{2}{5}$ of 80 → 80 ÷ 5 = 16 → 16 × 2 = 32

18 + 10 = 28 students travel by car

SET?

A. In a class of 35 students:

8 of the 14 boys are left-handed

9 girls are right-handed

Complete the frequency tree.

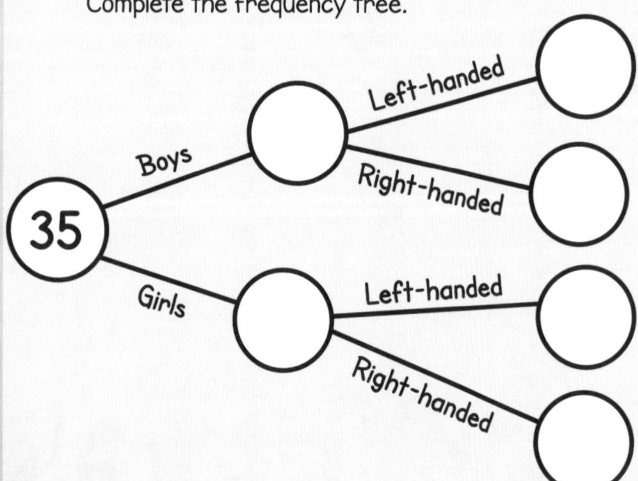

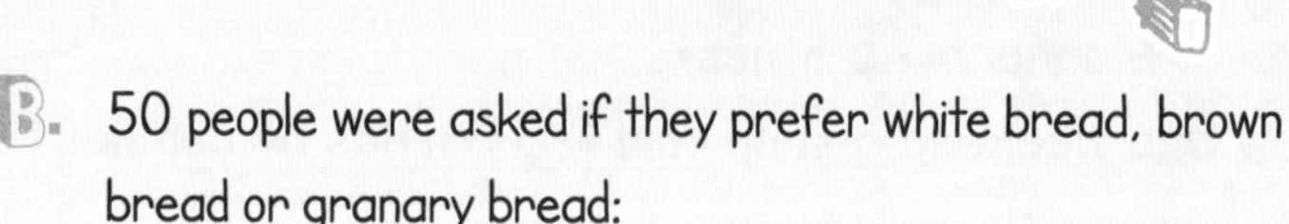

B. 50 people were asked if they prefer white bread, brown bread or granary bread:

21 of the people are male

11 of the males prefer brown bread

8 of the females prefer white bread

4 of the 9 people who prefer granary bread are male

Use a frequency tree to work out the number of people who prefer brown bread.

FREQUENCY TREES

Cool!

1. The two-way table shows the hot drink preferences of 100 people:

	Tea	Coffee	Other	Total
Male	28	10	8	46
Female	14	34	6	54
Total	42	44	14	100

Represent this information as a frequency tree.

2. Milk is sold in $\frac{1}{2}$ pint bottles, in 1 pint bottles and in 2 pint bottles.

One weekend a shop sold 100 bottles of milk.

46 of the bottles were sold on Sunday.
15 of the bottles sold on Sunday were 2 pint bottles.

31 of the bottles sold on Saturday were $\frac{1}{2}$ pint bottles.

22 of the bottles sold were 2 pint bottles.

30 of the bottles sold were 1 pint bottles.

How many 1 pint bottles were sold on Sunday?

3. At a cinema, films are shown on screen A and screen B. Customers pay full price or discounted Tuesday prices. At a film on a Tuesday:

There are three times as many people in screen B as screen A.

68 customers paid the discounted rate.

87 are in screen A of which 15 paid the discounted rate.

Find the difference between the number of full price tickets sold for screen A and the number of full price tickets sold for screen B.

READY?

Rounding to a number of decimal places

Decimal places are digits that are after the decimal point so this is where we start counting.

Rounding to a number of significant figures

We start counting significant figures from the first non-zero digit (basically the start of the number providing it's not a zero).

REMEMBER:

A decimal point separates the whole number part from the fractional part

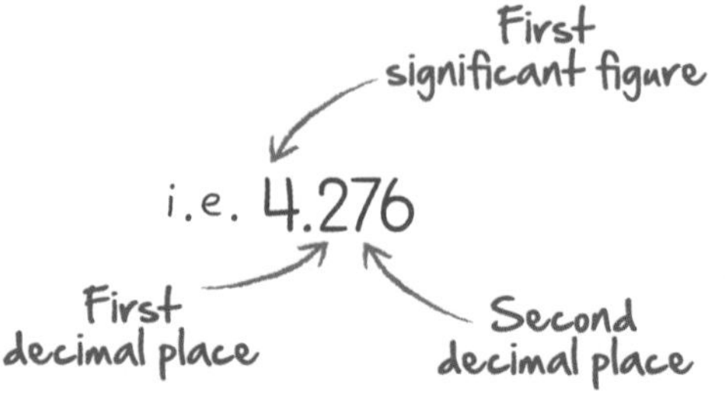

e.g. 1 Round 4.736428 to 1 decimal place.

4 If the digit to the right of the chop line is less than 5, leave the digit to the left of the chop line alone
If the digit to the right of the chop line is 5 or above, round the digit to the left of the chop line up one

So 4.7|3 → 4.7

e.g. 2 Round 0.043984 to 4 decimal places.

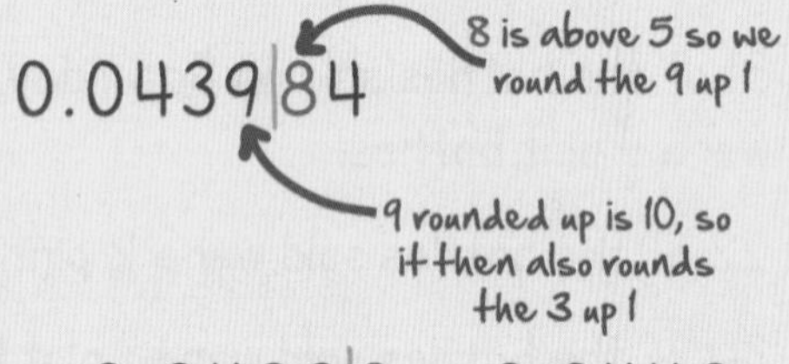

So 0.0439|8 → 0.0440

e.g. 3 Round 12.745428 to 3 significant figures.

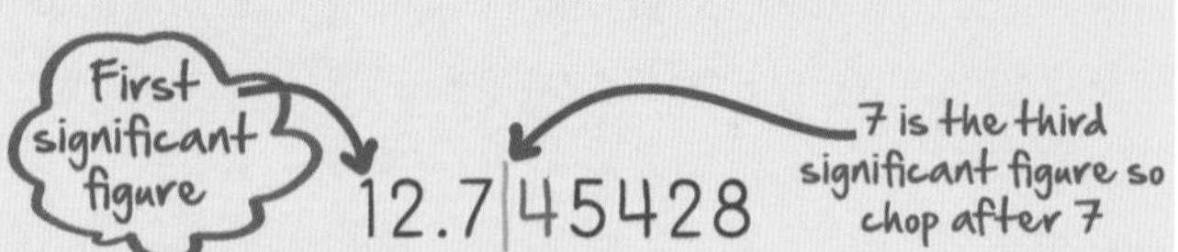

The rule about looking to the right of the chop line is still the same

So 12.7|4 → 12.7

e.g. 4 Round 0.0074739 to 3 significant figures.

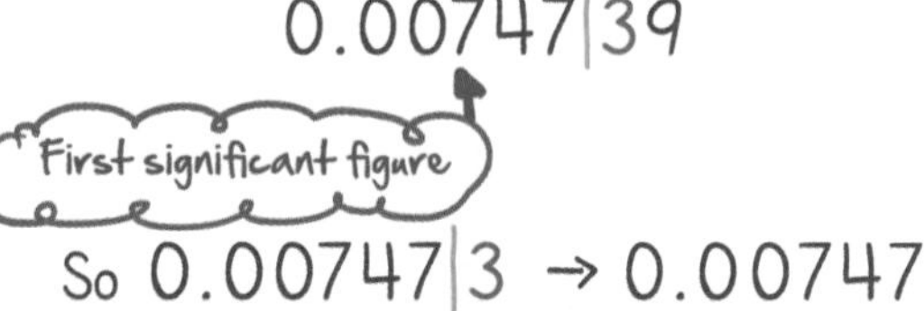

So 0.00747|3 → 0.00747

e.g. 5 Round 148 to 1 significant figure.

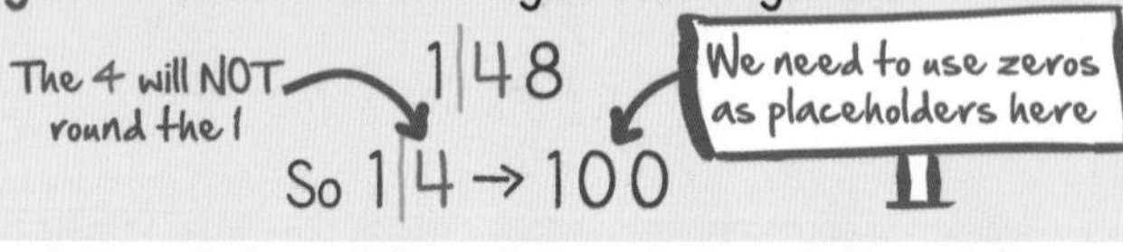

SET?

Complete this table:

Round to ...	1 decimal place	2 decimal places	3 decimal places	1 significant figure	2 significant figures	3 significant figures
(i) 6.5881						
(ii) 78.8894						
(iii) 0.071545						
(iv) 188.04779						

GO! ROUNDING

Very good!

1. Clarissa rounds 2.49901 to 1 significant figure. Here is her working:

   2.4|9901 so 2.5 to 1 s.f.

   Do you agree? Justify your answer.

2. A number rounded to one significant figure is 1000.

   What is the smallest whole number that this could be?

3. y = 2.6 rounded to 1 decimal place.
   What is the smallest possible value of y?

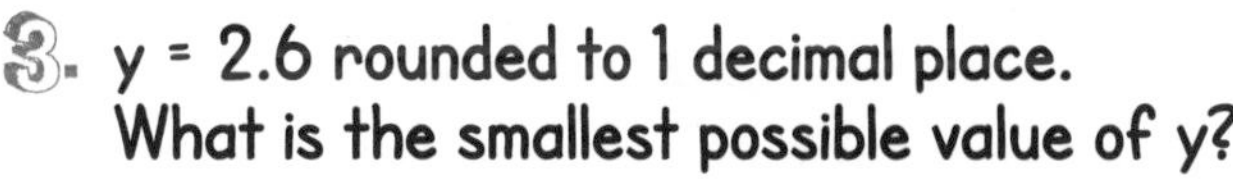

   2.65   2.5   2.55   2.59

4. Oona is asked to round 128,607 to two significant figures. She writes the answer 13.

   Do you agree? Explain why.

5. Paul won a race with a time of 81.3 seconds rounded to the nearest tenth of a second.

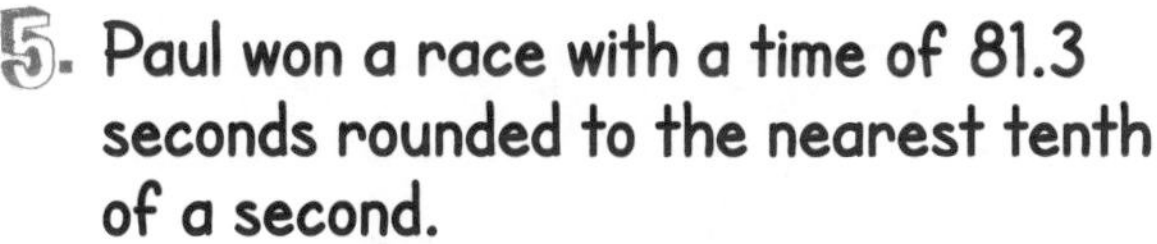

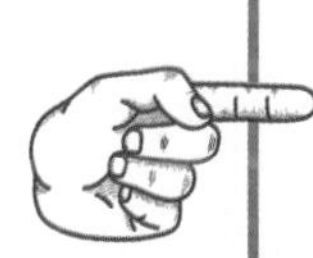

   What is the fastest time in which he could have completed the race? Explain your answer.

READY?

An **error interval** is the range of values a number could have taken before being rounded (or truncated). To find the error interval, we need to identify the upper and lower bounds of the number.

It's REALLY USEFUL to:

⇨ Be able to round and truncate values to:
- The nearest whole number, the nearest 10, 100, 1000 and a number of decimal places (d.p.) and significant figures (s.f.)

⇨ Understand bounds for rounding:
- The Lower Bound (LB) is the smallest value that would round up to the number in question.
- The Upper Bound (UB) is the smallest value above the number that does NOT round to that number.

e.g. 1 A number is rounded to 60 to the nearest 10 (Degree of accuracy)

Complete the error interval: ______ ≤ number < ______

1. Find the smallest value that rounds up to 60 to the nearest 10 → 55 (LB), 60
2. Find the smallest value that rounds up to 70 (the next value to the nearest 10) → 55 (LB), 60, 65 (UB)

__55__ ≤ number < __65__

55 rounds to 60 so we use ≤ — 65 does not round to 60 so we use <

e.g. 2 A number, n, is rounded to 17.4 to one decimal place. (Degree of accuracy)

Find the error interval.

1. Find the smallest value that rounds up to 17.4 to one d.p.
2. Find the smallest value that rounds up to 17.5 (the next value to one d.p.)

These all round UP to 17.4	These all round DOWN to 17.4
17.3|5...	17.4|0...
17.3|6...	17.4|1...
17.3|7...	17.4|2...
17.3|8...	17.4|3...
17.3|9...	17.4|4...

The Lower Bound is 17.35 — The Upper Bound is 17.45

The error interval is 17.35 ≤ n < 17.45

Ensure the symbols are correct

e.g. 3 Cody is drawing an equilateral triangle. The length of each side is 4 cm to one significant figure. (Degree of accuracy)

a) Write the error interval for the length of one side.

1. Find the smallest value that rounds up to 4 to one s.f. → 3.5 (LB), 4
2. Find the smallest value that rounds up to 5 (the next value to one s.f.) → 3.5 (LB), 4, 4.5 (UB)

The error interval is 3.5 ≤ length < 4.5

b) Write the error interval for the perimeter of the triangle.

We use the length error interval to calculate the perimeter error interval

(3 × 3.5) (3 × 4.5)

10.5 ≤ perimeter < 13.5

BE CAREFUL

Sometimes **truncation** can be used. The error interval can be found in the same way as rounding, we just need to think carefully about the lower and upper bounds.

e.g. 4 A number, n, is truncated to 8.4 to one decimal place. (Degree of accuracy)

Find the error interval.

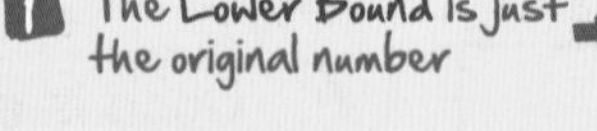

1. The Lower Bound is just the original number → 8.4 (LB)
2. The Upper Bound is the original number + degree of accuracy → 8.4 (LB), 8.5 (UB)

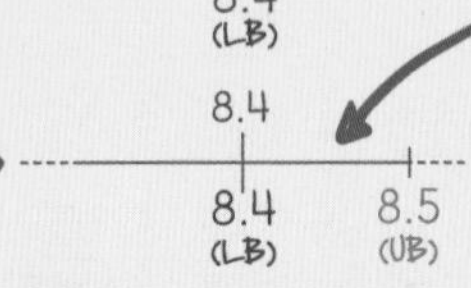

All the values here truncate to 8.4

The error interval is 8.4 ≤ n < 8.5

A. x = 3500 to the nearest 100, circle the smallest value of x.

3449 3450 3495 3499

B. A number is rounded to 6 to the nearest whole number.
Complete the error interval.

______ ≤ number < ______

C. A length is rounded to 5.2 to one decimal place.
Complete the error interval.

______ ≤ length < ______

D. A number, n, is rounded to the nearest 10
The result is 290
Write down the error interval for n.

E. A number, n, is rounded to 2 significant figures.
The result is 4.3
Write down the error interval for n.

F. A number, n, has been rounded to two decimal places.
The answer is 12.34
Find the error interval for n.

______ ≤ n < ______

G. A number, n, is truncated to 1 decimal place to 7.2
Complete the error interval.

______ ≤ n < ______

H. Izzy used her calculator to work out the value of a number y. The answer on her calculator display began 9.4...
Complete the error interval.

______ ≤ y < ______

HINT: TRUNCATING IN DISGUISE

Stunning!

1. The side length of a square is 5 cm to the nearest whole number.

   Maura works out that the perimeter of the square is 20 cm. She then writes the error interval for the perimeter as:

   $$19.5 \leq \text{perimeter} < 20.5$$

   Do you agree with Maura? Explain why.

2. A number, x, has been rounded to 2 significant figures.

   The answer is 0.52

   Use inequalities to write the error interval for x.

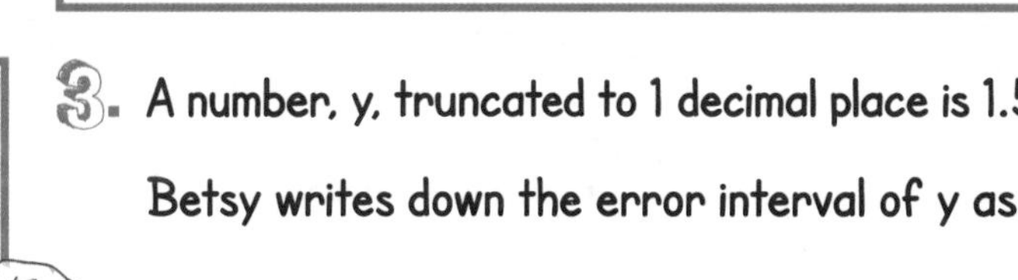

3. A number, y, truncated to 1 decimal place is 1.5

   Betsy writes down the error interval of y as:

   $$1.45 \leq y < 1.55$$

   Explain the mistake she has made.

4. The length of a piece of wood is 4.3 m truncated to 1 decimal place.

   The length of metal rod has been rounded to 4.4 m to one decimal place.

   Explain how the piece of wood could be longer than the metal rod.

READY?

We can estimate the answer to a calculation by using approximate values. When we are working with exact answers, we use the equals symbol (=) but when we are estimating, we use a symbol that means "is approximately equal to":

$\approx$ (a wavy equals sign!)

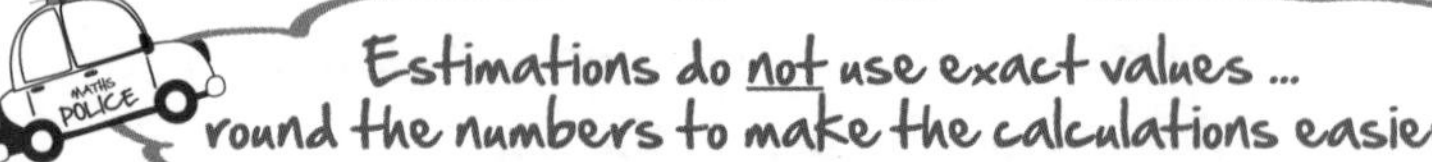

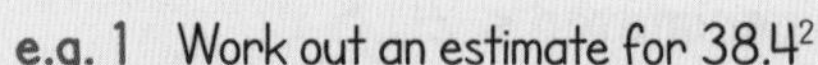

e.g. 1 Work out an estimate for 38.4^2

1 Round $38.4 \approx 40$ (a much easier number)

2 Calculate $40^2 = 40 \times 40 = 1600$

so $38.4^2 \approx 1600$

e.g. 2 Estimate: $\frac{3860}{232 \times 4.85}$

1 Round
$3860 \approx 4000$
$232 \approx 200$
$4.85 \approx 5$

2 Calculate $\frac{4000}{200 \times 5} = \frac{4000}{1000} = 4$

so $\frac{3860}{232 \times 4.85} \approx 4$

e.g. 3 Work out a sensible estimate of: $\frac{53 \times 9.87}{0.509}$

Dividing by a half is the same as multiplying by 2

1 Round
$53 \approx 50$
$9.87 \approx 10$
$0.509 \approx 0.5$ ($0.509 \approx 0.5$ (not 1))

2 Calculate $\frac{50 \times 10}{0.5} = \frac{500}{0.5} = 1000$

so $\frac{53 \times 9.87}{0.509} \approx 1000$

Estimations can also appear in more wordy problems.

e.g. 4 a) Tristan is organising a charity concert.
Each ticket for the event will cost £9.95
Tristan is hoping to sell 196 tickets.
The costs Tristan has to pay are:

£708 for the hire of the venue and
£213 transport costs for the band.

Any money left will be donated to charity.
Work out an estimate for the amount of money Tristan expects to raise for the charity.

$9.95 \approx 10$
$196 \approx 200$
$708 \approx 700$
$213 \approx 200$

Money from ticket sales $\approx 10 \times 200 =$ £2000
Costs to be paid $\approx 700 + 200 =$ £900
Estimated money left = £2000 - £900 = £1100

Tristan will raise about £1100

You also need to be able to explain the impact of rounding.

e.g. 4 (continued) b) Is your answer to a) an underestimate or an overestimate? Give a reason for your answer.

My answer will be an overestimate.
He will raise less than £1100 because both numbers used to calculate the total ticket sales were rounded up and the numbers used to calculate the costs were rounded down.

Estimate:

A. $313.76 + 2843.8$

B. 7.3×18

C. 6.2^2

D. 0.93×89.2

Show clearly what calculation could be used to estimate each of the below:

E. Half of 69.456

F. Double 119.3478890

G. Square root of 35

HINT: Use the nearest square number

Estimate:

H. $\frac{21.6}{108}$

I. $\frac{1.84 \times 2.03}{0.49}$

ESTIMATION

Perfect!

1. Without working out exact answers, match each question to its solution.

Show all your working out.

Question	Solution
35.2×29	487.6
92×5.3	786.87
$112 \div 12$	120
$\sqrt{72.25}$	9.3
6.3×124.9	1020.8
$60.12 \div 0.501$	8.5

2. Vinnie writes down the following:

$$4.5 \times 0.54 = 24.3$$

Without doing the exact calculation, explain why Vinnie's answer cannot be correct.

3. Adam and Beth both use a calculator to work out:

$$\sqrt[3]{4.1 + 2.3 + 1.35}$$

Adam writes down: 2.583

Beth writes down: 1.978945805

Without using a calculator, who is correct? Explain your answer.

4. A unit of electricity costs £0.124 per unit.

On average, Abbie uses 102.3 units of electricity a week.

a) Work out an estimate for the total cost of Abbie's electricity usage in one year.

b) Is your estimate to part a) an underestimate or an overestimate? Explain why.

READY?

Use the same calculator at home that you use in class. Different models label some of the same functions differently; e.g. $x^{\blacksquare}$ and ^ both find powers

Here are some of the most useful calculator functions to know.

Key	Function	Key	Function
 x^2	Squares a number	 Ans	Uses the previous answer in the next calculation
 $\sqrt{\blacksquare}$	Finds the positive square root	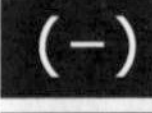 (−)	Inputs a negative number
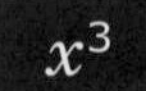 x^3	Cubes a number		Enters a fraction
 $\sqrt[3]{\blacksquare}$	Finds the cube root (you might need to press **SHIFT**)		Enters a mixed number
 $x^{\blacksquare}$	Finds any power of a number	 S⇔D	Converts between an exact answer (e.g. fraction) and a decimal
 $\sqrt[\blacksquare]{\square}$	Finds any root of a number (you might need to press **SHIFT**)	 ( )	Two separate buttons (one for each bracket)

When doing complex calculations, try to make your display look identical to the calculation, (or you can work out different parts separately).

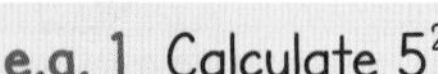

e.g. 1 Calculate 5^2

5 x^2 = 25

e.g. 2 Calculate $\sqrt[3]{64}$

 $\sqrt[3]{\blacksquare}$ 6 4 = 4

e.g. 3 Calculate 4^6

4  $x^{\blacksquare}$ 6 = 4096

e.g. 4 Calculate $\sqrt[4]{16}$

4 $\sqrt[\blacksquare]{\square}$ 1 6 = 2

e.g. 5 Use your calculator to work out the value of $\frac{12.7 \times 0.8}{9.78 + 6.4}$ as a decimal. Write down all the figures on the display.

Use the buttons on your calculator to make a copy of the calculation:

 1 2 ·  7 × 0 · 8  9 · 7 8 + 6 · 4 = S⇔D

0.6279357231

is the 'down' key

1 Work out the 'top' part

1 2 · 7 × 0 · 8 = 10.16

2 Then work out the 'bottom' part

9 · 7 8 + 6 · 4 = 16.18

3 Carry out the division

1 0 · 1 6 ÷ 1 6 · 1 8 = 0.6279357231

e.g. 6 Work out $\sqrt{\frac{8-2^2}{\pi}}$. Give your answer to 3 significant figures.

 $\sqrt{\blacksquare}$ 8 − 2 x^2 (down key) SHIFT $\times 10^x$ =

1.128379167 = 1.13 to 3 s.f.

Most calculators don't have a π button

OR

1 8 − 2 x^2 = 4

2 Ans ÷ SHIFT $\times 10^x$ = 1.273239545

3 $\sqrt{\blacksquare}$ Ans = 1.128379167 = 1.13 to 3 s.f.

Work out these calculations. Write your answer as a decimal.

A. $\frac{18.7}{13.8 + 4.36}$

B. $\frac{18.7 + 4.36}{13.8^2}$

C. $\frac{18.7^2}{13.8 + 4.36}$

D. Work out $\frac{4.65 \times 0.8}{15.4 - 9.76}$

Give your answer to 2 decimal places.

E. Use your calculator to work out:

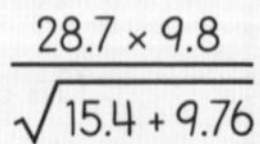

$$\frac{28.7 \times 9.8}{\sqrt{15.4 + 9.76}}$$

(i) Write down all the figures on your calculator display.

(ii) Write the answer to 3 significant figures.

F. Use your calculator to work out:

$$(2 + \sqrt[5]{14})^3$$

Write down all the figures on your calculator display.

HINT: Use the ▷ key

HIGHEST COMMON FACTOR AND LOWEST COMMON MULTIPLE

Love it!

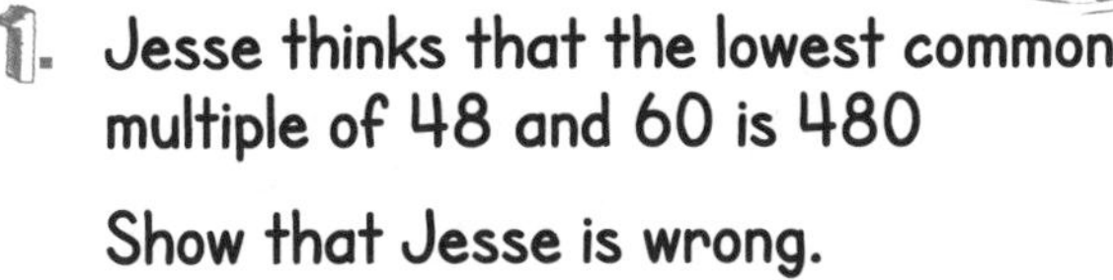

1. Jesse thinks that the lowest common multiple of 48 and 60 is 480

   Show that Jesse is wrong.

2. One lighthouse flashes its lights every 90 seconds.

   A second lighthouse flashes its lights every 70 seconds.

   If both lighthouses start to flash their lights at the same time, after how many seconds will they next flash their lights at the same time?

3. Find the highest common factor of 42, 56 and 70

HINT: Use the same method with 3 numbers as you would use with 2

4. Using:

   $$540 = 2^2 \times 3^3 \times 5$$

   a) Work out the highest common factor of 440 and 540

   b) Work out the lowest common multiple of 440 and 540

READY?

We can use lowest common multiples (LCM) to help solve problems.

REMEMBER:
Counting up in 7's from zero is 7, 14, 21 etc. ... these are all multiples of 7. The lowest common multiple (LCM) of two or more numbers is the lowest number that is a multiple of them all.

e.g. 1 Find the the LCM of 8 and 6

8 → 8, 16, (24), 32, 40 ...

6 → 6, 12, 18, (24) ... LCM of 6 and 8 = 24

e.g. 2 Buses to Worcester leave a bus station every 30 minutes.

Buses to Hereford leave the same bus station every 40 minutes.

A bus to Worcester and a bus to Hereford both leave the bus station at 09:20

At what time will a bus to Worcester and a bus to Hereford next leave the bus station at the same time?

1 List some of the multiples of 30 and 40

2 Find the LCM

Multiples of 30 → 30, 60, 90, (120), 150, ...

Multiples of 40 → 40, 80, (120), 160, ...

120 mins = 2 hours, so 09:20 + 2 hours

The next time both buses leave at the same time is 11:20 am

OR

Worcester (every 30 mins):

09:20, 09:50, 10:20, 10:50, (11:20), 11.50 ...

Hereford (every 40 mins):

09:20, 10:00, 10:40, (11:20), 12:00 ...

So, 11:20 am

e.g. 3 Gail is making cheeseburgers for a party. Each cheeseburger consists of one bun, one burger and one cheese slice. She buys cheese in packets of 20 slices, burgers in boxes of 12 burgers and buns in packets of 10 buns.

Gail buys the same number of cheese slices, burgers and buns. She uses everything she buys.

a) What is the least number of cheeseburgers she can make for the party?

	Cheese (20's)		Burgers (12's)		Buns (10's)
(1)	20	(1)	12	(1)	10
(2)	40	(2)	24	(2)	20
(3)	(60)	(3)	36	(3)	30
	80	(4)	48	(4)	40
		(5)	(60)	(5)	50
			72	(6)	(60)

The number of cheeseburgers she can make is 60

b) For your answer in part a) complete the information:

Gail buys:

3 packets of cheese

5 boxes of burgers

6 packets of buns

120 is also in all 3 lists but it is not the LCM

SET?

A. Trains to Sheffield leave a station every 25 minutes.

Trains to Leeds leave the same station every 45 minutes.

A train to Sheffield and a train to Leeds both leave the train station at 14:30

At what time will a train to Sheffield and a train to Leeds next leave the train station at the same time?

B. A motorised model of a planet with three moons is built.

- One moon orbits the planet every 40 seconds
- Another moon orbits the planet every 60 seconds
- The third moon orbits the planet every 12 seconds

When the model starts running all three planets are lined up together.

After what length of time are the three planets next all lined up together back at their starting positions?

C. Mathilda and Erin run around a track.

Each lap takes Mathilda 50 seconds to complete.
Each lap takes Erin 80 seconds to complete.

Mathilda and Erin start running at the same time.

How many laps will they each have run when they are next at the start line together?

REAL LIFE MULTIPLES

Brill!

1. Rich and Cameron are riding around the track at a velodrome.
    - Rich completes a lap every 24 seconds
    - Cameron completes a lap every 20 seconds

    They begin at the start line together. How many laps has Cameron completed when they next pass the start line together?

2. Buses to Coventry leave a bus station every 40 minutes. Buses to Leicester leave the same bus station every 30 minutes.

    Buses to Coventry and Leicester leave together at 18:00 on Monday. Erica says:

    30 × 40 = 1200 mins, 1200 ÷ 60 = 20 hrs

    They next leave together at 2pm on Tuesday

    Erica is wrong. Explain why.

3. Two gears are meshed together.
    - The large gear has 40 teeth
    - The small gear has 16 teeth

    Emmett starts to turn the gears.

    After how many turns of the small gear will both gears return to their starting position?

Not an accurate diagram

4. Lesley is buying cakes and buns.

    The cakes are sold in boxes. There are 12 cakes in each box.
    Each box of cakes costs £2.50

    The buns are sold in packs. There are 8 buns in a pack.
    Each pack of buns costs £1.20

    Lesley wants to buy more than 60 cakes and more than 60 buns. She wants to buy exactly the same number of cakes as buns.

    What is the least amount of money Lesley will have to pay?

You REALLY NEED to know:

* The **numerator** is the top number of a fraction
* The **denominator** is the bottom number of a fraction
* How to find equivalent fraction: e.g. $\frac{1}{2} = \frac{2}{4}$
* That a whole number can be written as a fraction very easily: $4 = \frac{4}{1}$

+ AND -

For adding and subtracting fractions we use the same method ... the fractions must have a common denominator before carrying out the addition or subtraction. (the "same")

e.g. 1 $\frac{1}{7} + \frac{2}{7} = \frac{3}{7}$ — The denominators are already the same so just add the numerators

Sometimes one fraction needs dealing with first.

e.g. 2 $\frac{7}{20} + \frac{1}{4}$

Look!! Different denominators

$1 \times 5 = 5$
$4 \times 5 = 20$

Multiply top AND bottom of $\frac{1}{4}$ by 5 to get 20 as the denominator

$= \frac{7}{20} + \frac{5}{20}$

$= \frac{12}{20}$

Only simplify your answer if you are asked to do so

Sometimes both fractions need dealing with.

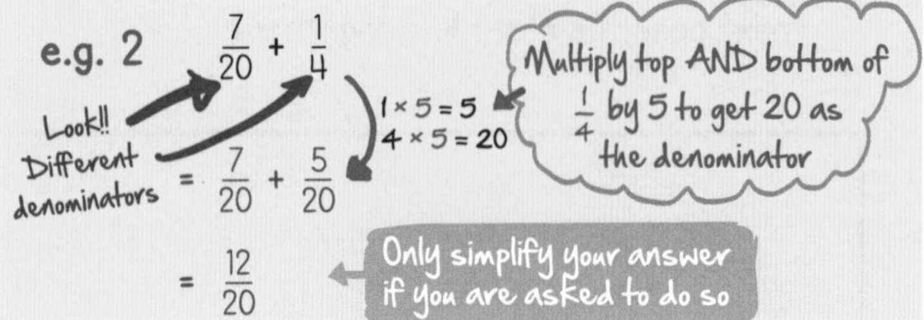

e.g. 3 Work out $\frac{7}{15} - \frac{1}{6}$ giving your answer in its simplest form.

$\frac{7}{15} - \frac{1}{6}$

$7 \times 2 = 14$, $15 \times 2 = 30$; $1 \times 5 = 5$, $6 \times 5 = 30$

$= \frac{14}{30} - \frac{5}{30}$

You need to look for multiples of 6 and 15 to find a common denominator

Look!! Not in its simplest form

$= \frac{9}{30} = \frac{3}{10}$

$9 \div 3 = 3$, $30 \div 3 = 10$

× AND ÷

Multiplying is the easy one.

e.g. 4 $\frac{1}{2} \times \frac{3}{13}$

$= \frac{1 \times 3}{2 \times 13}$

$= \frac{3}{26}$

e.g. 5 $\frac{2}{7} \times 3$

Don't multiply both top and bottom by 3

$= \frac{2}{7} \times \frac{3}{1}$ ($3 = \frac{3}{1}$)

$= \frac{6}{7}$

Dividing can be done by converting the calculation to one that involves multiplication.

e.g. 6 $\frac{4}{9} \div \frac{2}{3}$ (Keep, Flip)

$= \frac{4}{9} \times \frac{3}{2} = \frac{12}{18}$

Don't do $4 \div 2$ or $9 \div 3$

e.g. 7 $5 \div \frac{1}{4}$

$= \frac{5}{1} \times \frac{4}{1}$

$= \frac{20}{1} = 20$

e.g. 8 $\frac{1}{4} \div 5$

$= \frac{1}{4} \times \frac{1}{5}$

$= \frac{1}{20}$

Good to know: the reciprocal of 7 is $\frac{1}{7}$, the reciprocal of $\frac{1}{2}$ is $\frac{2}{1} = 2$, the reciprocal of $\frac{2}{3}$ is $\frac{3}{2}$, etc.

A. Work out:

(i) $\frac{4}{13} + \frac{3}{13}$

(ii) $\frac{4}{15} - \frac{1}{15}$

(iii) $\frac{7}{15} + \frac{2}{5}$

(iv) $\frac{5}{6} - \frac{1}{24}$

(v) $\frac{3}{8} + \frac{1}{6}$

(vi) $\frac{5}{8} - \frac{2}{5}$

B. Work out:

(i) $\frac{2}{3} \times \frac{4}{9}$

(ii) $\frac{1}{30} \times 5$

(iii) $\frac{5}{8} \times \frac{1}{2} \times \frac{4}{9}$

C. Work out:

(i) $\frac{3}{11} \div \frac{2}{3}$

(ii) $7 \div \frac{2}{9}$

(iii) $\frac{7}{12} \div 5$

D. Work out: $1 - \frac{1}{4} - \frac{2}{5}$

E. Work out: $\frac{2}{3} \times \frac{3}{8} \times \frac{3}{4}$

Simplify your answers where possible

FRACTIONS 1

1. Stefan works out $\frac{4}{7} + \frac{2}{5}$. Here is his working:

$$\frac{4}{7} + \frac{2}{5} = \frac{6}{12} = \frac{1}{2}$$

Stefan is wrong.

Explain his mistake and show the correct answer.

2. Are these statements true or false?

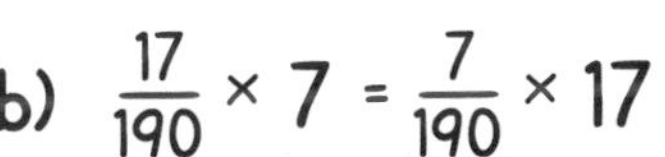

a) $\frac{2}{5} \times 2 = \frac{1}{2} - \frac{1}{10}$

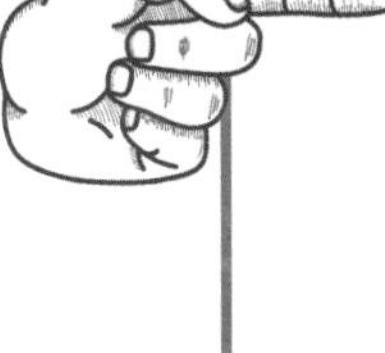

b) $\frac{17}{190} \times 7 = \frac{7}{190} \times 17$

Explain your reasons.

3. $\frac{5}{12}$ of the students in a school get a bus to school.

$\frac{3}{10}$ of the students come to school in a car and $\frac{1}{5}$ of the students walk to school.

All of the other students cycle to school.

There are 720 students in the school. How many of them cycle to school?

4. Maria has 30 metres of ribbon. She needs $\frac{4}{5}$ of a metre to tie a bow for wrapping birthday presents.

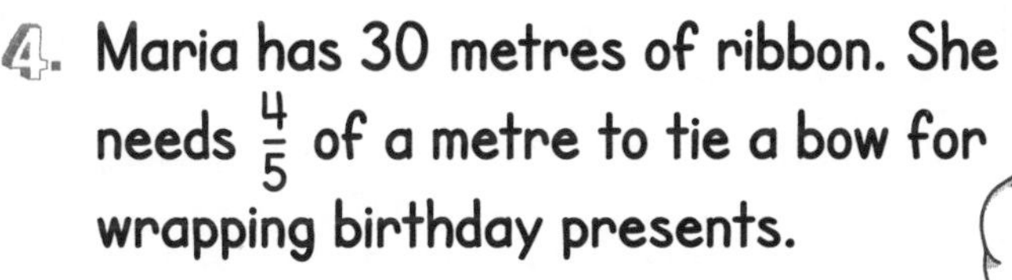

How many bows can Maria make from the ribbon?

READY?

When adding and subtracting with mixed numbers, it is useful to change any mixed numbers into improper fractions first.

e.g. 1 Calculate $2\frac{1}{5} + \frac{4}{15}$. Write your answer as a mixed number.

$= \frac{11}{5} + \frac{4}{15}$

1 Convert $2\frac{1}{5}$ to an improper fraction

$2\frac{1}{5} \rightarrow \frac{11}{5}$ ($2 \times 5 + 1 = 11$)

($11 \times 3 = 33$, $5 \times 3 = 15$)

$= \frac{33}{15} + \frac{4}{15}$

2 Remember the denominators must be the same when adding or subtracting fractions

$= \frac{37}{15}$

3 Check if the question asks to simplify, and/or write the answer as a mixed number

$= 2\frac{7}{15}$

$\frac{37}{15} \rightarrow 2\frac{7}{15}$ (15 divides into 37 two whole times with a remainder of 7)

e.g. 2 $3\frac{1}{6} - 2\frac{2}{9}$

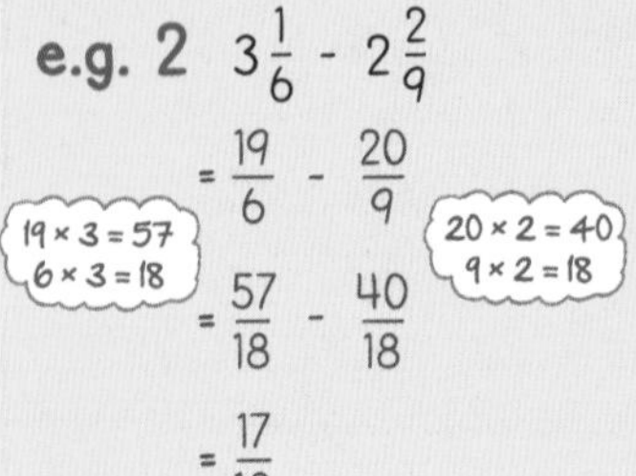

$= \frac{19}{6} - \frac{20}{9}$

($19 \times 3 = 57$, $6 \times 3 = 18$) ($20 \times 2 = 40$, $9 \times 2 = 18$)

$= \frac{57}{18} - \frac{40}{18}$

$= \frac{17}{18}$

Look out for the lowest common mulitple (LCM) of the denominators to make the calculations easier ... the LCM of 6 and 9 is 18

Improper fractions are also useful for multiplying ...

e.g. 3 Calculate $1\frac{3}{8} \times 2\frac{1}{5}$. Write your answer as a mixed number.

$\frac{11}{8} \times \frac{11}{5}$

1 Convert the mixed numbers to improper fractions

$= \frac{11 \times 11}{8 \times 5}$

2 Multiply both the numerators and the denominators

$= \frac{121}{40} = 3\frac{1}{40}$

3 Write the answer as a mixed number

... and dividing mixed numbers.

e.g. 4 Work out $3\frac{1}{2} \div 1\frac{5}{8}$

Write your answer as a mixed number in its simplest form.

$\frac{7}{2} \div \frac{13}{8}$

1 Convert the mixed numbers to improper fractions

$= \frac{7}{2} \times \frac{8}{13}$

2 Dividing can be done by converting the calcuation to one that involves multiplication

$= \frac{56}{26} = 2\frac{4}{26}$

3 Write the answer as a mixed number

$2\frac{4}{26} = 2\frac{2}{13}$

4 Give your answer in its simplest form

Look out for the mixed number button on your calculator:

Pressing the following 2 buttons on some calculators will convert an improper fraction to a mixed number:

SHIFT S⇔D

You **REALLY NEED** to know:

* Improper fractions are fractions where the **numerator** (the top number) is larger than the **denominator** (the bottom number)
* How to change between a **mixed number** and an improper fraction, e.g. $3\frac{1}{2} = \frac{7}{2}$ $(3 \times 2 + 1)$

the denominators stay the same

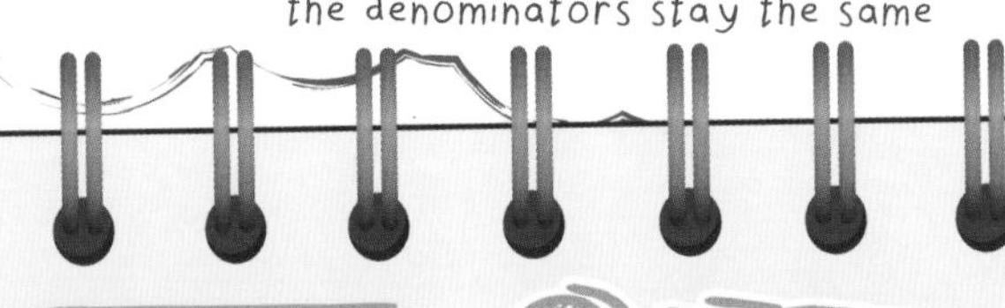

Give your answers as mixed numbers in their simplest form

A. Work out:

(i) $3\frac{1}{4} + 1\frac{5}{7}$

(ii) $2\frac{3}{4} - \frac{5}{6}$

(iii) $1\frac{5}{6} \times \frac{7}{8}$

(iv) $5\frac{2}{5} \div 3\frac{3}{4}$

B. Work out:

(i) $2\frac{3}{5} \times 4$

(ii) $1\frac{2}{3} \times 2\frac{2}{11}$

(iii) $1\frac{2}{3} \times 2\frac{2}{11} \times 3$

C. Work out:

(i) $5\frac{7}{10} \div 5$

(ii) $4 \div 1\frac{2}{3}$

HINT: $4 = \frac{4}{1}$

GO! FRACTIONS 2

Good stuff!

1. Work out:

a) $\left(3\frac{2}{3}\right)^2$

b) $\left(2\frac{1}{4} \times 1\frac{5}{6}\right) + 1\frac{1}{8}$

2. Darran rides a bike for $59\frac{1}{5}$ kilometres.

$1\frac{3}{5}$ kilometres is approximately 1 mile.

Work out how far his journey is in miles.

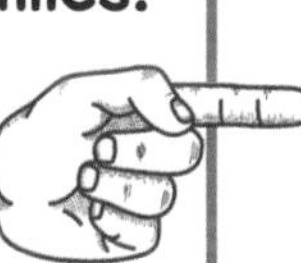

3. Sarah is working out $3\frac{2}{7} - 1\frac{3}{4}$

Here is her working:

$$\frac{3}{4} - \frac{2}{7} = \frac{21}{28} - \frac{8}{28} = \frac{13}{28} \text{ and } 3 - 1 = 2$$

$$\text{So } 3\frac{2}{7} - 1\frac{3}{4} = 2\frac{13}{28}$$

Do you agree with Sarah?
Explain your answer.

4. American paper sizes use measurements in inches.

A piece of paper measures $5\frac{1}{2}$ inches by $8\frac{1}{2}$ inches.

Find the area of a side of this piece of paper. Give your answer as a mixed number in its simplest form.

READY?

It is **REALLY USEFUL** to know:

* the symbol **:** is used to describe ratios
* how to simplify ratios ... 6 : 4 is the same as 3 : 2 and 15 : 6 is the same as 5 : 2

A ratio describes how the size of one quantity compares to the size of another quantity.

e.g. 1 Mel and Chris share £80 in the ratio 3 : 5
How much money does each person receive?

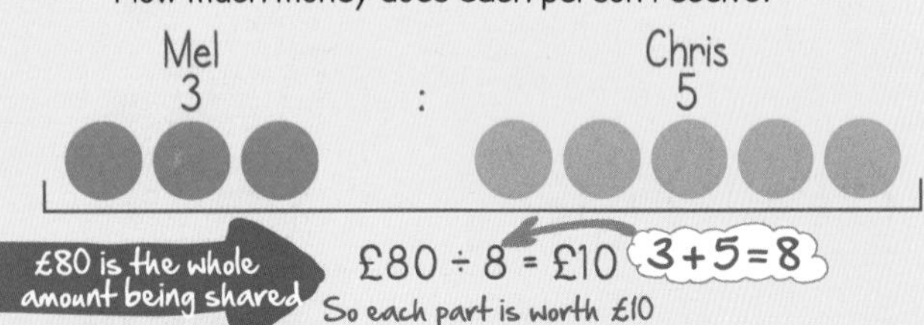

£80 is the whole amount being shared

£80 ÷ 8 = £10 (3 + 5 = 8)

So each part is worth £10

£10 £10 £10 £10 £10 £10 £10 £10

Mel = 3 × £10 = £30 Chris = 5 × £10 = £50

e.g. 2 Mel and Chris share some money in the ratio 3 : 5
If Chris receives £40, how much money did they share?

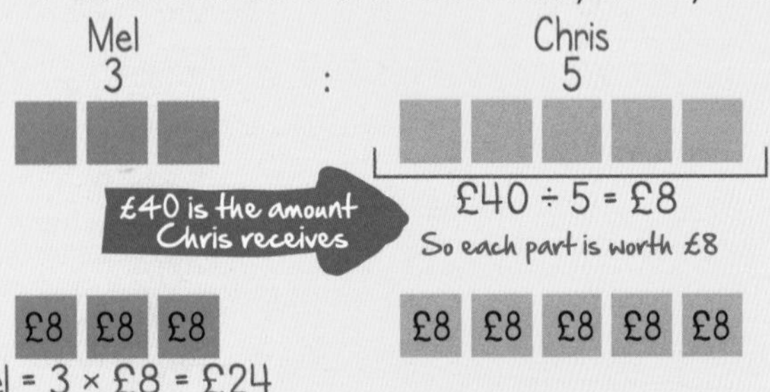

Mel = 3 × £8 = £24

Total amount shared = £24 + £40 = £64

e.g. 3 Mel and Chris share some money in the ratio 3 : 5
Chris receives £14 more than Mel.
How much money did Mel receive?

Mel = 3 × £7 = £21 Chris = 5 × £7 = £35

Mel receives £21

e.g. 4 Mel, Chris and Fize share some sweets.
Chris gets three times as many sweets as Mel.
Fize gets twice as many sweets as Chris.
Mel's sweets : Chris' sweets : Fize's sweets = 1 : n : m
Work out the values of n and m.

Mel 1 : Chris 3 × 1 : Fize 2 × 3 = 6

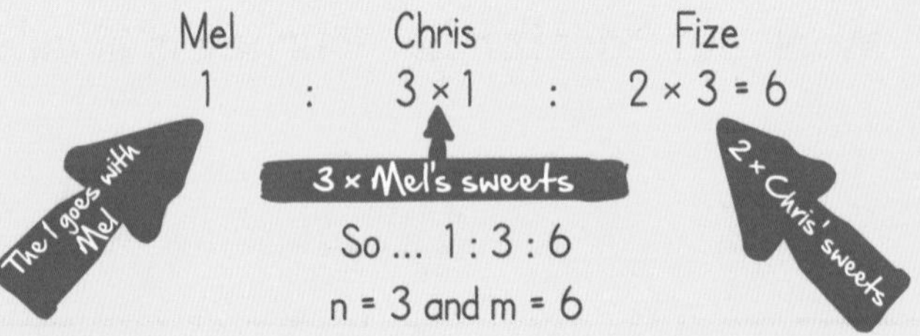

So ... 1 : 3 : 6

n = 3 and m = 6

e.g. 5 Mel and Chris share some money in the ratio 1 : 3

What fraction of the total does Mel receive?

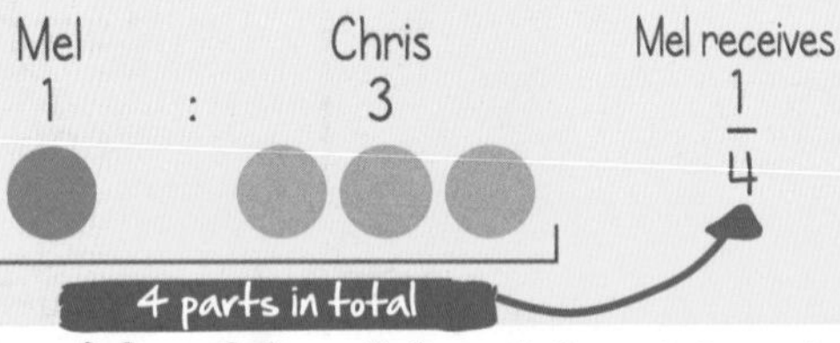

Mel receives $\frac{1}{4}$

SET?

A. Share £60 in the ratio:

(i) 1 : 4

(ii) 3 : 7

(iii) 4 : 11

(iv) 3 : 17

(v) 1 : 2 : 3

B. Ezra and Isla are sharing money in the ratio 2 : 5

(i) If Ezra receives £12, how much money does Isla receive?

(ii) If Isla receives £12.50, how much money do they share in total?

C. Evie and Steve share some money in the ratio 2 : 7
Steve receives £55 more than Evie.
How much money do Evie and Steve have in total?

D. Tom is sending some letters.
3 out of every 4 letters are sent first class.
If 18 letters are sent first class, how many letters are sent altogether?

E. Elijah and Mia share some money in the ratio 1 : 4

(i) What fraction does Elijah get?

(ii) What fraction does Mia get?

F. Sweets are shared in the ratio n : 3, where n is a positive integer.
There are 24 sweets in total.
Find 3 possible values for n.

G. John, Kam and Liam share some money in the ratio 5 : 6 : 9
In total, John and Liam receive £56.
Work out the amount of money Kam receives.

GO!

Good work!

1. The ratio of the angles in a triangle is:

   1 : 5 : 6

   Fatima thinks the triangle is right-angled.

   Do you agree? Explain your answer.

2. Harley and Lucy shared some sweets in the ratio 7 : 4

   Harley got 21 more sweets than Lucy.

   Maya thinks Lucy got 12 sweets because:

   $21 \div 7 = 3$ and $3 \times 4 = 12$

   Do you agree? Explain your answer.

3. There are between 20 and 38 students in a class. The ratio of girls to boys is 5 : 7

   How many students could there be in the class?

4. There are 60 people in a club.

   Half of the people in the club are women.

   The number of women in the club is three times the number of men in the club.

   The rest of the people are children.

   The ratio of the number of children in the club to the number of men in club is n : 1

   Work out the value of n.

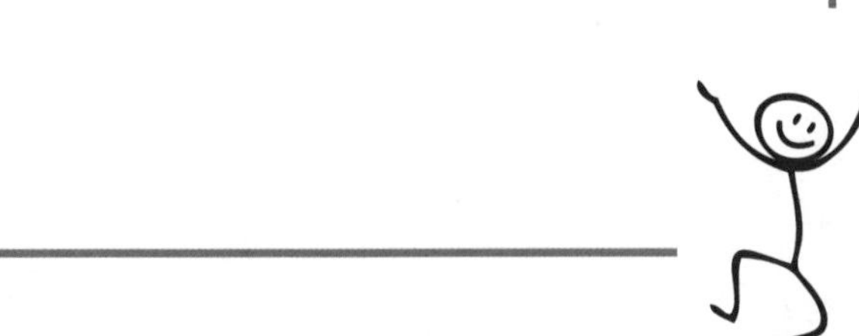

READY?

It is **REALLY USEFUL** to know how to find equivalent ratios
e.g. 2 : 3 is equivalent to 4 : 6, 6 : 9, 8 : 12 etc.

Two or more ratios can be combined into one single ratio (or used to create another ratio). For example, if you know x : y and y : z you can then find the ratios x : y : z and x : z.

e.g. 1 a : b = 8 : 5 and b : c = 3 : 4

b is the common letter so we need to get the same value for b in both ratios

a) Find the ratio a : b : c

a : b = 8 : 5 (×3) → 24 : 15
b : c = 3 : 4 (×5) → 15 : 20

b is now the same value in both ratios

So ... a : b : c
24 : 15 : 20

It is important when multiplying a ratio you multiply all parts by the same value

b) Find the ratio a : c in its simplest form.

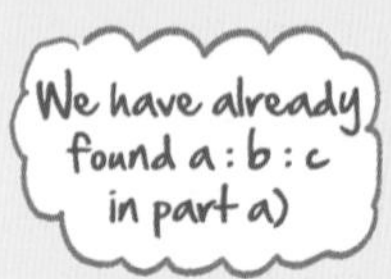

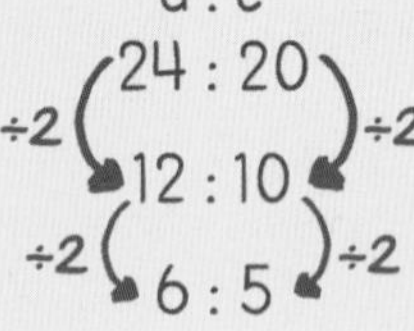

e.g. 2 On a farm:
The number of sheep and the number of cows are in the ratio 6 : 5
The number of goats and the number of cows are in the ratio 1 : 2
The total number of goats, cows and sheep on the farm is 216
How many cows are there on the farm?

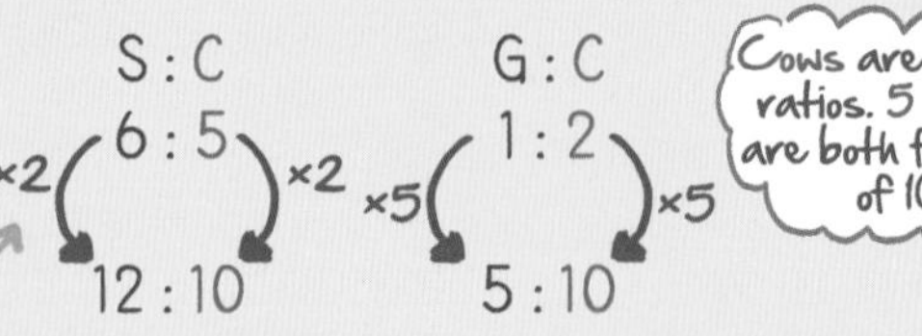

Sheep : Cows : Goats
12 : 10 : 5
Total on the farm → 216

12 + 10 + 5 = 27 parts

So ... 216 ÷ 27 = 8 and 10 × 8 = 80

There are 80 cows on the farm

e.g. 3 At a school event, the ratio of men to women is 5 : 3
The ratio of women to children is 7 : 4
Show that more than half of the people at the event are men.

So just like in e.g. 1 and e.g. 2:

1. Get the common letter the same value in each ratio
2. Re-write as a new ratio

m : w = 5 : 3 (×7) → 35 : 21
w : c = 7 : 4 (×3) → 21 : 12

w is the common letter ... 3 and 7 are both factors of 21

So ... m : w : c
35 : 21 : 12

The fraction of men = $\frac{35}{68}$ which is more than half the people

half would be $\frac{34}{68}$

A. a : b = 1 : 3 b : c = 4 : 3
Find the ratio a : b : c

B. x : y = 5 : 2 y : z = 5 : 2
Find the ratio x : y : z

C. a : b = 3 : 5 b : c = 4 : 3
Find the ratio a : c in its simplest form.

D. A bag contains blue, red and green beads.
The ratio of blue to red beads is 2 : 3
The ratio of red to green beads is 4 : 5

(i) Find the ratio:
blue beads : red beads : green beads

(ii) If there are 45 green beads, what is the total number of beads?

E. In a village:
Women : Children = 11 : 3
Men : Children = 5 : 2

(i) Find the ratio of Men : Women.

(ii) There are 36 children in the village.
Find the total population of the village.

Champion!

1. Find a : b : c : d if:

a : b = 2 : 3

b : c = 5 : 2

b : d = 1 : 2

2. At a school show:

The ratio of men to women is 5 : 4

The ratio of women to children is 4 : 5

Anya says that the number of children and men must be the same.

Is Anya correct? Explain your answer.

3. The colours of cars at a garage are in the ratios:

white : red = 7 : 3
red : blue = 5 : 2

Sam thinks the ratio of white : blue is 7 : 2

Explain the mistake that Sam has made and give the correct ratio.

4. The number of mints and the number of jelly beans are in the ratio 5 : 6

The number of chocolates and the number of jelly beans are in the ratio 11 : 4

The total number of mints, jelly beans and chocolates in a jar is 220

How many jelly beans are there in the jar?

READY?

If two things (let's call them x and y ... but they could be called almost anything!) are in **direct proportion**, a multiplicative relationship connects them (they can be expressed as multiples of each other).

e.g. 1 The cost of 3 ice creams is £5.10
What is the cost of 2 ice creams?

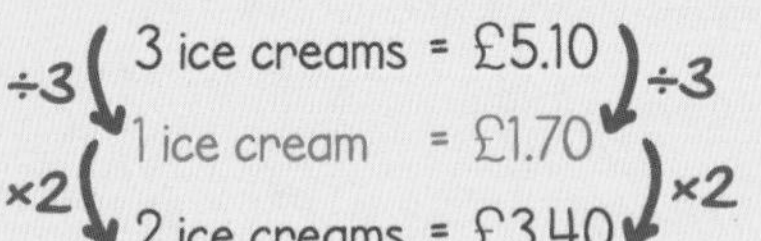

It can be helpful to use a table to find the multipliers between each variable (a variable is an amount that can have different values).

e.g. 2 q is directly proportional to p.
q is 24 when p = 4

Look out for other multipliers

a) Find q when p = 12

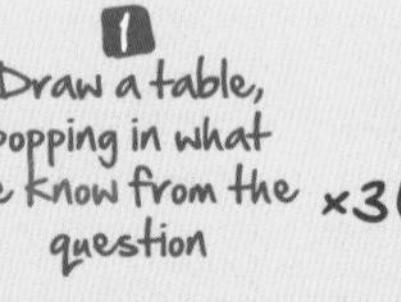

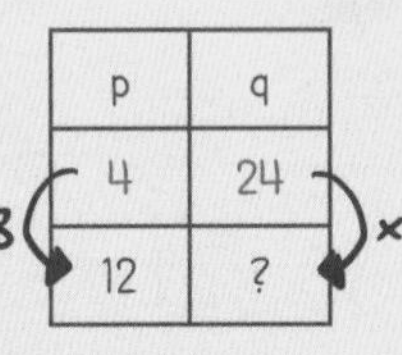

p	q
4	24
12	?

2 Find and use a multiplier connecting 2 of the values ($4 \times 3 = 12$)

$q = 24 \times 3 = 72$

b) Find p when q = 18

1 Table and numbers

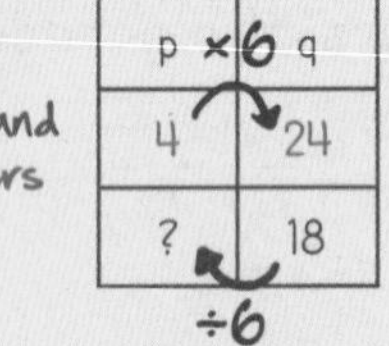

p	q
4	24
?	18

2 Find and use a multiplier

$p = 18 \div 6 = 3$

From p to q is ×6, so q to p must be ÷6

YOU REALLY NEED TO KNOW:

When x is **directly proportional** to y, if x is doubled then y is also doubled, if x is halved then y is also halved etc. It's easy to see this relationship on a graph between x and y:

It's a straight line through the origin.

(0,0)

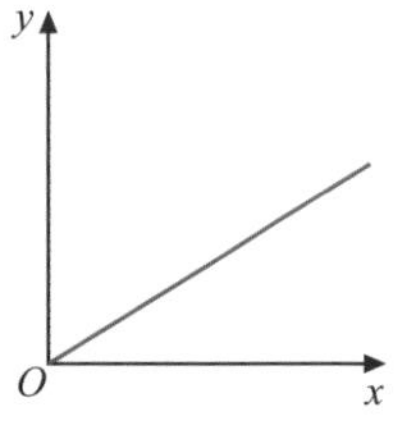

You need to be prepared to work with other areas of maths too, such as money, ratio, percentages, etc.

e.g. 3 The ratio of the cost of one metre of nylon fabric to the cost of one metre of wool fabric is 2 : 5
Complete the table of costs:

	2 m	6 m	8 m	9 m
Nylon	£6			
Wool				

1 Use the ratio 2 : 5 and the fact that 2 m of nylon = £6 to find the cost of 2 m of wool

N : W
×3 2 : 5 ×3
6 : 15

So 2 m of wool = £15

2 Find the cost of 1 m for both by dividing the 2 m costs by 2

	1 m	2 m	6 m	8 m	9 m
Nylon	£3	£6	£18	£24	£27
Wool	£7.50	£15	£45	£60	£67.50

÷2 ×3 ×4 ← 8 m + 1 m

3 Find the multipliers and complete the table

WATCH OUT: Multipliers are not always whole numbers

A. y is directly proportional to x.
y is 32 when x = 8
Find the value of y when x = 24

B. A is directly proportional to B.
A is 9 when B = 6
Find the value of A when B = 10

C. P is directly proportional to Q.
P is 21 when Q = 7
Find the value of Q when P = 36

D. Each table shows a set of numbers with a direct proportional relationship. Find the missing values.

(i)

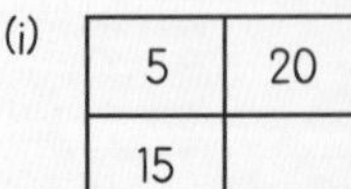

5	20
15	

(ii)

4	20
6	

(iii)

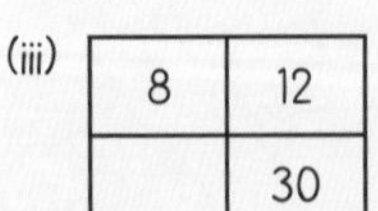

8	12
	30

(iv)

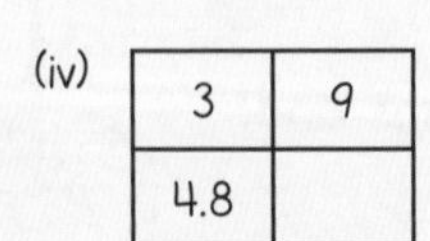

3	9
4.8	

E. The ratio of sheep to cows in a field is 5:2
Complete the table.

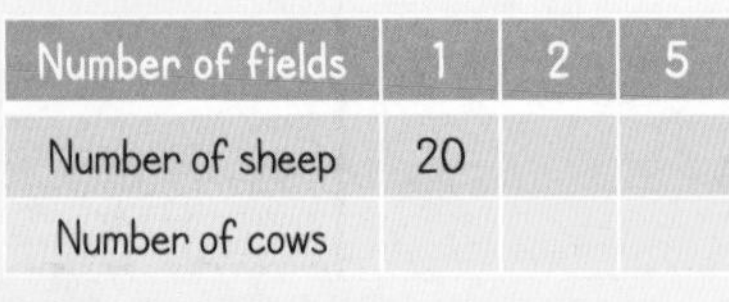

Number of fields	1	2	5
Number of sheep	20		
Number of cows			

F. The mass of a piece of wire is directly proportional to its length.

A piece of wire is 12 cm and weighs 4 g.

Calculate the mass of a 30 cm piece of similar wire.

GO!

DIRECT PROPORTION

Bostin!

1. y is directly proportional to x.

y is 30 when x = 20

Find the value of x when y = 7.5

2. T is directly proportional to L.

Catriona says when L is doubled, the value of T is halved.

Explain why Catriona is incorrect.

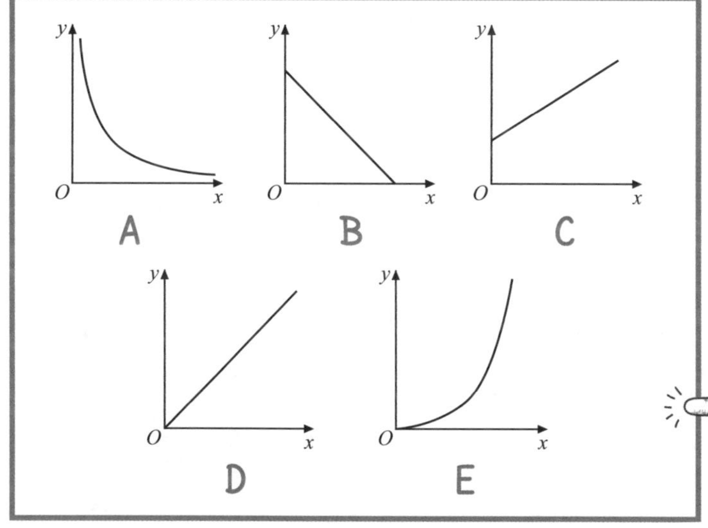

3. Aamir thinks that both graphs C and D show that y is directly proportional to x.

Do you agree? Explain why.

4. The amount of money (m) Terri earns is directly proportional to the number of hours (h) she works.

Terri works 12 hours and earns £105

a) Find a formula linking m and h.

b) Terri earns £166.25
Use the formula to calculate how many hours she worked.

HINT: m = multiplier × h

READY?

It is **USEFUL** to be able to:

* Order decimals, e.g. 0.292 is larger than 0.29 (0.29 = 0.290)
* Use decimals in real life, e.g. £0.292 is 29.2p

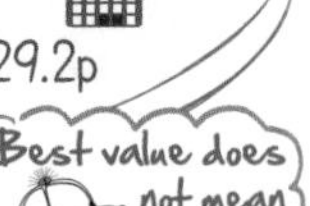

A best value problem will ask to compare two (or more) options to see which is the best value for money.

Best value does not mean cheapest

e.g. 1 A supermarket sells 8 kg of potatoes for £3.52
A farm shop sells 10 kg of the same potatoes for £4.30
Which is the better value for money option?

Supermarket ⟷ Find the cost per kg at both places ⟷ Farm Shop

Supermarket	Farm Shop
8kg → £3.52	10kg → £4.30
÷8 ÷8	÷10 ÷10
1kg → £0.44	1kg → £0.43

The farm shop is better value as 43p is less than 44p per kg

e.g. 2 Milk is sold in two sizes of bottle.
A 4 pint bottle of milk costs £1.15
A 6 pint bottle of milk costs £1.68
Which bottle of milk is the best value for money?

Write all the digits on your calculator display

4 pints	6 pints
4 pints → £1.15	6 pints → £1.68
÷4 ÷4	÷6 ÷6
1 pint → £0.2875	1 pint → £0.28

A 6 pint bottle is better value as 28p < 28.75p per pint

OR

Find LCM of 4 and 6

4, 8, (12) → 3 × 4 pints = 12 pints, 3 × £1.15 = £3.45
6, (12) → 2 × 6 pints = 12 pints, 2 × £1.68 = £3.36

A 6 pint bottle is better value: £3.36 < £3.45 for 12 pints

Sometimes there might be a shortcut.

e.g. 3 75 ml of toothpaste costs 80p.
225 ml of the same toothpaste costs £2.10
Which size gives the best value for money option?

1 Notice that:

75 ml × 3 = 225 ml

2 Work out what 3 lots of the small tube of toothpaste would cost:

80p × 3 = £2.40

The 225 ml size is better value
(as it's £2.10 for the same amount)

Sometimes we work with three or more items.

e.g. 4 Jars of coffee are sold in three different sizes.

12 servings £5.65

20 servings £9.20

35 servings £15.75

Which size jar gives the best value for money?

12 → £5.65	20 → £9.20	35 → £15.75
÷12 ÷12	÷20 ÷20	÷35 ÷35
1 → £0.4708...	1 → £0.46	1 → £0.45

The 35 servings jar is the best value for money as it is the least value per serving

A. Which box of teabags is the better value for money?

120 teabags
£2.00

300 teabags
£4.80

B. A 4 pint bottle of milk costs £1.15
A 6 pint bottle of milk costs £1.75
Which bottle is the best value for money?

C. Plants are sold in three different sizes of tray:

- A small tray of 30 plants costs £6.50
- A medium tray of 40 plants costs £8.95
- A large tray of 50 plants costs £10.99

Which size tray is the best value for money?

D. A 500 g bag of sugar costs 70p.
A 1.5 kg bag of sugar costs £2
Which size of bag gives the better value for money?

HINT: Look at the units

GO!

PROPORTION: BEST VALUE

Superb!

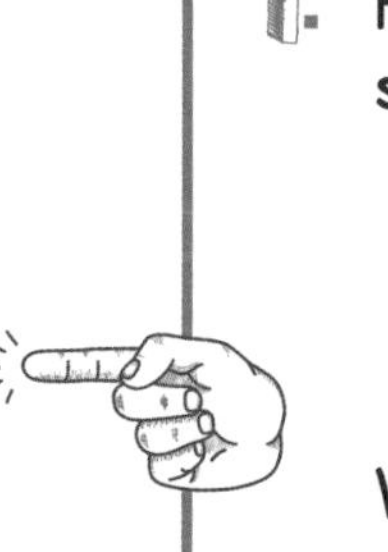

1. Flour can be bought in three different pack sizes:

   750 grams for 81p

   900 grams for 99p

   1.5 kg for £1.65

   Which pack size gives the best value for money?

2. Shampoo is sold in two sizes of bottle:

   250 ml for £1.80 and 400 ml for £3

   Roger works out which size gives the best value.

   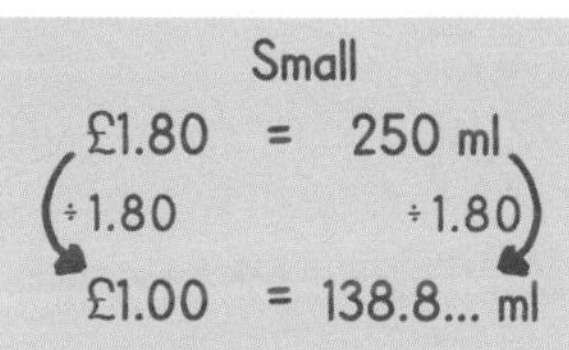

   Large
   £3.00 = 400 ml
   ÷3.00 ÷3.00
   £1.00 = 133.3... ml

   The small bottle is better value

   Do you agree with Roger?
   Justify your answer.

3. Two garden centres sell the same tray of plants for the same price. They offer different deals:

   Garden Centre A
   3 trays for the price of 2

   Garden Centre B
   Buy one tray, get a second for half price

   Jude is buying 12 trays of plants.
   Which garden centre offers the best value for money for Jude?

4. Breakfast cereal is sold in two different sizes:

   - Standard: 450 grams for £1.60
   - Family: 790 grams for £2.50

   The family pack is better value for money.

   For a limited time, a special offer on the standard pack offers 25% extra free.

   Is the family pack still better value for money?

   Explain your answer.

READY?

It is **REALLY USEFUL** to remember how to convert between metric measures using the facts:

1 kg = 1000 g 1 litre = 1000 ml

We can solve proportion problems by scaling up and/or scaling down: i.e. if we know a recipe for 3 people, we can work out the recipe for 1 person (divide by 3) and then multiply by 4, 5, 6, 7, etc to work out the recipe for 4, 5, 6, 7, etc people.

e.g. 1 The ingredients for Victoria Sponge Cake are shown here:

a) How much flour is needed to make the cake for 12 people?

From the recipe ...

×2 6 people → 200 g flour ×2
12 people → 400 g flour

400 g of flour is needed

b) How many eggs are needed to make the cake for 3 people?

From the recipe ...

÷2 6 people → 4 eggs ÷2
3 people → 2 eggs

2 eggs are needed

c) How much cream is needed to make the cake for 15 people?

From the recipe ...

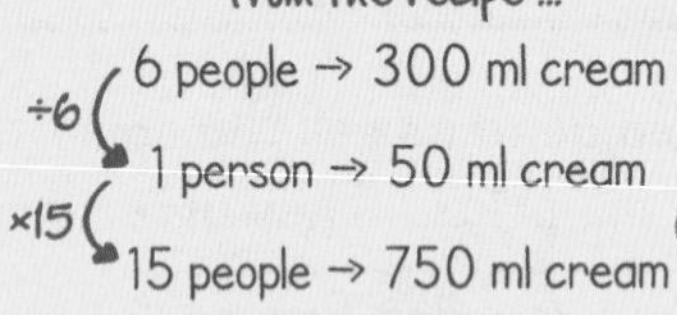

750 ml cream is needed

e.g. 2 A drink is made by mixing 25 ml of cordial with 200 ml of lemonade.
Ross has 200 ml of cordial and $1\frac{1}{2}$ litres of lemonade. (1500 ml)
What is the maximum number of drinks he can make?

He does not have enough lemonade for 8 drinks

The maximum number of drinks he can make is 7

e.g. 3 Here are the ingredients needed to make 12 cakes.

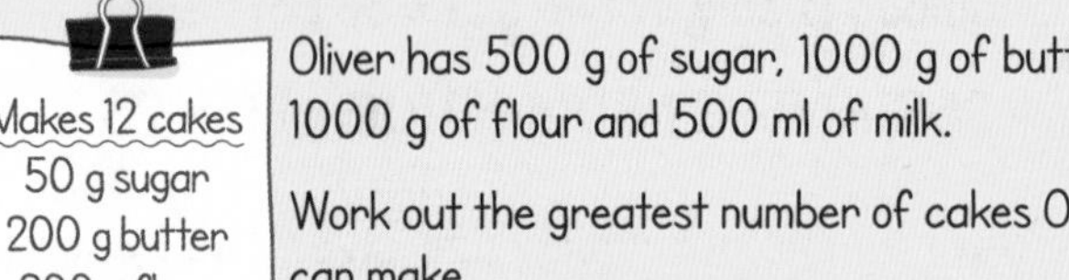

Oliver has 500 g of sugar, 1000 g of butter, 1000 g of flour and 500 ml of milk.

Work out the greatest number of cakes Oliver can make.

Sugar:

×10 50 g → 12 cakes ×10
500 g → 120 cakes

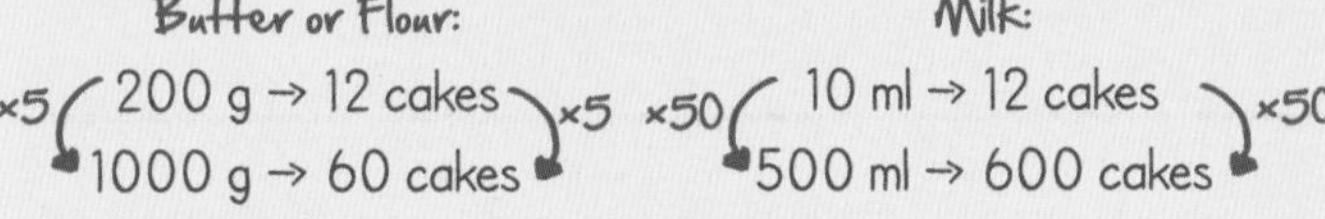

The butter and flour limit how many cakes he can make

The greatest number of cakes he can make is 60

A. The recipe for Corned Beef Casserole (serves 6 people) uses:

600 g corned beef 1 onion
300 ml of gravy stock 3 carrots

(i) Work out the recipe to serve 18 people.

(ii) Work out the recipe to serve 3 people.

(iii) Work out the recipe to serve 9 people.

B. The recipe for Amanda's Lush Cake (serves 4 people) uses:

2 eggs 80 g of sugar
150 g of flour 60 g of margarine

(i) How much flour is needed to make the cake for 8 people?

(ii) How many eggs are needed to make the cake for 20 people?

(iii) How much sugar is needed to make the cake for 10 people?

(iv) Kai has 150 g of margarine and plenty of the other ingredients. How many people can he make cake for?

(v) Write the recipe for 6 people.

C. The recipe to make 800 ml of Mango Smoothie uses:

$1\frac{1}{2}$ cups mango juice
1 banana
1 cup of mango chunks
200 ml Greek yogurt

Amber has 500 ml of Greek yogurt, 2 bananas and plenty of mango juice and mango chunks.

What is the maximum amount of Mango Smoothie she can make?

PROPORTION: RECIPES

Cracking!

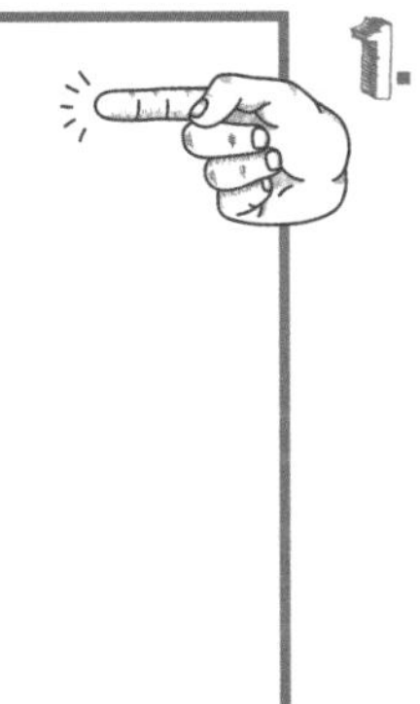

1. The recipe for Grandma Margaret's famous Butterfly Cakes uses:

2 eggs	150 g margarine
100 g sugar	120 g flour

The recipe makes 12 cakes.

Paige has 10 eggs, 600 g each of sugar, margarine and flour. She thinks that the maximum number of cakes she can make is 48. Is Paige correct? Explain why.

2. The recipe for Lizzie's Jam Cake (serves 6 people) uses:

1 egg	1 cup of sugar
2 cups of flour	60 g of margarine

Jam to spread

Keanu thinks he needs 1 kg of margarine to make Jam Cake for 10 people.

Do you agree? Explain your answer.

3. <u>Carrot soup (serves 4)</u>

400 g carrots

600 ml vegetable stock

Salt and pepper

Maisie has 1.5 kg of carrots and 3 litres of vegetable stock.

What is the maximum number of people she can make carrot soup for?

4. The recipe for Evan's Fabulous Tuna Pasta Bake (serves 4 people) uses:

6 ounces pasta	2 ounces mushrooms
1 tin of tuna	$\frac{1}{2}$ pint of tomato soup
1 onion	1 ounce margarine
2 ounces cheese	Crisps to sprinkle on the top

Match the people to ingredients (one has been done for you) and find the missing values.

People	Ingredient
6	..... ounces pasta
3	100% more onions
1	$1\frac{1}{4}$ pints of tomato soup
10	$\frac{1}{2}$ ounce cheese
.....	50% more tuna

READY?

REALLY USEFUL to know:
Different countries around the world use different currencies. The exchange rate states how one currency matches to another.

In currency exchange questions, it can really help to set the facts out in a table so you can use multipliers to work out missing values. Be careful, sometimes the multiplier might not be obvious.

e.g. 1 Jonathan is travelling from the UK to Switzerland. He wants to exchange £150 for Swiss francs. The exchange rate in the UK is:

£1 = 1.30 Swiss francs

a) How many Swiss francs does Jonathan get?

1 Draw a table

£	Swiss francs

2 Pop in what you know and find a multiplier

£	Swiss francs
1	1.30
×150 → 150	

3 Use the same multiplier in the other column

£	Swiss francs
1	1.30
×150 → 150	195 ← ×150

Look out for other multipliers

Jonathan gets 195 Swiss francs

e.g. 1 continued At the end of his trip Jonathan has 39 Swiss francs left and wants to change them back to pounds. The exchange rate remains the same in the UK and the exchange rate in Switzerland is:

1 Swiss franc = £0.79

b) Will he get more pounds (£) in Switzerland, or should he wait until returning to the UK?

In Switzerland:

£	Swiss francs
0.79	1
×39 → 30.81	39 ← ×39

In the UK:

£	Swiss francs
1	1.30
÷1.30 → 0.769	1 ← ÷1.30
×39 → 30	39 ← ×39

He has 39 Swiss francs ... first work out the value of 1 Swiss franc

Jonathan gets more money if he exchanges in Switzerland as £30.81 is more than £30.00

e.g. 2 Kanav is going to America and needs to change some money into dollars.

Kanav wants to change up to £700 into dollars.

The exchange rate is £1 = $1.21

What is the maximum number of 50 dollar notes he can get?

£	Dollars
1	1.21
×700 → 700	847 ← ×700

Do not round up to 17

847 ÷ 50 = 16.94

So he can get sixteen 50 dollar notes

A. Ruth spends £350 buying some Swedish krona. The exchange rate is:

£1 = 12 Swedish krona

How many Swedish krona does Ruth get?

B. Estelle buys some Jordanian dinar. She exchanges £150 using the rate:

£1 = 0.92 Jordanian dinar

How many Jordanian dinar does Estelle get?

C. Thomas changes £385 using the exchange rate:

1 Australian dollar = £0.55

How many Australian dollars does Thomas get?

D. Rebekah buys some Bahraini dinar using the exchange rate:

1 Bahraini dinar = £2.05

She spends £492. How many Bahraini dinar does she get?

E. Jonah buys some euros using the exchange rate:

£1 = 1.14 euros

He wants to change up to £200 into euros and wants as many €20 notes as possible. What is the maximum number of €20 notes can he get?

PROPORTION: EXCHANGE RATES

Outstanding!

Rand or pounds is fine

1. In South Africa, Mason sees a camera for 14,000 rand.

   In the UK, the same camera is on sale for £900

   The exchange rate is £1 = 17.63 rand.

   Work out the difference between the cost of the camera in South Africa and the UK.

2. Cole is going on holiday to Iceland. He wants to buy some spending money in Icelandic krona.

   Cole has £30 to exchange. All the money he buys will be given in 500 krona notes.

   The exchange rate is £1 = 155.87 krona.

   Cole buys as many 500 krona notes as possible. How much change to the nearest penny does he get?

3. Hannah wants to change some pounds to Polish zloty.

   In the UK the exchange rate is £1 = 4.80 zloty.

   In Poland the exchange rate is 1 zloty = £0.20

   In which country would Hannah get more zloty for her pounds? You must show your working out.

4. Faisal is working out how many Japanese yen he can buy.

   He knows that:

   10 Japanese yen = £0.07

   Faisal has £200 to exchange. He works out:

   200 ÷ 0.07 = 2857.1 yen

   Do you agree? Explain why.

READY?

If two variables are **inversely proportional** to each other then when one variable increases the other variable decreases at the same rate.

* When x is directly proportional to y, if x is doubled then y is also doubled.
* When x is **inversely proportional** to y, if x is doubled then y is halved. The graph of two variables in inverse proportion looks like this:

e.g. 1 a) If it takes 2 people 3 days to paint a fence, how long will it take 4 people to paint the fence?

Day 1 Day 2 Day 3

2 people → 3 days (This means it would take 1 person 6 days to paint the fence)

Total number of 'work days' = 2 × 3 = 6

So if we have 4 people, we still have 6 work days

6 ÷ 4 = 1.5

It will take 4 people 1.5 days to paint the fence

b) What assumption have you made in part a) and if your assumption is incorrect, how would this affect your answer?

The people work at the same rate as each other. (Assumption)
If they work at a faster rate, it will take less time. If they work at a slower rate it will take more time.

Setting the information out in a table can help.

e.g. 2 3 people take 2 hours to put some letters into envelopes. Find the difference in time between 3 people and 5 people to pack the letters.

1. Draw a table popping in what we know from the question
2. Work out how long it would take one person
3. Work out how long for five people

Number of People	Time (hours)
3	2
÷3 → 1	×3 → 6
×5 → 5	÷5 → 1.2

Do the INVERSE operation!

It will take 1.2 hours for 5 people to put the letters into envelopes

1.2 hours = 1 hour 12 minutes

(1.2 × 60 = 72 mins = 1 hr 12 mins) (1.2 hours is NOT 1 hour 20 mins)

2 hours - 1 hour 12 minutes = 48 minutes

It will take 48 minutes less

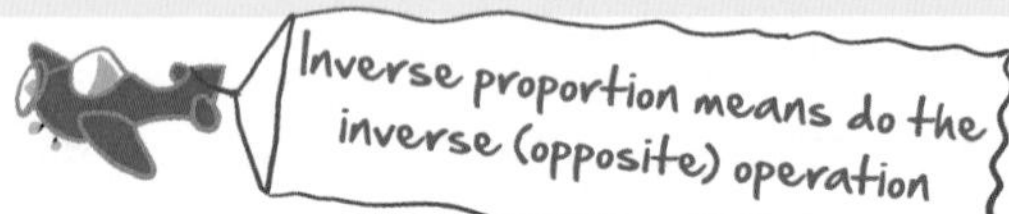

e.g. 3 y is inversely proportional to x.
Complete the table:

x	1	4	60	
y		7.5		12

1. Choose two values next to each other

4	60
7.5	0.5

×15, ÷15

2. Complete the table

x	1	4	60	2.5
y	30	7.5	0.5	12

÷4, ÷24, ×4, ×24

SET?

A. A swimming pool takes 36 minutes to fill with water using a hosepipe.
How long will it take if the rate of flow of water is doubled?

B. It takes 2 people 4 days to build a shed.
How long would it take 8 people to build the same shed if they work at the same rate?

C. A journey takes 3 hours travelling at 40 mph.
How long would the journey take travelling at 60 mph?

D. Given that y is inversely proportional to x, complete the table:

x	3	9		
y		7	84	210

E. y is inversely proportional to x.
Which graph shows this?

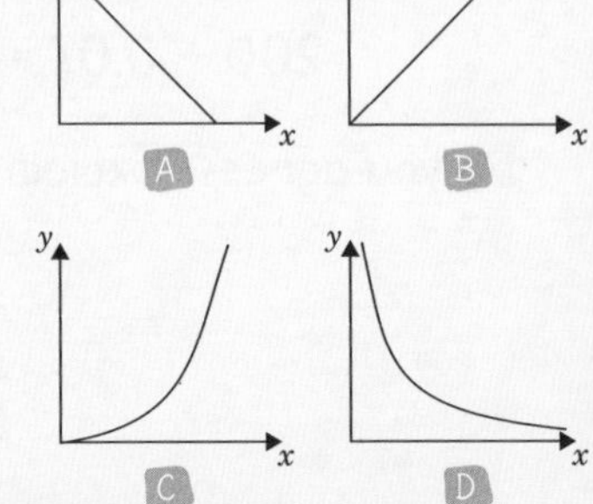

INVERSE PROPORTION

Worthy!

1. 4 workers take 5 days to paint a house.

   Monika thinks it would have taken 8 workers 10 days to paint a house working at the same rate.

   Do you agree with Monika?
   Explain your answer.

2. Two students are asked to identify which graph represents inverse proportion:

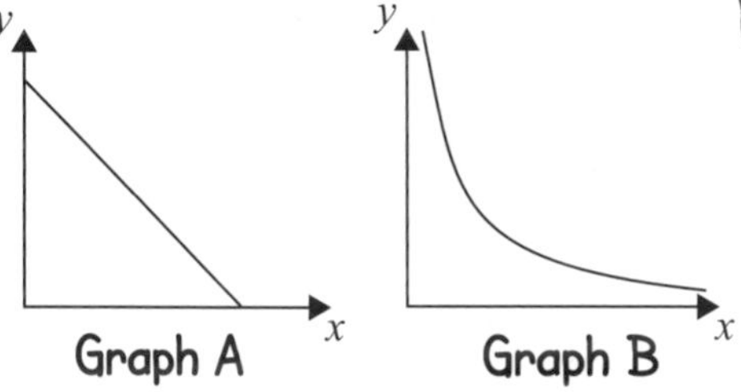

   Lindsey thinks Graph A because it is the opposite to direct proportion.

   Sadie thinks Graph B because when one amount doubles, the other amount is halved.

   Tick the correct statement.

   A Both Lindsey and Sadie are correct

   B Only Lindsey is correct

   C Only Sadie is correct

   D Both Lindsey and Sadie are incorrect

3. Suz and Alec are putting leaflets into envelopes. They take 3 hours to put 120 leaflets into envelopes.

   Patrick, Ashley and Vincent start to help them.

   Working at the same rate, how long will it take the five of them to put another 120 leaflets into envelopes? Give your answer in minutes.

4. 7 builders take 90 days to build a house.

   a) How many more builders must be employed to build the same house in 15 days?

   b) State an assumption you have made in your answer to part a).

READY?

We really need to know how to find a percentage of an amount both with and without a calculator.

REMEMBER:

* To find 10% of a number, you just need to divide by 10
* To find 1%, you simply divide the 10% value by 10 again

Dividing by 10 to find 10% is a special case ... don't try this for other percentages

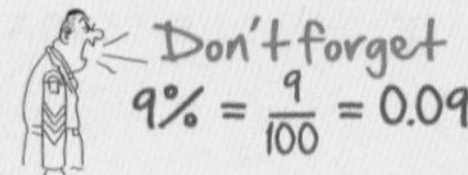

e.g. 1 Find 35% of 620

1. Find 10% — 10% of 620 → 620 ÷ 10 = 62
2. Half of the 10% — 5% of 620 → 62 ÷ 2 = 31
3. 3 of the 10%'s — 30% of 620 → 62 × 3 = 186
4. Add the 30% and 5% — 35% of 620 → 186 + 31 = 217

e.g. 2 Find 12% of 250

10% of 250 → 250 ÷ 10 = 25

1% of 250 → 25 ÷ 10 = 2.5 (Divide the 10% by 10 again to get 1%)

So 2% of 250 → 2.5 × 2 = 5

So 12% of 250 → 25 + 5 = 30

When using a calculator it is far quicker and easier to write the percentage as a decimal first.

e.g. 3 Find 27% of 420

0.27 × 420 = 113.4

e.g. 4 Find 9% of 250

0.09 × 250 = 22.5

Don't forget $9\% = \frac{9}{100} = 0.09$

e.g. 5 Find 22.5% of 46

0.225 × 46 = 10.35

e.g. 6 Find 1.7% of £148

0.017 × 148 = 2.516 → £2.52

Money must be rounded to two d.p.

e.g. 7 John bought a car for £6000 plus VAT at 20%. John paid £3000 when he got the car. He then paid the rest in 10 equal monthly payments.

How much was each monthly payment?

1. Find 10% — 10% of £6000 = £600
2. 2 × 10% — 20% of £6000 = £1200
3. Full cost of the car — £6000 + £1200 = £7200
4. Take off the £3000 — £7200 - £3000 = £4200
5. Divide by 10 — £4200 ÷ 10 = £420

So each monthly payment was £420

SET?

A. Find 60% of 120

B. Find 55% of 240

C. Find 21% of 300

D. Find 7% of 85

E. Find 12.5% of 140

F. Which is greater:
25% of 88 or 88% of 25?

G. A computer costs £360 plus VAT at 20%.

How much does the computer cost?

H. A vacuum cleaner costs £85

Stan gets 10% discount off the price in a sale.

How much does Stan pay for the vacuum cleaner?

PERCENTAGES 1

Good job!

1. Stuart is working out 4% of $435

He types the following into his calculator:

0.4 × 435

and writes the answer as $174

Do you agree with Stuart?
Justify your answer.

2. Two shops sell the same phone. In both shops it is £196. One shop increases the price by 17.5%. The other shop increases the price by 22.5%.

Calculate the difference between the new prices of the phone in the two shops.

3. Elise is working out 20% of 600 kg.

She types 600 ÷ 20 into her calculator.

Elise writes down the answer: 30 kg

What is Elise's mistake?

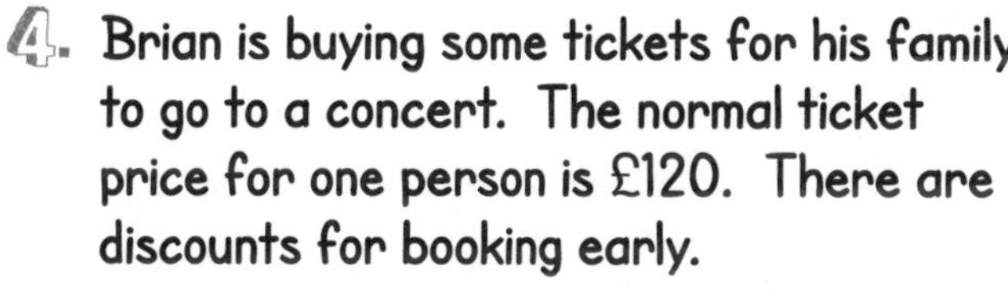

4. Brian is buying some tickets for his family to go to a concert. The normal ticket price for one person is £120. There are discounts for booking early.

- Adult tickets have 30% off the normal price.
- A child's ticket has 60% off the normal price.

Brian buys two adult tickets and three child's tickets with the discount.

Work out how much he pays.

READY?

You **REALLY NEED** to know how to write one amount as a fraction of another:
36 as a fraction of 45 can be written as $\frac{36}{45}$

Converting between fractions, decimals and percentages is useful when asked to write one amount as a percentage of another.

e.g. 1 What is 36 out of 45 as a percentage?

$36 \div 45 = 0.8$ and $0.8 \times 100 = 80\%$

e.g. 2 What is 11 out of 20 as a percentage?

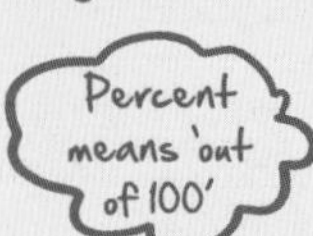

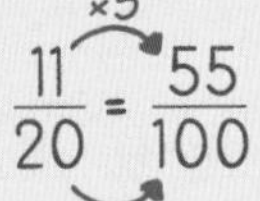

$\frac{11}{20} = \frac{55}{100}$ (×5) and $\frac{55}{100} = 55\%$

We also need to be able to work out a percentage change (an increase or decrease):

$$\text{Percentage change} = \frac{\text{actual change}}{\text{original amount}} \times 100$$

e.g. 3 The average number of students absent from a school decreases from 56 to 35
Calculate the percentage decrease. (Original amount)

1. Find actual decrease (the 'change') $56 - 35 = 21$
2. Use the formula $\frac{21}{56} \times 100 = 37.5\%$

e.g. 4 A puppy weighed 2 kg.
Ten weeks later the puppy weighed 3.5 kg.
Calculate the percentage increase.

1. Find actual increase (the 'change') $3.5 - 2 = 1.5$ kg
2. Use the formula $\frac{1.5}{2} \times 100 = 75\%$

In financial contexts we often deal with profit (increase) and loss (decrease).

e.g. 5 Lisa bought her house for £200,000 and sold it for £240,000
Calculate the percentage profit.

Actual profit = 240,000 - 200,000 = 40,000

Percentage profit = $\frac{40,000}{200,000} \times 100 = 20\%$

e.g. 6 Bobby buys a bike for £120. He sells the bike for £105
Calculate the percentage loss.

Actual loss = 120 - 105 = 15

Percentage loss = $\frac{15}{120} \times 100 = 12.5\%$

Using multipliers speeds up calculations.

e.g. 7 Increase £420 by 22%

An increase of 22% = original (100%) + 22% = 122%
122% → a multiplier of 1.22
420 × 1.22 = £512.40

e.g. 8 Decrease £420 by 22%

A decrease of 22% = original (100%) − 22% = 78%
78% → a multiplier of 0.78 (Not 0.22)
420 × 0.78 = £327.60

A. What is 7 out of 10 as a percentage?

B. Mo scores 32 out of 40 in a test. What percentage did he get?

C. A car is bought for £1500
It is sold for £1250
Calculate the percentage loss to one decimal place.

D. A shirt is bought for £10
It is sold online for £22.50
Calculate the percentage profit.

E. The population of a town increases from 22,500 to 42,750
Calculate the percentage change.

F. Increase £120 by 62%

G. Decrease £85 by 6%

H. Increase 80 kg by 17%

GO! PERCENTAGES 2

Magic!

1. In 2006 Chris bought his house for £215,000

   In 2009 he sold his house for £176,000

   Work out his percentage change to 1 d.p.

2. Edwina buys a dress for £135 and sells it for £90. She works out her percentage loss to be:

$$\frac{45}{90} \times 100 = 50\%$$

   Explain why Edwina is incorrect.

3. Roberta says:

   'If I increase an amount by 25% by multiplying by 1.25 then I must multiply the new amount by 0.75 to get back to the original amount'

   Do you agree with Roberta? Give reasons for your answer.

4. Percentage error is calculated as the actual error as a percentage of the correct amount.

   Joey measured his heart rate as 99 beats per minute. His actual heart rate was 90 beats per minute.

   What is the percentage error?

5. Freya sells cars.

   In January, she sold 40 cars.

   In February, Freya sold 15% more cars than in January.

   In March, Freya sold 25% fewer cars than in January.

   Calculate the percentage change in her sales from February to March. Give your answer to one decimal place.

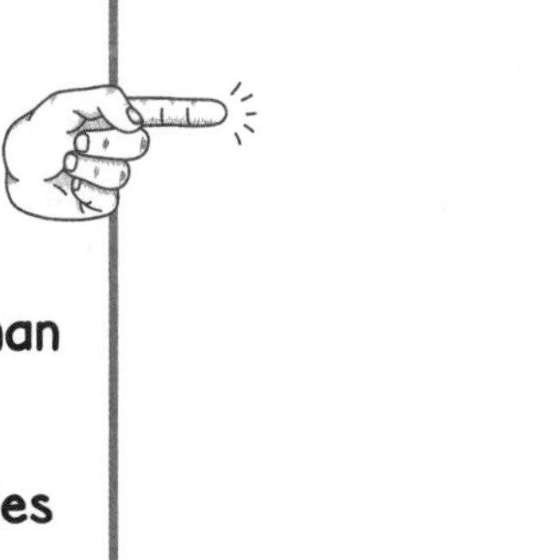

READY?

Interest is the charge made for borrowing money or the payment received for investing money (e.g. in a bank account). There are two ways in which interest can be calculated ... simple or compound.

You **REALLY NEED** to know how to:

- Find a percentage of an amount with and without a calculator
- Use multiplier methods with percentage increase:
  e.g. Increase 340 by 5% → 340 × 1.05 = 357
  100% + 5% = 105%

SIMPLE INTEREST: The simplest way to calculate interest.

e.g. 1 £500 is invested in a savings account.
A simple interest rate of 5% per year is offered.
How much interest is earned over four years?

Let's create a table

÷2 10% of 500 = 50 → 5% of 500 = 25 ÷2

Year	Amount at year start	Interest at year end	Amount at year end
1	£500	£25	£525
2	£525	£25	£550
3	£550	£25	£575
4	£575	£25	£600

4 × £25 = £100, so £100 interest is earned over 4 years

COMPOUND INTEREST: Builds up more quickly. It is the most common way of calculating interest.

e.g. 2 £600 is invested in a savings account.
A compound interest rate of 4.5% per annum is offered.
How much is in the account after three years?

'annum' means 'year'

10% → 60
1% → 6
0.5% → 3
so 4.5% → 27
OR 600 × 0.045 = 27

Year	Amount at year start	Interest at year end	Amount at year end	Or using multipliers
1	£600	£27	£627	600 × 1.045
2	£627	£28.215 → £28.22	£655.22	627 × 1.045
3	£655.22	£29.4849 → £29.48	£684.70	655.22 × 1.045

At the end of 3 years there is £684.70 in the account

You could use: starting number × multiplier^{years} → 600×1.045^3

It is not always about interest and money.

e.g. 3 The population P, of a town t years after January 1st 2018 is given by this formula:

$$P = 4300 \times 1.04^t$$

Original population (4300); Multiplier = 1.04 so rate of growth = 4%; Number of years (t)

Using the formula, what should the population be at the start of 2021?

Jan 18 → Jan 19 → Jan 20 → Jan 21 = 3 years

Population = $4300 \times 1.04^3 = 4836.9152$

At the start of 2021 the population should be 4837 (nearest whole number)

A. £1000 is invested in an account that pays simple interest of 3% per year.
How much interest is earned over five years?

B. £480 is invested in an account paying simple interest of 2.5% per year.
How much is in the account after four years?

C. A savings account pays compound interest of 4% per year. £800 is invested in the account.
How much interest is earned over 3 years?

D. £1200 is invested in an account that pays compound interest of 3.2% per year.
How much is in the account after 2 years?

E. The population of a village is 3500 and it is growing at a rate of 2.5% per year.
Using the formula:

$$P = 3500 \times 1.025^t$$

What will the population be in 5 years time?

Always check whether you are being asked to calculate the amount of interest or the total amount

INTEREST AND GROWTH

Ace!

Year	Amount at year start	Interest at year end	Amount at year end
1	£2500	£100	£2600
2	£2600	£100	£2700
3	£2700	£100	£2800

After 3 years I will have £2800

1. Fiona is working out the amount she should have in a savings account after 3 years. She invests £2500 at a compound interest rate of 4%.

   Here is her working.

   Explain the mistake that Fiona has made.

2. Bank A and Bank B offer different deals for savers.

Bank A	Bank B
Simple interest of 4.5% per year	3.5% in the first year. Compound interest of 5% in all other years

Isaac plans on saving £5000 for 3 years. Which bank offers him the greatest interest payment?

You must show workings to justify your decision.

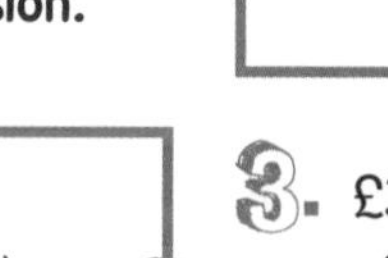

3. £3000 is invested at a compound interest rate of 3.2%. Two students work out the total amount at the end of four years.

Aarons' method	Emily's method
3.2% of £3000 = £96 £96 × 4 = £384 £3000 + £384 = **£3384**	$£3000 \times 1.032^4$ = **£3402.83**

Who is correct? Explain your answer.

4. At the beginning of 2019 the population of a city was 1,560,000.

   Lois assumes that the population will increase at a constant rate of 4.8% each year.

a) Use Lois' assumption to estimate the population at the beginning of 2020. Give your answer correct to 3 significant figures.

b) In which year will the population of the city reach 2 million?

c) If Lois' assumption about the rate of increase is too low, how could this affect your answer to part b)?

READY?

When items go down in value, their value has **depreciated**. Cars are a good example of items that can depreciate.

You **REALLY NEED** to know how to use multiplier methods with percentage decrease:

e.g. Decrease 340 by 15%
340 × 0.85 = 289

100% − 15% = 85%

e.g. 1 Mike buys a car for £12,000. He estimates that it will depreciate by 20% a year for the first three years. If Mike is correct, what will the car be worth after three years?

YEAR 1
Find 20% of 12,000
10% → 1,200
20% → 2,400
12,000 − 2,400 = 9,600
OR
80% of 12,000 = 0.8 × 12,000 = 9,600

YEAR 2
Find 20% of 9,600
10% → 960
20% → 1,920
9,600 − 1,920 = 7,680
OR 80% of 9,600 = 0.8 × 9,600 = 7,680

YEAR 3
Find 20% of 7,680
10% → 768
20% → 1,536
7,680 − 1,536 = 6,144
OR
80% of 7,680 = 0.8 × 7,680 = 6,144

Year	Amount at year start	20%	Amount at year end
1	£12,000	£2,400	£9,600
2	£9,600	£1,920	£7,680
3	£7,680	£1,536	£6,144

If Mike is correct it will be worth £6,144 after 3 years

You could use: starting number × multiplier^{years} → $12{,}000 \times 0.8^3$

e.g. 2 In January 2008 a population of bats was estimated to be 700. Over the next five years the population reduced by 10% each year. What was the population at the end of this time?

Year	Start population	10%	End population
2008	700	70	630
2009	630	63	567
2010	567	56.7 → 57	510
2011	510	51	459
2012	459	45.9 → 46	413

(700 − 70 = 630)

You cannot have part of a bat!

There will be 413 bats remaining

You can choose to take a formula approach to these type of questions.

e.g. 3 The estimated number of red squirrels (S) that there will be in Scotland in n years after January 1st 2018 is given by:

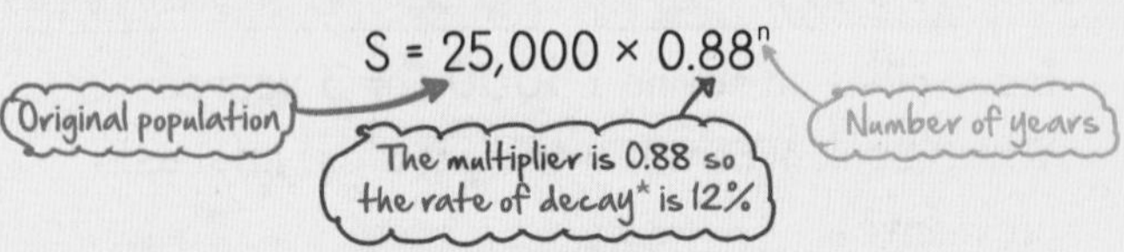

$S = 25{,}000 \times 0.88^n$

The multiplier is 0.88 so the rate of decay* is 12%

How many red squirrels will there be after 8 years?

Population = $25{,}000 \times 0.88^8$ = 8,990.86312
= 8,991 squirrels (to the nearest squirrel)

*Depreciation is to do with money. Populations and other things 'decay'

SET?

A. A car is worth £15,000 when new. It is expected to depreciate by 30% each year. What will its value be after 3 years?

B. Ralph buys a motorbike for £16,642. Its value falls by 11% each year for 2 years. What is it worth now?

C. Kathy buys a mountain bike for £4,500. She sells the bike after two years using a price based on depreciation by 13.4% every year. What is the selling price?

D. In 2014 the population of Harpleton was 45,000. The population fell by 10% every year for the next three years. What was the population in 2017?

E. The value of a £5,000 investment reduces by 6.5% per year. What is it worth after 3 years?

DEPRECIATION AND DECAY

Wow!

1. An investment of £38,000 is made.

Over the next three years, the value of the investment falls by 2.5% per year.

The money is withdrawn from the investment after three years.

How much money has been lost in this time?

2. A car was worth £16,000 when new.

It depreciated by 30% in the first year.

After that, it depreciated by 20% every year.

Tamara works out the value of the car after 4 years. Here is her working.

Tamara is wrong. Find the mistakes and correct her working.

$0.3 \times 16000 = 4800$

$0.2 \times 16000 = 3200$

$3200 \times 3 = 9600$

$16000 - 9600 - 4800 = 1600$

The car is now worth £1600

3. A population of 50,000 decreases by 2% a year. Two students work out the population at the end of two years.

Andy's method	Vicki's method
2% of 50,000 = 1000 50,000 - 1000 = 49,000 2% of 49,000 = 980 49,000 - 980 = **48,020**	$50{,}000 \times 0.98^2 =$ **48,020**

Circle the correct statement. Justify your decision.

Only Andy's method is correct
Only Vicki's method is correct
Andy and Vicki are both incorrect
Andy and Vicki are both correct

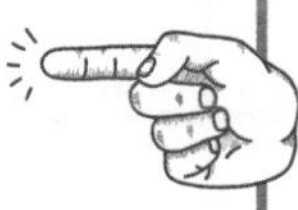

4. Throughout the second half of the 20th century it is thought that tropical rainforests were destroyed at a rate of 1.4% per year.

There were about 20 million square kilometres of tropical rainforest in 1960.

What was the area of tropical rainforest in 1965?
Give your answer to the nearest 1000.

READY?

REMEMBER:
The "original" is always 100%

When dealing with percentages, sometimes you will be given the final value and have to work out the original amount. It's a good idea to draw a picture (not a masterpiece ... just a sketch).

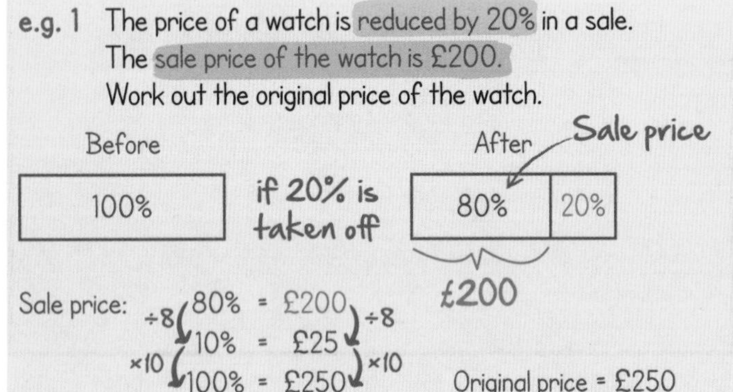

Sometimes you'll be given the reduction or increase (the amount that is taken off or added on) and have to work out either the original or the new value.

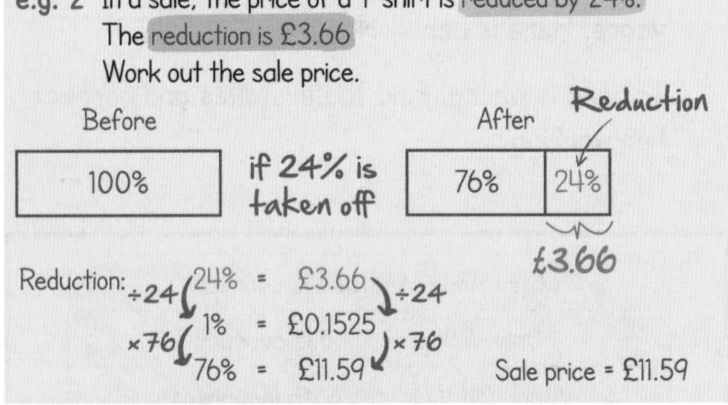

e.g. 3 Mal's wages are increased by 3%. After the increase, his annual salary is £29,355
What was his original salary?

Before

100% — if 3% is added on

After

100% | 3%

103% is £29,355 (new salary)

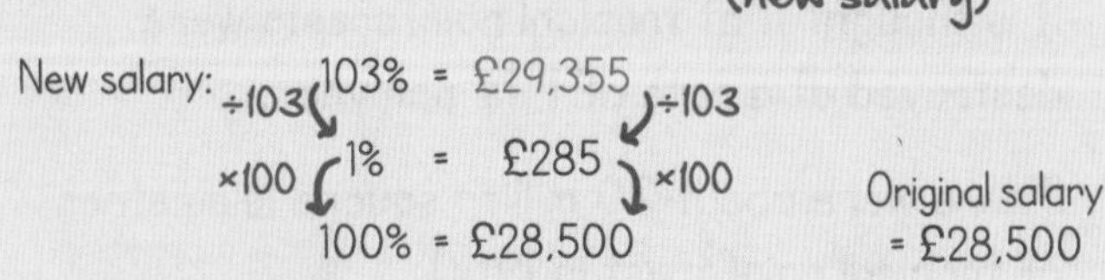

Annual means per year (so does 'per annum')

SET?

A. A bike is reduced by 40% in a sale.
The selling price is now £1500
What was the original cost of the bike?

B. The price of bread increases by 5%.
A loaf of bread now costs £1.26
What did it cost before the increase?

C. A packet of cereal is advertised as 20% extra free. There are 900 grams of cereal in the pack.
How much cereal was in the original pack?

D. An electronics store is advertising 30% off everything.
A TV is advertised as "£210 off".
What was the cost before the reduction?

E. A pair of shoes cost £60 in a sale.
They are advertised as 25% off.
What was the original price of the shoes?

ESREVER SEGATNECREP*

*reverse percentages!

Genius!

1. A clothes shop is advertising 20% off everything in a sale.

Gareth buys a pair of trousers for £40

He works out the original price as follows:

20% of £40 = £8 so £40 + £8 = £48

Gareth is wrong. Explain why.

2. During editing, the running time of a film is reduced by 16% to 2 hours and 6 minutes.

How long was the film before editing took place?

3. The price of a necklace is reduced by 30%.

One week later, the price is then increased by 30%.

The necklace is now on sale for £145.60

Which of these statements is correct?
You must give reasons for your answer.

A. The necklace originally cost less than £145.60

B. The necklace originally cost exactly £145.60

C. The necklace originally cost more than £145.60

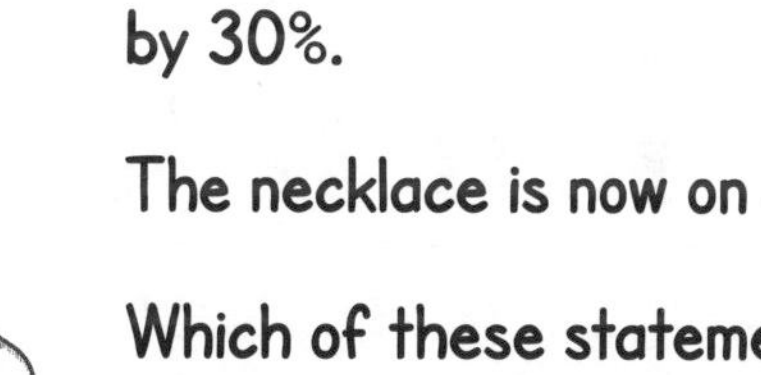

4. Matt's annual salary has increased by 4%.

The increase is £1553.60

Matt says that this increase will mean he now earns more than £40,000 per annum.

Is Matt correct? Explain your answer.

READY?

Powers (or **indices**) are a way of showing that a number is multiplied by itself a certain number of times; e.g.

$$2^3 = 2 \times 2 \times 2 = 8$$

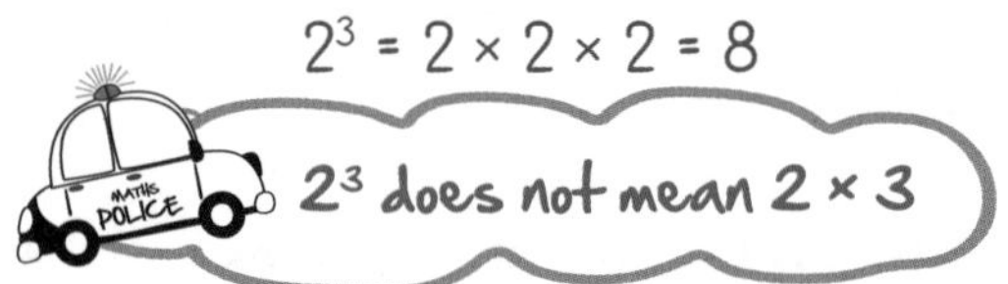

You **REALLY NEED** to remember:

- **Square** numbers are the result of multiplying a whole number by itself. They are 1, 4, 9, 16, 25, 36, 49 etc.
- **Cube** numbers are the result of multiplying a whole number by itself, then by itself again. They are 1, 8, 27, 64, 125 etc.
- There is a secret power of 1 on any letter or number on its own: e.g. $4 = 4^1$

Don't forget ... anything to the power of zero equals 1
$5^0 = 1$ $567^0 = 1$ $y^0 = 1$ etc.

1st Law of indices: $a^m \times a^n = a^{m+n}$ (add powers)

e.g. 1 $2^3 \times 2^2 = 2^{3+2} = 2^5$

e.g. 2 $y^5 \times y = y^5 \times y^{1} = y^{5+1} = y^6$

Write in the secret 1

2nd Law of indices: $a^m \div a^n = a^{m-n}$ (subtract powers)

e.g. 3 $3^5 \div 3^2 = 3^{5-2} = 3^3$

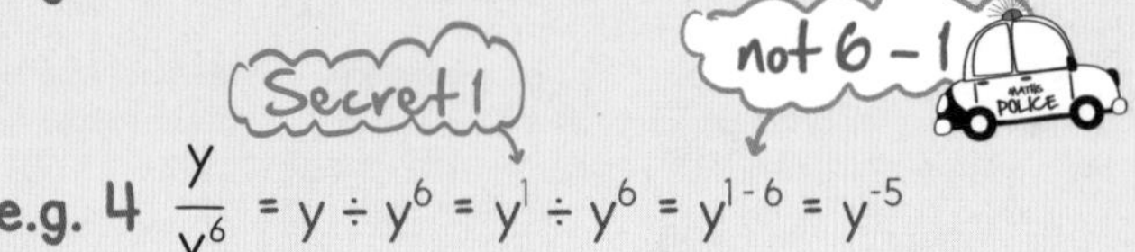

e.g. 4 $\dfrac{y}{y^6} = y \div y^6 = y^1 \div y^6 = y^{1-6} = y^{-5}$

3rd Law of indices: $(a^m)^n = a^{m \times n}$ (multiply powers)

e.g. 5 $(2^4)^3 = 2^{4 \times 3} = 2^{12}$

e.g. 6 $(2y^2)^3 = 2y^2 \times 2y^2 \times 2y^2$
$= 2 \times 2 \times 2 \times y^2 \times y^2 \times y^2$
$= 8y^{2+2+2}$
$= 8y^6$ **OR** $(2y^2)^3 = 2^3 \times (y^2)^3 = 8y^6$

4th Law of indices: $a^{-m} = \dfrac{1}{a^m}$

e.g. 7 $5^{-2} = \dfrac{1}{5^2} = \dfrac{1}{25}$ e.g. 8 $y^{-1} = \dfrac{1}{y^1} = \dfrac{1}{y}$

Sometimes different laws of indices need to be used together.

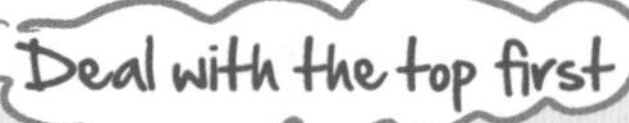

e.g. 9 $2y^4 \times 3y^5 = 2 \times 3 \times y^4 \times y^5 = 6y^{4+5}$
$= 6y^9$

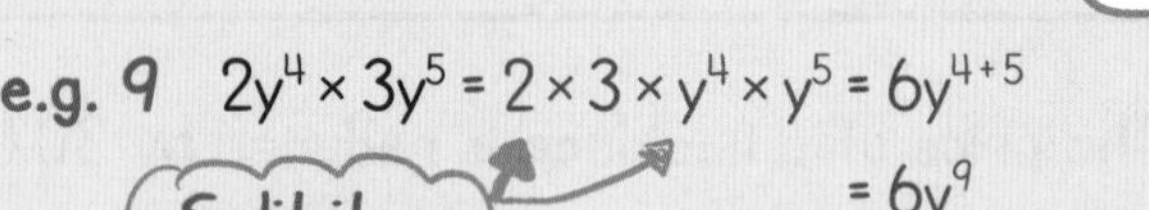

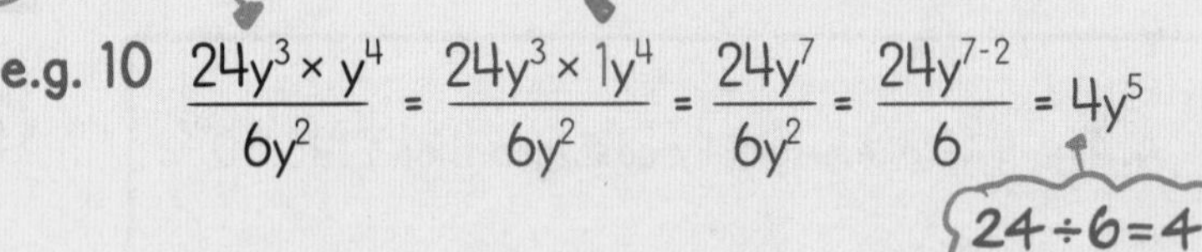

e.g. 10 $\dfrac{24y^3 \times y^4}{6y^2} = \dfrac{24y^3 \times 1y^4}{6y^2} = \dfrac{24y^7}{6y^2} = \dfrac{24y^{7-2}}{6} = 4y^5$

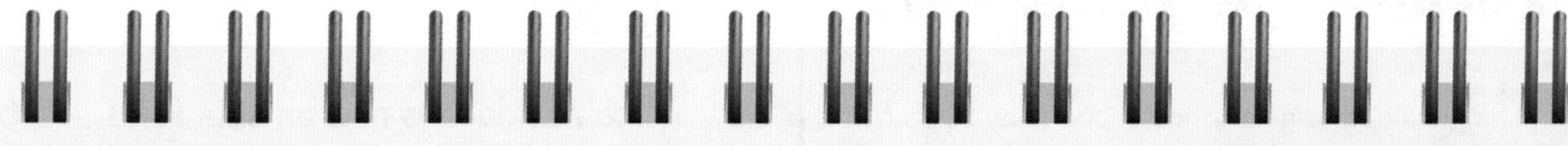

A. Write $4 \times 4 \times 4 \times 4 \times 4$ as a single power of 4

B. Simplify $p^4 \times p^4$

C. Evaluate $7^{-2} \times 7^6$
Leave your answer in index form.

D. Simplify $\dfrac{m^5}{m^2}$

E. Simplify $\dfrac{m^3 \times m^4}{m^2}$

F. Work out the following:

$$\frac{5^{10} \times 5}{5^4 \times 5^3}$$

Write your answer as a power of 5

G. Simplify $(m^4)^5$

H. Write down the value of 2^{-2}

I. Write down the value of 27^0

J. Write down the value of 3^{-1}

Howay man!

GO! INDEX LAWS

Be careful with part a)

1. Simplify the following:

a) $a^3 + a^3$ b) $m^3 \div m^8$

c) $m \times m^6$ d) $(p^{-3})^7$

e) $2 \times 2 \times 3 \times m \times m$ f) $(2h^3)^3$

2. Write as a single power of 4:

$$\frac{2^2 \times 4^7}{4^2}$$

3. For each of the below, work out the value of n:

a) $m^n \times m^2 = m^6$ b) $p^n = 1$

c) $(3m^2)^n = 27m^6$ d) $\frac{4m^3 \times m^n}{2m^5} = 2m^6$

4. Saira writes:

$$(4g^2)^3 = 4g^6$$

Saira is wrong. Explain why.

5. Simplify:

a) $5m^3r \times 4m^2r^5$ b) $(3x^2y^4)^3$

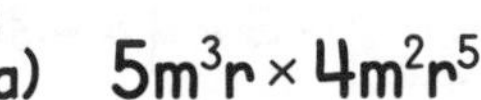

c) $4m^{-4}n^3 \times m^2n$ d) 4682^0

e) $\frac{5m^2 \times 3n^3}{2n^2 \times 6m}$ f) $\frac{36m^2n^3}{12m^3n^2}$

READY?

An important skill in algebra is simplification. You will often be asked to put something in its simplest form. One way to do this is collecting like terms.

e.g. 1 Simplify $2 + 5a + 4a^2 - 3a + 1$

1. Identify the like terms: $2 + 5a + 4a^2 - 3a + 1$
2. Collect the like terms: $3 + 2a + 4a^2$ ($+5a - 3a = +2a$)

Another important skill in algebra is expanding brackets. We multiply everything inside the brackets by the term outside the brackets.

e.g. 2 Expand $4(2m - 3n)$

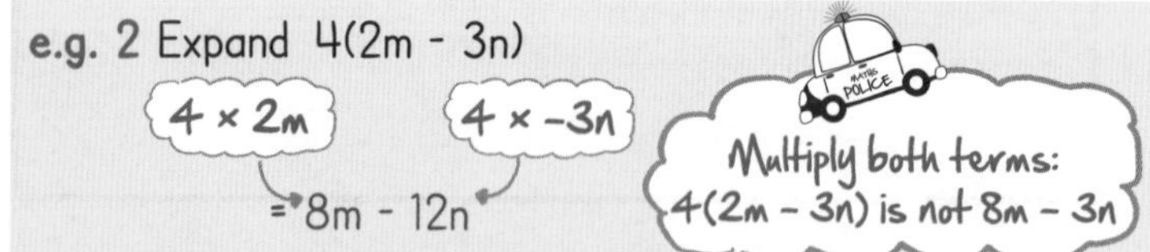

We need to be able to combine both of the above skills.

e.g. 3 Expand and simplify $3(2a + 5) + 5(a - 2)$

1. Expand the brackets: $3(2a + 5) = 6a + 15$ and $+ 5(a - 2) = + 5a - 10$
2. Identify the like terms: $6a + 15 + 5a - 10$
3. Collect the like terms: $11a + 5$

When expanding double brackets like this: $(x + 2)(x + 3)$, there are 4 different multiplications that need to be completed first.

e.g. 4 Expand and simplify $(y + 5)(y - 7)$

1. Write down the multiplications: $y \times y$ $y \times -7$ $5 \times y$ 5×-7
2. Identify the like terms: $y^2 - 7y + 5y - 35$
3. Collect the like terms: $y^2 - 2y - 35$ ($-7y + 5y = -2y$)

You could also use a grid method.

e.g. 5 Expand and simplify $(y - 3)(y - 6)$

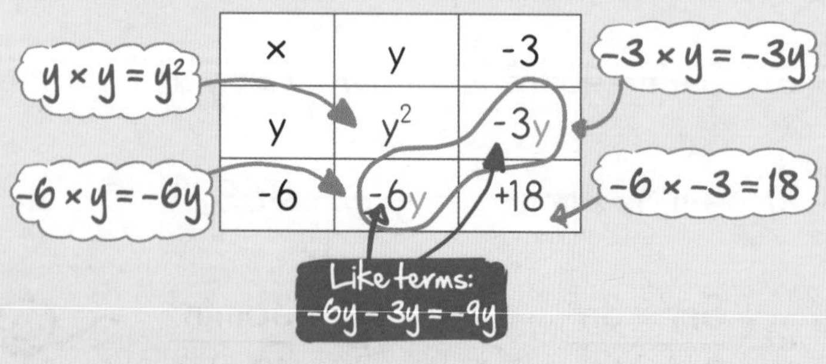

×	y	-3
y	y^2	$-3y$
-6	$-6y$	$+18$

Like terms: $-6y - 3y = -9y$

Collect the like terms: $y^2 - 9y + 18$

SET?

A. Simplify:

(i) $3a + 4 + 5a$

(ii) $5x + 2y + 2x + 3y$

(iii) $6x^2 + 2x - 2x^2$

(iv) $3a^2 + 2b - 2b^2 + 5b - 3b^2$

B. Expand:

(i) $3(a + 2)$

(ii) $4(2x + 3)$

(iii) $y(y - 6)$

Remember: $y \times y = y^2$

(iv) $h(7h + 3)$

(v) $4k(10 + k)$

(vi) $6m(2m - 1)$

C. Expand and simplify:

(i) $4(x + 2) + 3(x + 3)$

(ii) $3(2a + 3) - 5(a + 4)$

Hint: $-5 \times a = -5a$ and $-5 \times 4 = -20$

(iii) $2(4p + 3) - 6(2p - 3)$

D. Expand and simplify:

(i) $(x + 4)(x + 5)$

(ii) $(y - 3)(y + 6)$

(iii) $(p - 6)(p - 10)$

Legend!

GO!

EXPAND AND SIMPLIFY

1. Find the value of p:

$$3(2x + p) + 4(x - 2) = 10x + 1$$

2. Eve is expanding and simplifying this expression:

$$4(3x - 2) - 5(4x + 1)$$

She writes:

$$4(3x - 2) - 5(4x + 1)$$
$$= 12x - 8 - 20x + 5$$
$$= 32x - 3$$

She is wrong. Explain why.

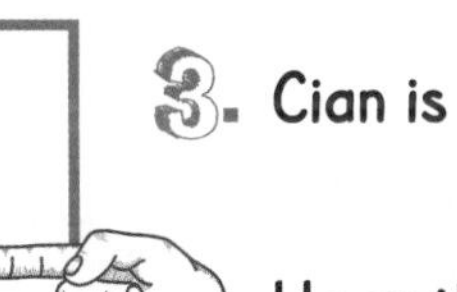

3. Cian is expanding and simplifying:

$$(y + 2)(y - 3)$$

He writes:

$$y^2 + 5y - 6$$

Do you agree? Explain your answer.

4. Expand and simplify:

a) $(2y + 8)(y + 6)$

b) $(x - 6)(x + 6)$

c) $(3a - 8)(4a - 5)$

d) $(2p + q)(p - 3q)$

5. ABGH is a square.

BCDG is a rectangle.

DEFG is a square.

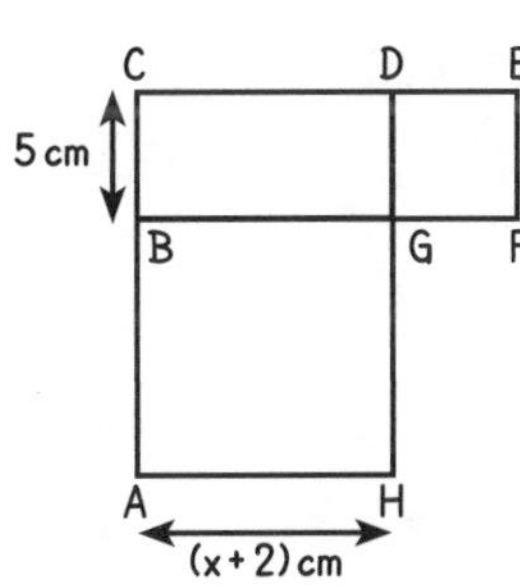

Show that the total area of the shape is $x^2 + 9x + 39\ cm^2$

When the position-to-term rule is written in algebra, it is known as the nth term. You can find a sequence from its nth term. If the numbers of a sequence increase or decrease by the same amount each time, it is a linear (or arithmetic) sequence.

e.g. 1 The nth term of a sequence is $6n - 5$
Find the first three terms of the sequence.

The first term (position 1) is the value of $6n - 5$ when $n = 1$

when $n = 1 \rightarrow (6 \times 1) - 5 = 6 - 5 = 1$

when $n = 2 \rightarrow (6 \times 2) - 5 = 12 - 5 = 7$

when $n = 3 \rightarrow (6 \times 3) - 5 = 18 - 5 = 13$

The first three terms of the sequence are: 1, 7, 13, ...

e.g. 2 The nth term of a sequence is $48 - 3n$.
Find the first three terms of the sequence.

The first term (position 1) is the value of $48 - 3n$ when $n = 1$

when $n = 1 \rightarrow 48 - (3 \times 1) = 48 - 3 = 45$

when $n = 2 \rightarrow 48 - (3 \times 2) = 48 - 6 = 42$

when $n = 3 \rightarrow 48 - (3 \times 3) = 48 - 9 = 39$

The first three terms of the sequence are: 45, 42, 39, ...

If the numbers increase or decrease by a different amount each time, it is a non-linear sequence.

e.g. 3 The nth term of a sequence is $n^2 - 2$
Find the first three terms of the sequence.

The first term (position 1) is the value of $n^2 - 2$ when $n = 1$

when $n = 1 \rightarrow 1^2 - 2 = 1 - 2 = -1$

when $n = 2 \rightarrow 2^2 - 2 = 4 - 2 = 2$

when $n = 3 \rightarrow 3^2 - 2 = 9 - 2 = 7$

The first three terms of the sequence are: -1, 2, 7, ...

You **REALLY NEED** to know that:

* A sequence is a list of numbers formed using a rule.
* The 1st number in a sequence is called the 1st term, the 2nd number is the 2nd term, and so on.

First term → 4, 7, 10, 13, ... ← Fourth term

* A term-to-term rule tells us how to get from each term to the next term:

4, 7, 10, 13, ... The term to term rule here is +3
(+3 +3 +3)

* A position-to-term rule tells us how to get from the position number to the term:

Position → 1 2 3 4
4, 7, 10, 13, ... The position to term rule here is ×3 then +1

You also need to be able to find the nth term for a linear sequence.

e.g. 4 Find the nth term of the sequence:

5, 8, 11, 14, 17, ...
(+3 +3 +3 +3)

1 Work out the difference between each term
(In this case, it goes up by 3 each time, so is connected to the 3 times table ... the nth term starts "3n")

2 Compare the sequence to the 3 times table

3 times table →	3	6	9	12	15
	+2	+2	+2	+2	+2
sequence →	5	8	11	14	17

3 This tells us what we need to add (or subtract) to each number in the 3 times table to get the sequence

The nth term is $3n + 2$

SET?

A. Find the first five terms in each of these sequences:

(i) $8n - 5$

(ii) $12n + 20$

(iii) $20 - 3n$

(iv) $2n - 7$

B. Find an expression for the nth term of these arithmetic sequences:

(i) 11, 18, 25, 32, 39, ...

(ii) 2, 8, 14, 20, 26, ...

(iii) 7, 8, 9, 10, 11, ...

(iv) -4, 0, 4, 8, 12, ...

C. A non-linear sequence is given by the nth term $n^2 + 7$

(i) Write down the first five terms of this sequence.

(ii) Write down the 10th term of this sequence.

SEQUENCES

Yay!

1. Work out the *n*th term of the sequence:

20, 18, 16, 14, 12, ...

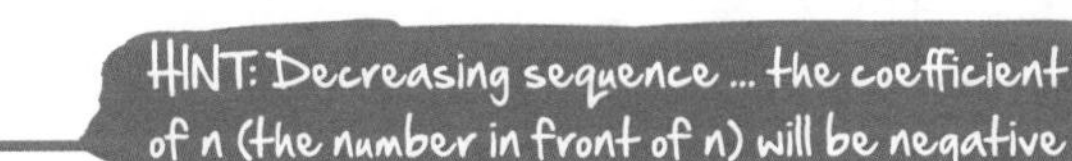

2. Amina thinks that the sequence

2, 7, 12, 17, 22, ...

has the *n*th term rule of $n + 5$.

Amina is wrong. Explain why.

3. The *n*th term of a sequence is $4n - 17$

Is the number 213 in this sequence?

Justify your answer.

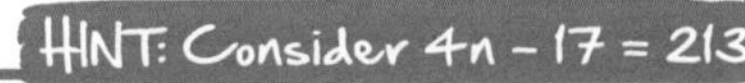

4. Circle any of the sequences that contain the number 18

$n^2 + 8$	$5n + 3$	$30 - 3n$
$40 - 9n$	$n^2 + 9$	$2n + 7$

5. Sequence A has *n*th term $2n^2 - 1$

Sequence B has *n*th term $40 - n^2$

Show that there is only one number that is the same in both of these sequences.

READY?

REMEMBER:

* Addition & subtraction are inverse operations. So are multiplication and division.
* The order of operations (some call it BIDMAS or BODMAS)

'Solve' means find the value of the unknown.

e.g. 1 Solve $7x + 6 = 41$

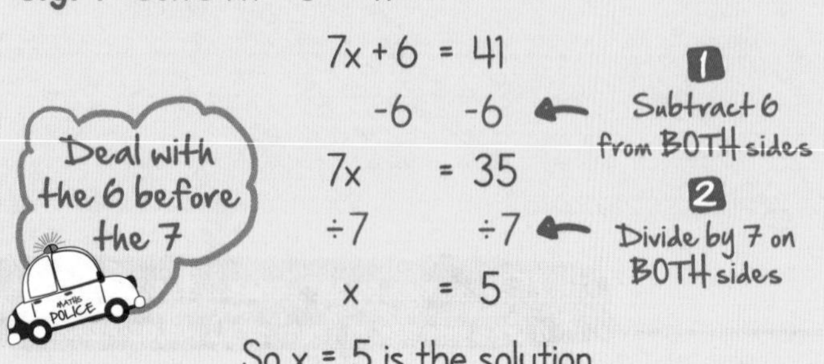

$$7x + 6 = 41$$
$$-6 \quad -6$$
$$7x = 35$$
$$\div 7 \quad \div 7$$
$$x = 5$$

1. Subtract 6 from BOTH sides
2. Divide by 7 on BOTH sides

Deal with the 6 before the 7

So $x = 5$ is the solution

The unknown could be on the right hand side.

e.g. 2 Solve $12 = 11 + 2m$

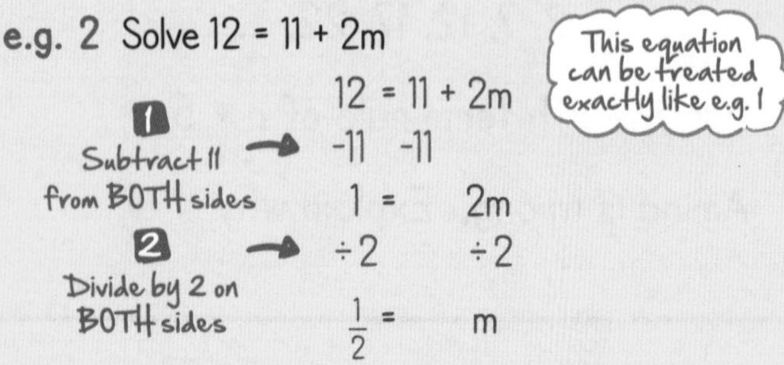

This equation can be treated exactly like e.g. 1

$$12 = 11 + 2m$$
$$-11 \quad -11$$
$$1 = 2m$$
$$\div 2 \quad \div 2$$
$$\frac{1}{2} = m$$

1. Subtract 11 from BOTH sides
2. Divide by 2 on BOTH sides

So $m = \frac{1}{2}$ (or 0.5) is the solution

We could have brackets to deal with.

e.g. 3 Solve $4(3m - 1) = 26$

1. Expand the brackets
2. Now solve like e.g. 1

$$4(3m - 1) = 26$$
$$12m - 4 = 26$$
$$+4 \quad +4$$
$$12m = 30$$
$$\div 12 \quad \div 12$$
$$m = \frac{30}{12}$$

So $m = \frac{30}{12}$ (or $\frac{5}{2}$, or 2.5) is the solution

Some equations have unknowns on both sides.

e.g. 4 Solve $9y - 5 = 4y + 41$

Eliminate the smaller value of y to make an equation with the unknown on one side only

$$9y - 5 = 4y + 41$$
$$-4y \quad -4y$$
$$5y - 5 = 41$$
$$+5 \quad +5$$
$$5y = 46$$
$$\div 5 \quad \div 5$$
$$y = \frac{46}{5}$$

Looks like e.g. 1 now

So $y = \frac{46}{5}$ (or 9.2) is the solution

Sometimes equations involve powers.

e.g. 5 Solve $2x^2 + 3 = 21$

Leave the power until last

$$2x^2 + 3 = 21$$
$$-3 \quad -3$$
$$2x^2 = 18$$
$$\div 2 \quad \div 2$$
$$x^2 = 9$$
$$x = \pm\sqrt{9}$$

2 answers? $(-3)^2 = 9$ and $3^2 = 9$

The inverse operation of $\square^2$ is $\sqrt{}$ so we $\sqrt{}$ both sides here to get x on its own

So $x = +3$ and $x = -3$ are the solutions

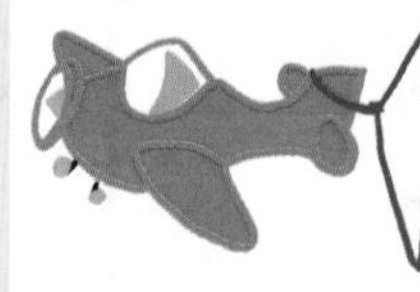

Solving equations, solving inequalities and changing the subject of a formula all use very similar skills

Solve these equations:

A. $4x - 7 = 29$

B. $5k + 3 = 14$

C. $7d + 30 = 2$

D. $2(a - 3) = 9$

E. $6x + 1 = 10x - 11$

F. $y + 3 = 4 - 2y$

G. $43 = 11 + 10k$

H. $2b^2 = 50$

GO!

SOLVING EQUATIONS

Hoot!

1. Henry is solving the equation $6(x - 2) = 36$
Here is his working:

$$6(x - 2) = 36$$
$$x - 2 = 6$$
$$x = 8$$

Do you agree with Henry? Explain why.

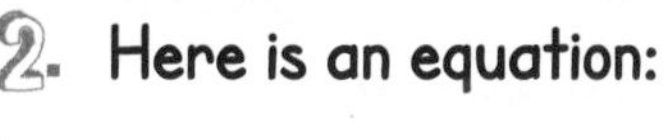

2. Here is an equation:

$$3x^2 - 2 = 46$$

How many solutions are there for x?

Justify your answer.

3. Match the equations with their correct solutions.

Equation	Solution
$3x + 2 = 8$	$x = -2$
$3x - 2 = 8$	$x = \frac{10}{3}$
$8 = 2 - 3x$	$x = 2$
$-8 = 2 + 3x$	$x = -\frac{10}{3}$

4. Solve these equations:

a) $\frac{4m}{3} - 2 = 6$

b) $\frac{4m - 2}{3} = 6$

We often use algebra to make it easier (OK, maybe not always easier, but definitely more efficient than playing around with numbers!) to solve problems by creating a formula or an equation.

e.g. 1 Ruby buys x packs of red pens and y boxes of green pens.
There are 6 red pens in a pack of red pens.
There are 8 green pens in a box of green pens.
Ruby buys a total of T pens.
Write down a formula for T in terms of x and y.

	Red	Green
Ruby buys:	x packs	y boxes
	6 pens per pack	8 pens per box

So ... $6 \times x = 6x$ red pens and $8 \times y = 8y$ green pens

This can be written as $6x + 8y$

$T = 6x + 8y$

Don't leave it as just an expression

Forming and solving an equation is not always the obvious thing to do.

Many of the situations where an equation is formed, you will need to use knowledge from other areas of maths too. This could be money, area, perimeter, angle facts, etc.... so many other topics!

e.g. 2 The perimeter of the triangle is the same as the perimeter of the square. Find the side length of the square.

The dashes on the sides tell us each side is the same length ... it's equilateral

(x + 4) cm 2(x - 1) cm

All sides of a square are equal

1 Create some expressions:

Perimeter of triangle $\rightarrow (x + 4) + (x + 4) + (x + 4) = 3x + 12$

Perimeter of square $\rightarrow 2(x - 1) + 2(x - 1) + 2(x - 1) + 2(x - 1)$
$= 2x - 2 + 2x - 2 + 2x - 2 + 2x - 2$
$= 8x - 8$

$2(x-1) = 2x-2$

2 Form an equation: $3x + 12 = 8x - 8$

3 Solve the equation:
$-3x \quad -3x$ — $-3x$ both sides eliminates $3x$
$12 = 5x - 8$
$+8 \quad +8$ — $+8$ both sides eliminates -8
$20 = 5x$
$\div 5 \quad \div 5$ — $\div$ both sides by 5 eliminates $\times 5$
$4 = x$

4 Find the length: $2(x - 1) = 2(4 - 1) = 2 \times 3 = 6$ cm

e.g. 3 Kate thinks of a number.
Jamal's number is 14 less than Kate's number.
The sum of Kate's and Jamal's numbers is 212
Find Jamal's number.

Let's say Kate's number is 'n' ... you can choose any letter

	Kate		Jamal	
1 Create:	n		n - 14	
2 Form:	n	+	n - 14	= 212

sum means +

$2n - 14 = 212$

3 Solve to find n:
$2n - 14 = 212$
$+14 \quad +14$
$2n = 226$
$\div 2 \quad \div 2$
$n = 113$

4 Find the numbers:

Kate's number	Jamal's number
n = 113	n - 14 = 113 - 14 = 99

So Jamal's number is 99

A. Batteries are sold in packets and boxes.
Each packet contains 4 batteries.
Each box contains 20 batteries.
Amelie buys **p** packets of batteries and **b** boxes of batteries.
Amelie buys a total of **N** batteries.
Write down a formula for **N** in terms of **p** and **b**.

B. ABCD is a square.

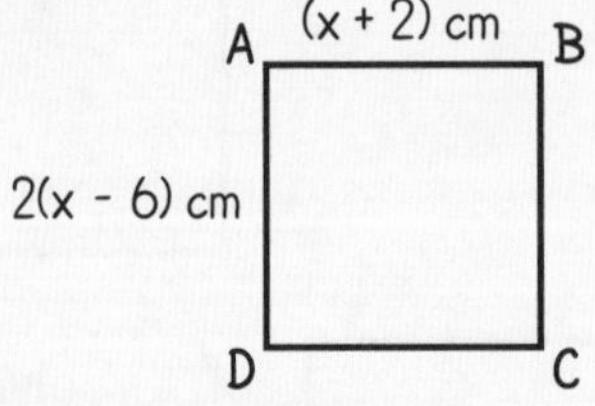

Find the side length of the square.

C. All angles in this triangle are in degrees.
Find the size of the largest angle.

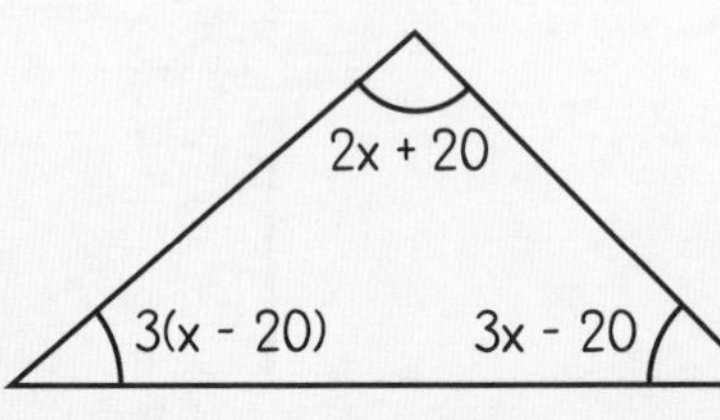

Use the fact that the sum of angles in a triangle = 180°

D. Sheena, Helen and James save some money.
- Sheena has £15 more than Helen.
- James has twice as much as Helen.
- Altogether they have saved £72

How much did each person save?

FORMING AND SOLVING

Supreme!

1. All angles in the quadrilateral are in degrees.
Find the size of the largest angle.

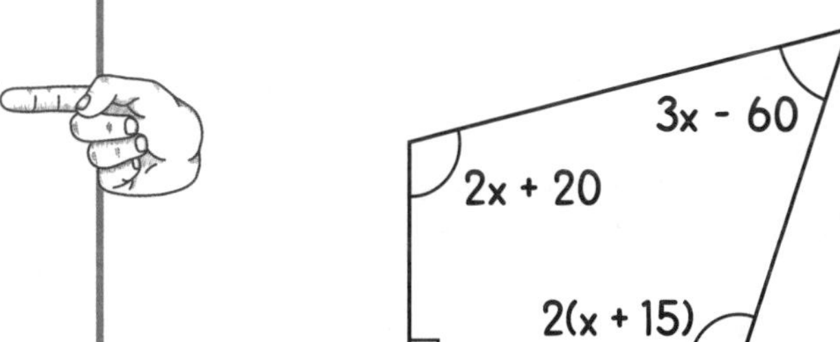

2. School A sent some students to a revision day.
School B sent twice as many students as School A.
School C sent 3 fewer students than School A.

Each student paid £10 for the revision day.
The students paid a total of £2170

Work out how many students were sent by each school to the revision day. You must show all your working.

HINT: 2170 ÷ 10 will tell you how many students in total

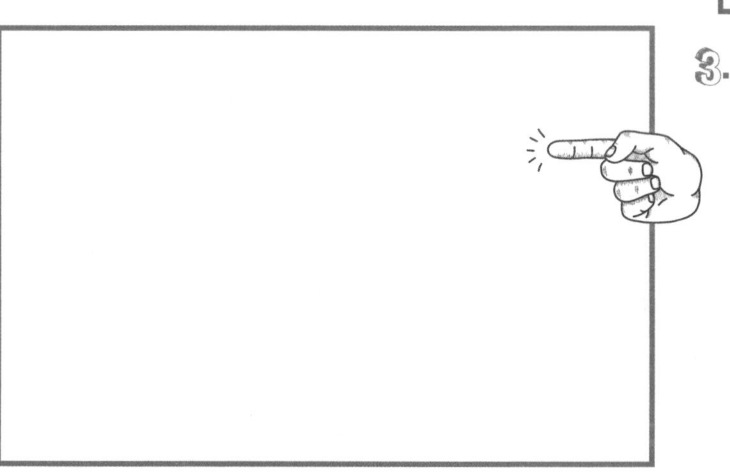

3. All lengths in these two shapes are in centimetres. The perimeters are the same.

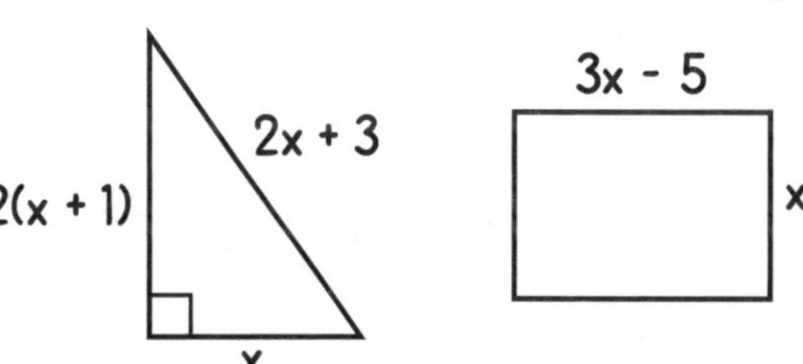

Calculate the area of the rectangle.

4. Rikke is solving this problem:

- Cath thinks of a number, n
- Dave's number is double Cath's number
- Ella's number is 5 less than Dave's number
- The sum of all the numbers is 135

Find the numbers.

Rikke's solution is incorrect.
Describe the mistake she has made.

Cath's number is n
Dave's number is 2n
Ella's number is 2(n - 5)

$n + 2n + 2(n - 5) = 135$
$3n + 2n - 10 = 135$
$5n - 10 = 135$
$5n = 145$
$n = 29$

Cath ... 29 .....
Dave ... 58 .....
Ella ..... 53 ......

READY?

You **REALLY NEED** to know:

- $<$ means "less than"
- $>$ means "greater than"
- $\le$ means "less than OR equal to"
- $\ge$ means "greater than OR equal to"

An **inequality** is a statement using any of the symbols $<$, $>$, $\le$ or $\ge$. We can be asked to show an inequality on a number line.

DRAWING INEQUALITIES:

e.g. 1 Show $x > 5$ on the number line.

$x > 5$ means that x is any number greater than 5

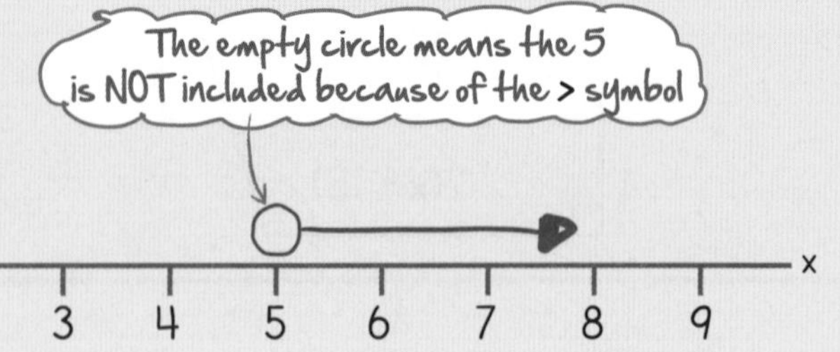

e.g. 2 Show $1 \le x < 5$ on the number line and state the integer values which satisfy the inequality.

$1 \le x < 5$ means x is between 1 and 5

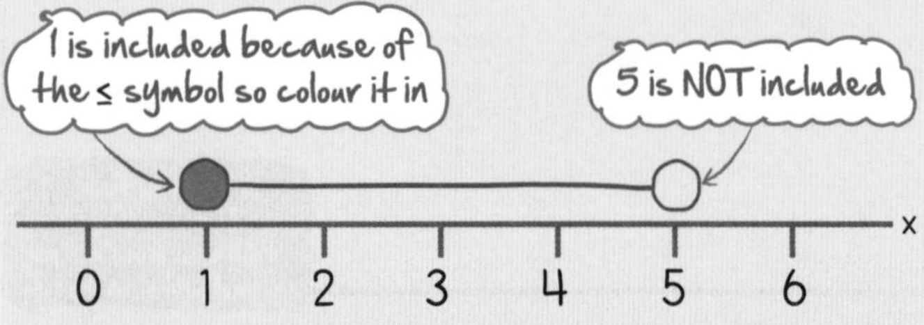

The integers that satisfy this inequality are 1, 2, 3 and 4

'Integer' means positive and negative whole numbers, and zero ... no decimals!

Solving an inequality is just like solving an equation.

SOLVING INEQUALITIES:

e.g. 3 Solve $2d + 5 > 13$

$2d + 5 > 13$ — **1** Subtract 5 from both sides

$-5 \quad -5$

$2d > 8$

2 Divide both sides by 2: $\div 2 \quad \div 2$

$d > 4$

So the solution is $d > 4$

Don't change this symbol to an =

On a number line it would look like this:

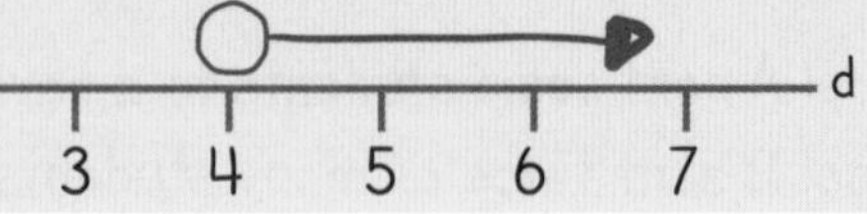

We can deal with more complex inequality statements in a similar way.

e.g. 4 Solve $-3 < 4w + 1 \le 21$

$-3 < 4w + 1 \le 21$ — **1** Subtract 1 from all 3 parts

$-1 \quad -1 \quad -1$

$-4 < 4w \le 20$ — **2** Now divide all 3 parts by 4

$\div 4 \quad \div 4 \quad \div 4$

$-1 < w \le 5$

So the solution is $-1 < w \le 5$

On a number line it would look like this:

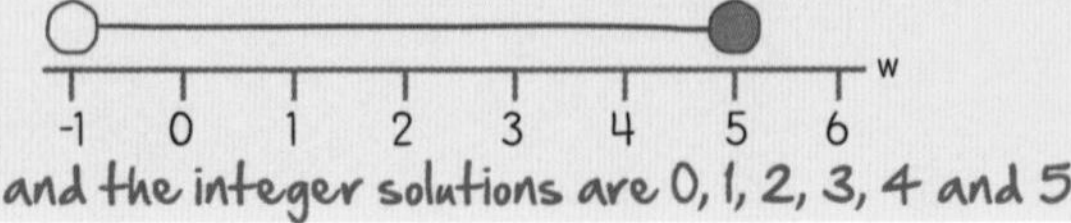

... and the integer solutions are 0, 1, 2, 3, 4 and 5

A. Write the inequality shown on this number line.

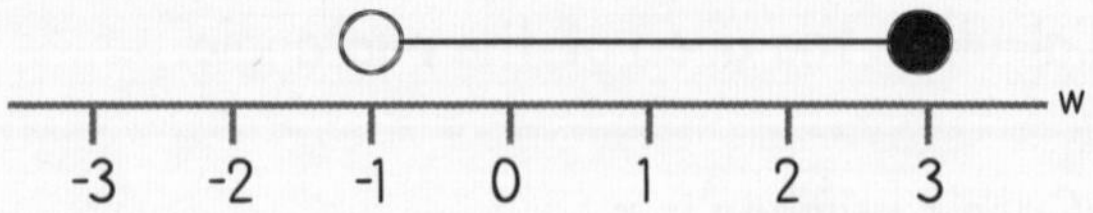

(Number line: -3 -2 -1 0 1 2 3, w; empty circle at -1, filled circle at 3)

B. Write all the integers that satisfy:

(i) $-3 \le n < 4$

(ii) $12 < 3n < 30$

(iii) $7 \le 2n - 1 \le 11$

C. Solve $3x + 4 > 25$

D. Solve $4x - 13 \le 15$
Show the solution on a number line.

E. Solve $20 < 5(p - 4)$

F. Solve $\frac{g + 7}{3} > 7$

GO! INEQUALITIES

Fantastic!

1. Abbi is solving the inequality $2x - 10 \geq 8$
Here is her working:

$$2x - 10 \geq 8$$
$$-10 \quad -10$$
$$2x \geq -2$$
$$\div 2 \quad \div 2$$
$$x \geq -1$$
$$\text{so } x = -1$$

There are errors in Abbi's work. Describe the mistakes that she has made.

2. Here are two inequalities:

$2y - 12 \leq 16$ and $5(y + 3) > 100$

Explain why it is not possible to find a value of y that satisfies both inequalities.

3. $-9 < 6x + 3 \leq 33$

a) Solve the inequality.

b) Show your solution on a number line.

c) Write down the integer values of x.

4.

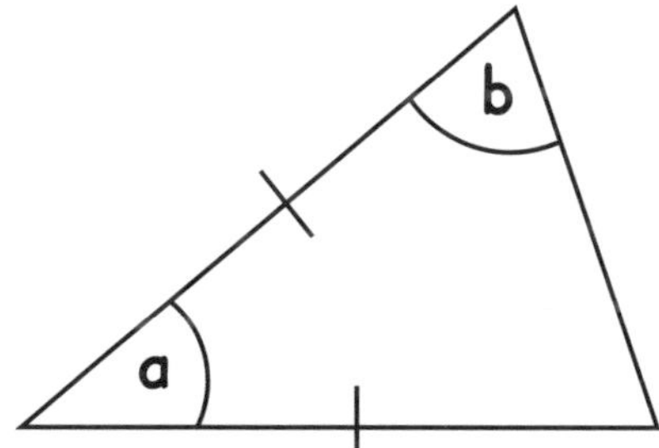

Angle a > 26°

Show that b < 77°

You must show each stage of your working.

In order to factorise an algebraic expression, we need to find the highest common factor of all the terms.

LOOK:

"Factorising" is the process of finding factors.
It is the opposite of expanding

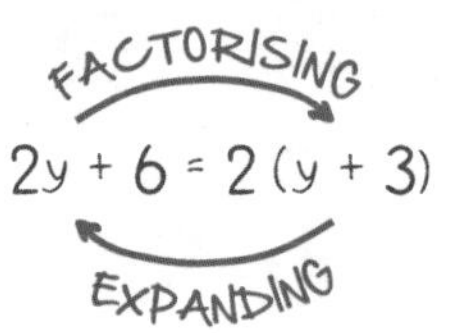

e.g. 1 Factorise $10x + 16$

1. List the factors of 10 and 16 then find the highest common factor (HCF):

   $10 \rightarrow 1, 2, 5, 10$

   $16 \rightarrow 1, 2, 4, 8, 16$

   Highest common factor = 2

2. Place the factor 2 outside some brackets:

   2(.........)

3. Work out the expression inside the brackets ... what multiplied by 2 gets $10x + 16$?

   $2(5x + 8)$

   $2 \times 5x = 10x$ $\quad$ $2 \times 8 = 16$

e.g. 2 Factorise fully $18m - 24n$

1. List the factors of 18 and 24, and find the HCF:

   $18 \rightarrow 1, 2, 3, 6, 9, 18$

   $24 \rightarrow 1, 2, 3, 4, 6, 8, 12, 24$

   Highest common factor = 6

2. Place the factor 6 outside some brackets:

   6(.........)

3. Work out the expression inside the brackets:

   $6(3m - 4n)$

Some expressions include powers.

e.g. 3 Factorise completely $3y^2 + 12y$

1. Factors of $3 \rightarrow 1, 3$

   Factors of $12 \rightarrow 1, 2, 3, 4, 6, 12$

   Highest common factor = 3

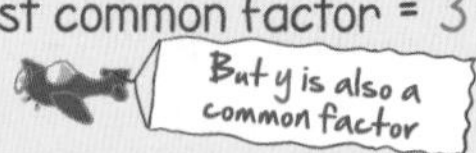

   $3y^2 = 3 \times y \times y$ and $12y = 3 \times 4 \times y$

2. Place the factors 3 and y outside some brackets:

   3y(.........)

3. $3y(y + 4)$ $\quad$ $3y \times y = 3y^2$ and $3y \times 4 = 12y$

e.g. 4 Factorise fully $9pq^3 + 12pq^2 + 15pq$

Factors of $9 \rightarrow 1, 3, 9$

Factors of $12 \rightarrow 1, 2, 3, 4, 6, 12$

Factors of $15 \rightarrow 1, 3, 5, 15$

Highest common factor = 3

There are other common factors:

$9pq^3 = 3 \times 3 \times p \times q \times q \times q$

$12pq^2 = 3 \times 4 \times p \times q \times q$

$15pq = 3 \times 5 \times p \times q$

3, p and q outside some brackets:

$3pq(3q^2 + 4q + 5)$

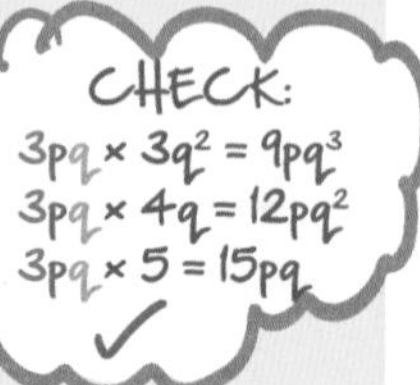

SET?

A. Factorise:

(i) $2x + 10$

(ii) $9 + 15y$

(iii) $14s - 21$

(iv) $-11a + 22$

B. Factorise fully:

(i) $4a + 28b$

(ii) $20p - 10q$

(iii) $20t - 36u$

(iv) $45a + 60d$

C. Factorise completely:

(i) $x^2 - x$

(ii) $y^2 + y$

(iii) $12a^2 - 4a$

(iv) $10s^3 - 20s^2 - 15s$

D. Factorise completely:

(i) $15x + 5y - 40z$

(ii) $8x - 12y - 20z$

(iii) $15a + 25ab - 40ac$

GO! FACTORISING 1

Fabulous!

1. Factorise completely:

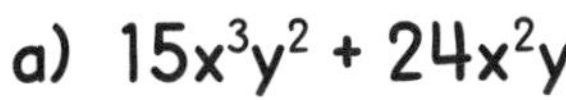

a) $15x^3y^2 + 24x^2y$

b) $12pq^3 - 12pq^2 + 15pqr$

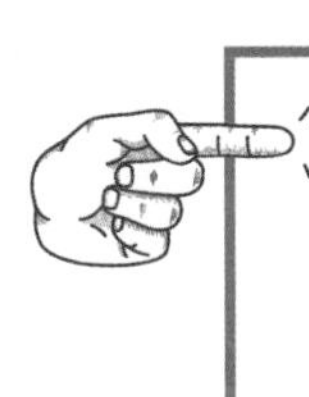

HINT: x^2 is the common factor of x^3 and x^2

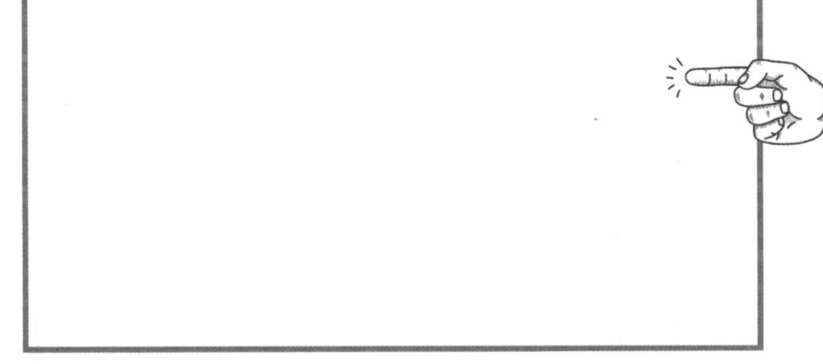

2. Faiza is asked to factorise completely the expression $12p + 36$. She writes:

$$12p + 36 = 2(6p + 18)$$

Do you agree with Faiza? Explain your answer.

3. Tyler and Rosa are writing formulae to find the perimeter, P, of the rectangle:

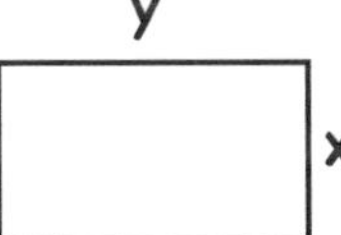

Tyler thinks the formula is $P = 2y + 2x$

Rosa thinks the formula is $P = 2(x + y)$

Which of these statements is correct?

A Only Tyler is correct

B Only Rosa is correct

C Both Tyler and Rosa are incorrect

D Both Tyler and Rosa are correct

4. Write different numbers in the boxes to make the statement correct.

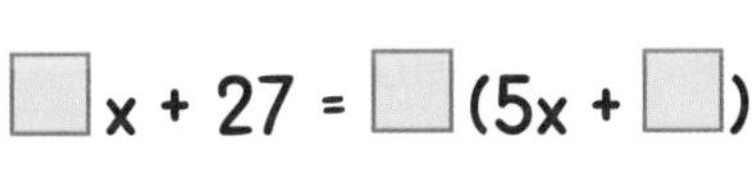

$\square x + 27 = \square(5x + \square)$

READY?

If we expand $(x + 3)(x + 4)$ we get the quadratic expression $x^2 + 7x + 12$. We also need to be able to start with $x^2 + 7x + 12$ and work sdrawkcab* to get to $(x + 3)(x + 4)$ by factorising.

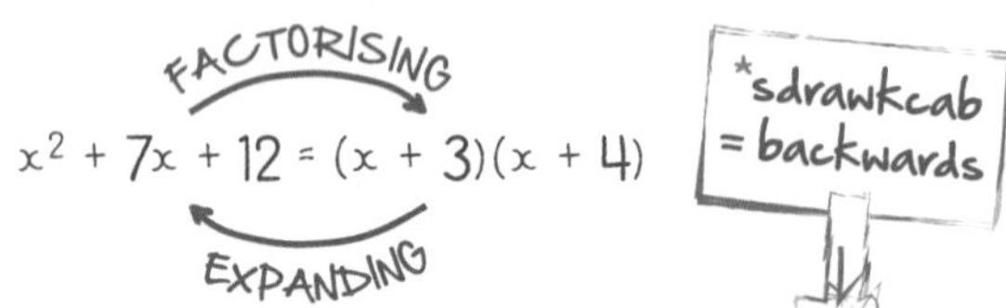

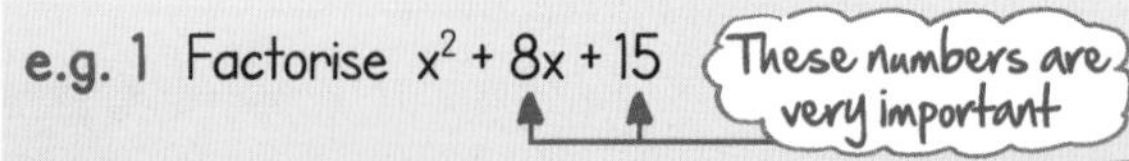

e.g. 1 Factorise $x^2 + 8x + 15$

product → 'x'

1 Find two whole numbers with a product of +15:

$1 \times 15 = 15,\ 3 \times 5 = 15,\ -3 \times -5 = 15$, or $-1 \times -15 = 15$

2 Choose the pair whose sum is +8: $3 + 5 = 8$

sum → '+' both positive

3 Create the expression in each set of brackets:

$(x + 3)(x + 5)$

e.g. 2 Factorise $x^2 - 7x + 10$ (Important numbers ... again!)

1 Find two whole numbers with a product of +10:

$1 \times 10 = 10,\ 2 \times 5 = 10,\ -2 \times -5 = 10$, or $-1 \times -10 = 10$

2 Choose the pair whose sum is −7: $-2 + -5 = -2 - 5 = -7$

3 Create the expression in each set of brackets:

$(x - 2)(x - 5)$

You might find it helpful to use the grid when factorising

×	x	-2
x	x^2	-2x
-5	-5x	+10

Special case: difference of two squares.

e.g. 3 Factorise $x^2 - 16$

As there is no x term, the 2 numbers must sum to 0:

1 $4 \times -4 = -16$ **2** $4 + -4 = 0$ (no x term) **3** $(x + 4)(x - 4)$

Factorising can also be used to solve a quadratic equation.

e.g. 4 Solve $x^2 - 7x + 10 = 0$

1 Factorise: $(x - 2)(x - 5) = 0$ (As in e.g. 2)

2 Set each pair of brackets equal to 0:

$x - 2 = 0$ and $x - 5 = 0$

3 Solve each equation:

$x - 2 = 0$ and $x - 5 = 0$

Add 2 to both sides → $+2\ \ +2$ $\quad$ $+5\ \ +5$ ← Add 5 to both sides

$x = 2$ and $x = 5$

Sometimes one solution is zero.

e.g. 5 Solve $y^2 - 4y = 0$ (Easy to factorise)

1 $y(y - 4) = 0$

2 $y = 0$ and $y - 4 = 0$

3 Solutions are $y = 0$ and $y = 4$

SET?

A. Factorise:

(i) $x^2 + 8x + 12$

(ii) $y^2 + 13y + 12$

(iii) $h^2 - 6h - 16$

(iv) $p^2 - 15p + 50$

B. Factorise:

(i) $x^2 - 100$ (ii) $a^2 - 36$

(iii) $m^2 - 1$ (iv) $a^2 - b^2$

C. Solve:

(i) $a^2 + 11a + 24 = 0$

(ii) $p^2 + 11p + 30 = 0$

(iii) $y^2 - 3y - 28 = 0$

(iv) $0 = x^2 - 8x + 7$

D. Solve:

(i) $x^2 + 10x = 0$

(ii) $x^2 - 6x = 0$

E. Solve: $x^2 - 9 = 0$

GO! FACTORISING 2

Wicked!

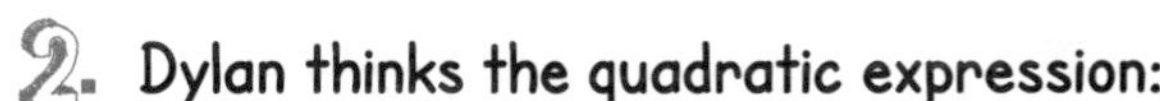

1. The area of a rectangle is given by the expression:

$$y^2 + 10y + 9$$

Find expressions for the length and width of the rectangle.

2. Dylan thinks the quadratic expression:

$$x^2 - 169$$

cannot be factorised.

Do you agree with Dylan?
Explain your answer.

3. Ayesha is asked to factorise the quadratic expression:

$$x^2 + 10x + 21$$

She writes:

$$x(x + 10) + 21$$

Do you agree with Ayesha?
Explain your answer.

4. Dean writes:

$$p^2 + 3p - 18 = 0$$

So $(p - 6)(p + 3) = 0$

So $p = 6$ and $p = -3$

Dean is wrong.
Explain why.

5. $x^2 + ax + 24 = (x + b)(x + c)$

a is a positive odd number.

Find possible values for b and c.

READY?

Changing the subject is very similar to solving equations and solving inequalities

The subject of a formula (or equation) is the variable (letter) which is on its own and it is usually on the left hand side of the equals symbol. To **change the subject** of a formula means rearranging it so that a different variable (letter) is on its own.

e.g. 1 Make x the subject of $y = 4x + 3$

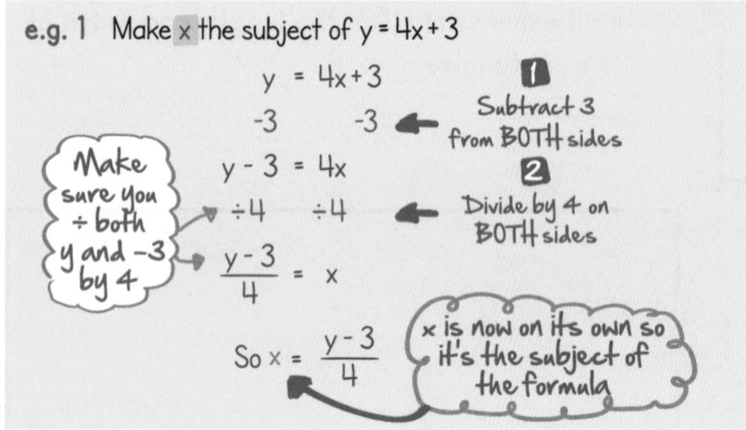

Sometimes we need to deal with brackets.

e.g. 2 Make q the subject of $p = 12(3 - q)$

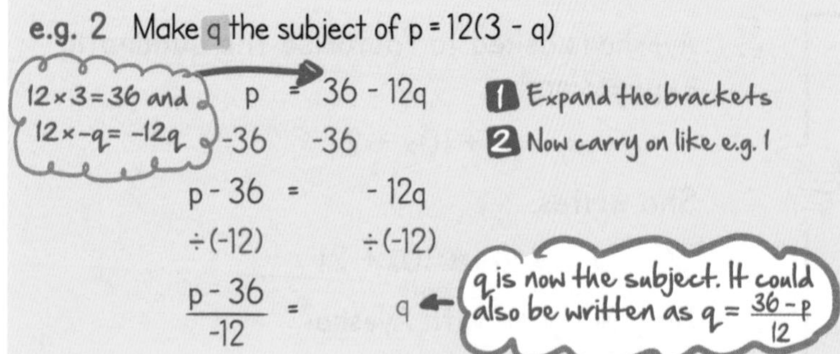

The method is no different with even more letters.

e.g. 3 Make u the subject of $v = u + 3t$

$$v = u + 3t$$
$$-3t \qquad -3t$$
$$v - 3t = u$$
$$\text{So } u = v - 3t$$

These are the same, u is the subject in both

We might be given formulae with powers or roots.

e.g. 4 Make y the subject of $x = \sqrt{\frac{y+m}{2}}$

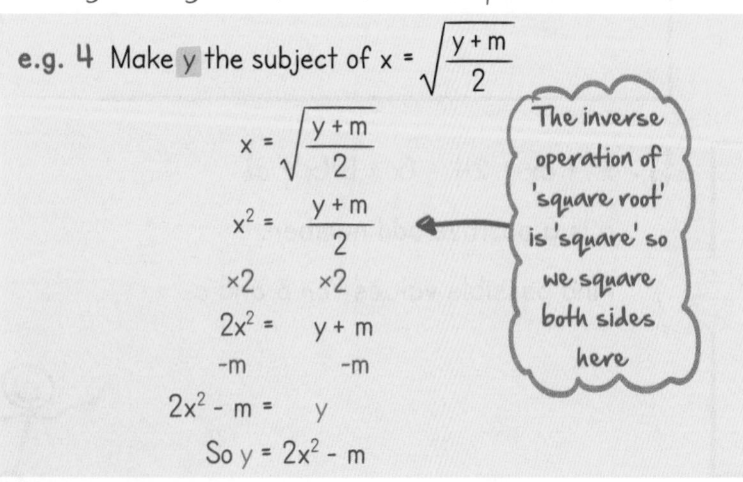

A. Make n the subject of $T = 5n$

B. Make c the subject of $a = b + c$

C. Make x the subject of $y = \sqrt{x}$

D. Rearrange $s = 2t - 1$ to make t the subject.

E. Make p the subject of $s = 1 - 2p$

F. Rearrange $y = \frac{1}{2}x + 6$ to make x the subject.

G. Make r the subject of $A = \frac{r+s}{2}$

H. Rearrange $p = 5 + \sqrt{q}$ to make q the subject.

GO! CHANGING THE SUBJECT

Amazing!!

1. Todd is asked to make h the subject of:

$$T = \frac{5h - 13}{2}$$

He gives the answer:

$$\frac{2(T + 13)}{5} = h$$

Do you agree with Todd? Explain why.

2. Show that $x = \sqrt{\frac{y + 21}{15}}$ can be rearranged to give:

$$y = 15x^2 - 21$$

3. The formula for the area of a circle is given by $A = \pi r^2$ where r is the radius.

a) Rearrange this formula to make r the subject.

b) Use your formula to find the radius of a circle when the area is 200 cm^2. Give your answer correct to 2 decimal places.

4. Here are six formulae.

Which two pairs of formulae are equivalent?

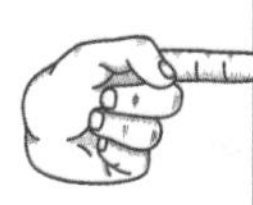

$t = \frac{3 + v}{10}$	$t = \frac{3 - v}{10}$
$v = 3 - 10t$	$t = \frac{v + 10}{3}$
$t = \frac{v - 3}{10}$	$v = 10t + 3$

READY?

Standard form is a useful way of writing very LARGE or very small numbers, but any number can be written in this form. Numbers written in this format have two parts:

$$8.42 \times 10^4$$

A number greater than or equal to 1 but less than 10

Always ×10 with a negative or positive power

We can convert between 'ordinary' numbers and standard form by considering where the decimal point needs to be.

The decimal point is at the end if you can't see one

e.g. 1 Write 384000 in standard form.

1. To make a number between 1 and 10, the decimal point needs to be between the 3 and 8
2. Now count how many hops are needed to make this happen ... this number will be the power

5 hops

$3.84000. \rightarrow 3.84000. \rightarrow 3.84 \times 10^5$

e.g. 2 Write 0.0037 in standard form.

1. To make a number between 1 and 10, the decimal point needs to be between the 3 and 7
2. Now count how many hops are needed to make this happen ... this number will be the power

3 hops

Negative power

$0.003.7 \rightarrow 0.003.7 \rightarrow 3.7 \times 10^{-3}$

We can also go from standard form to ordinary numbers.

e.g. 3 Write 2.86×10^4 as an ordinary number.

1. The power tells us how many hops. It is positive so hop to the right.

4 hops

2.86 _ _.

2. Use a zero to fill in any gaps

28600. ← The decimal point is here but no need to write it

e.g. 4 Write 6.4821×10^{-3} as an ordinary number.

1. The power tells us how many hops. It is negative so hop to the left.

3 hops

_ . _ _ 6.4821

2. Use a zero to fill in any gaps

→ 0.0064821

WATCH OUT!

423×10^5 is NOT standard form ... 423 is not between 1 and 10

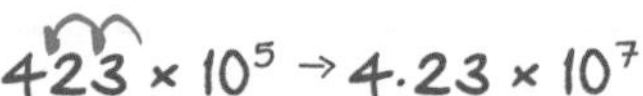

$423 \times 10^5 \rightarrow 4.23 \times 10^7$

A. Write these numbers in standard form:

(i) 8000 (ii) 31400

(iii) 461610 (iv) 11111

B. Write these numbers in standard form:

(i) 0.0006 (ii) 0.00543

(iii) 0.761 (iv) 0.010101

C. Write these as ordinary numbers:

(i) 7×10^5 (ii) 7.8×10^4

(iii) 2.23×10^6 (iv) 9.909×10^2

(v) 4.0892×10^4 (vi) 6.4×10

D. Write these as ordinary numbers:

(i) 5×10^{-5} (ii) 6.5×10^{-4}

(iii) 2.28×10^{-3} (iv) 9.842×10^{-2}

(v) 9.999×10^{-7} (vi) 1×10^{-1}

STANDARD FORM 1

Mega!

1. Zoe thinks that 28 000 written in standard form is 28×10^3

Do you agree?
Explain your answer.

2. Write forty thousand in standard form.

3. What is 150,000 less than 10 million?
Give your answer in standard form.

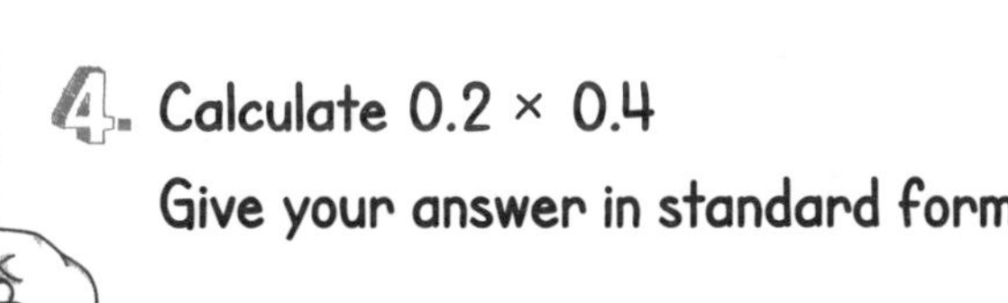

4. Calculate 0.2×0.4
Give your answer in standard form.

5. a) Match each statement in column A to one statement in column B.

b) Write the missing value in column B as a number in standard form.

A	B
16×10^2	1.6×10^4
160×10^{-3}	1.6×10^2
0.16×10^3	......
0.016×10^6	1.6×10^{-4}
0.16×10^{-3}	1.6×10^{-1}

READY?

It is **REALLY USEFUL** to remember:
$10^a \times 10^b = 10^{a+b}$ and $10^a \div 10^b = 10^{a-b}$

It is possible to do calculations with numbers written in standard form with and without a calculator.

e.g. 1 Calculate:

With + and − change to ordinary numbers first

a) $(8 \times 10^5) + (2 \times 10^3)$

$= 800\,000 + 2000 = 802\,000 = 8.02 \times 10^5$

b) $(8 \times 10^4) - (2.5 \times 10^3)$

$= 80\,000 - 2500 = 77\,500 = 7.75 \times 10^4$

With × and ÷ use the index laws

c) $(6 \times 10^5) \times (2.5 \times 10^3)$

Add the powers $10^5 \times 10^3 = 10^8$

$= 6 \times 2.5 \times 10^5 \times 10^3$

$= 15 \times 10^8 = 1.5 \times 10^9$

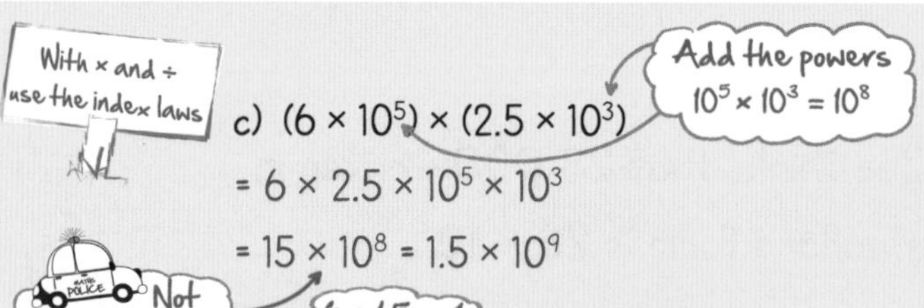

$6 \div 1.5 = 4$

d) $(6 \times 10^{-5}) \div (1.5 \times 10^3)$

Subtract the powers $10^{-5} \div 10^3 = 10^{-5-3} = 10^{-8}$

$= 4 \times 10^{-8}$

OR Using the ×10ˣ or EXP button:

a) (8 ×10ˣ 5) + (2 ×10ˣ 3) = 8.02×10^5

b) (8 ×10ˣ 4) − (2 · 5 ×10ˣ 3) = 7.75×10^4

c) (6 ×10ˣ 5) × (2 · 5 ×10ˣ 3) = $15 \times 10^8 = 1.5 \times 10^9$

d) (6 ×10ˣ (−) 5) ÷ (1 · 5 ×10ˣ 3) = 4×10^{-8}

e.g. 2 Order from smallest to largest:

				Smallest
	250 000	0.025×10^6	2.5×10^6	0.25×10^4
As ordinary numbers ...	250 000	25 000	2 500 000	2500
	3rd	2nd	4th	1st
... then in order	0.25×10^4	0.025×10^6	250,000	2.5×10^6

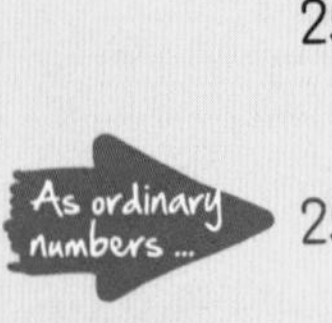

Look for patterns

$2500 = 250 \times 10^1 = 25 \times 10^2$
$= 2.5 \times 10^3 = 0.25 \times 10^4$

only these versions are in standard form

$0.00025 = 0.0025 \times 10^{-1}$
$= 0.025 \times 10^{-2} = 0.25 \times 10^{-3} = 2.5 \times 10^{-4}$

SET?

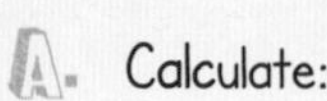

Give all your answers in standard form

A. Calculate:

(i) $(3 \times 10^5) + (2 \times 10^3)$

(ii) $(5 \times 10^6) + (1.5 \times 10^6)$

(iii) $(3 \times 10^6) - (3 \times 10^4)$

(iv) $(5 \times 10^6) - (1.5 \times 10^6)$

B. Calculate:

(i) $(3 \times 10^5) \times (2 \times 10^3)$

(ii) $(3 \times 10^8) \times (2 \times 10^{-3})$

(iii) $(4 \times 10^5) \times (3 \times 10^3)$

(iv) $(6 \times 10^9) \div (2 \times 10^3)$

(v) $(9 \times 10^6) \div (3 \times 10^{-3})$

(vi) $(1.2 \times 10^5) \div (4 \times 10^{-2})$

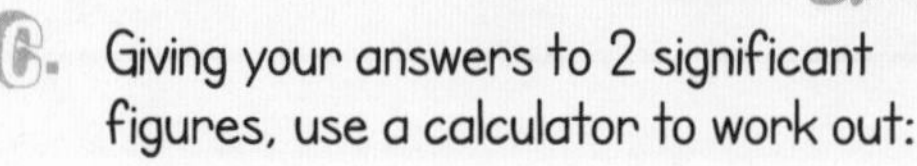

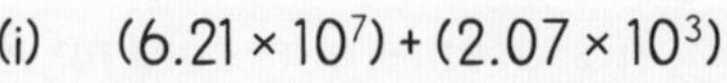

C. Giving your answers to 2 significant figures, use a calculator to work out:

(i) $(6.21 \times 10^7) + (2.07 \times 10^3)$

(ii) $(3.47 \times 10^{-2}) + (1.69 \times 10^{-5})$

(iii) $(9.5 \times 10^7) - (4.89 \times 10^3)$

(iv) $(8.34 \times 10^{-3}) - (5.7 \times 10^{-7})$

(v) $(4.2 \times 10^4) \times (1.6 \times 10^5)$

(vi) $(9.2 \times 10^{-4}) \times (5.6 \times 10^6)$

(vii) $(1.2 \times 10^4) \div (2.5 \times 10^6)$

(viii) $(1.23 \times 10^{-4}) \div (4.56 \times 10^6)$

GO! STANDARD FORM 2

Brilliant!

1. Order from smallest to largest:

a) 0.6×10^5, 6 million, 60×10^4, 0.06×10^5

b) 0.046, 4.6×10^{-1}, 0.46×10^{-3}, 46×10^{-6}

2. Charlie thinks that:

$$(5 \times 10^5) \times (1.5 \times 10^3) = 7.5 \times 10^{15}$$

Do you agree?

Explain your answer.

3. Find the values of a, b, c and d.

$$7 \times 10^a + 6 \times 10^b = 700{,}600$$

$$(4 \times 10^c) \times (d \times 10^{-2}) = 0.0000012$$

4. A snail has a top speed of 2.8×10^{-3} metres per second. The distance from Manchester to London is 2.6×10^5 metres.

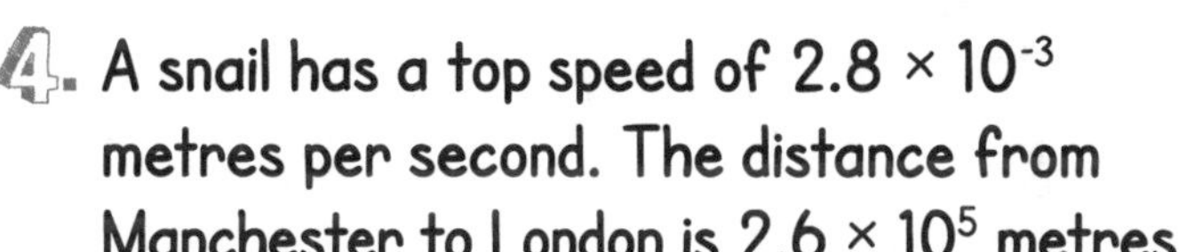

Work out the number of seconds it would take a snail to crawl from Manchester to London.

Give your answer in standard form and to 2 significant figures.

HINT: speed = $\frac{\text{distance}}{\text{time}}$

5. One sheet of paper is 9×10^{-3} cm thick.

Fern wants to put 500 sheets of paper into the paper tray of her printer.

The paper tray is 5 cm deep.

Is the paper tray deep enough for 500 sheets of paper?

You must explain your answer.

It is **REALLY USEFUL** to remember:

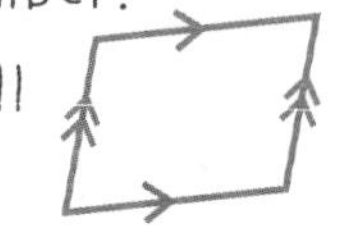

* Parallel lines are lines that will never meet (like train tracks)
* The notation for parallel lines is > or >>
* The sum of the angles in a triangle is 180°
* The sum of the angles at a point is 360° and on a straight line is 180°
* Vertically opposite angles are equal

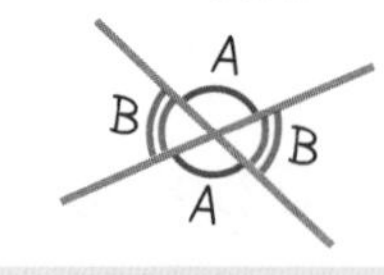

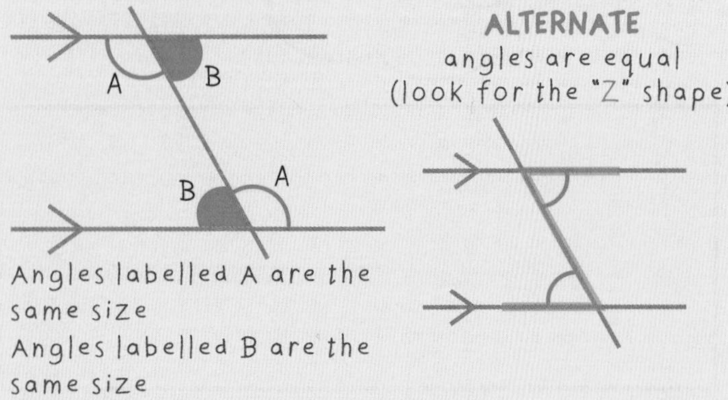

ALTERNATE angles are equal (look for the "Z" shape)

Angles labelled A are the same size
Angles labelled B are the same size

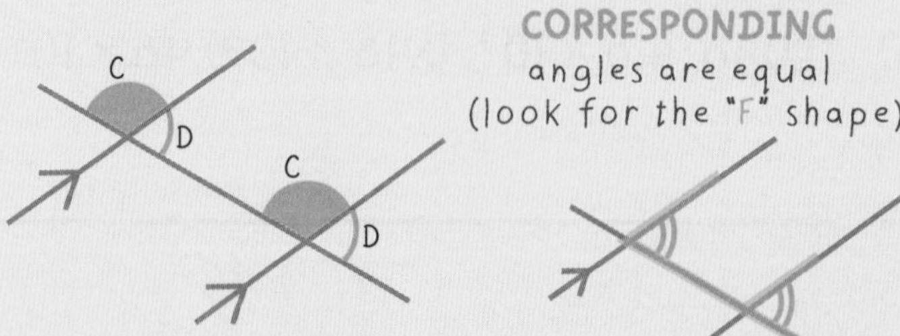

CORRESPONDING angles are equal (look for the "F" shape)

Angles labelled C are the same size
Angles labelled D are the same size

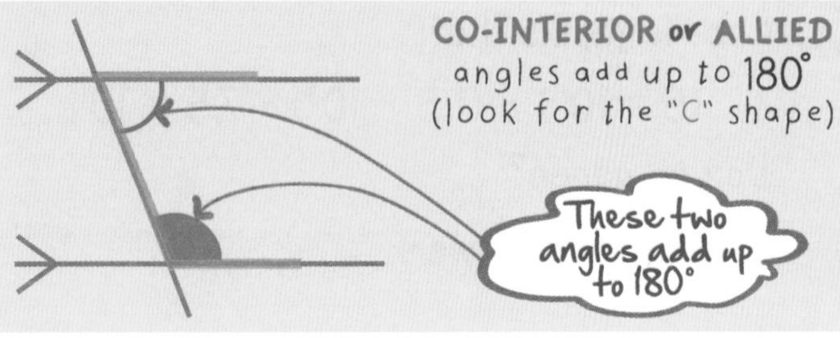

CO-INTERIOR or ALLIED angles add up to 180° (look for the "C" shape)

These two angles add up to 180°

Don't measure angles when you are asked to work them out

e.g. 1 Calculate the value of x. Give reasons for your answer.

* The sum of the angles on a straight line = 180°
* Corresponding angles are equal so ... x = 39°

e.g. 2 Giving reasons, calculate the value of y.

* The sum of the angles in a triangle = 180°
* Alternate angles are equal so ... y = 54°

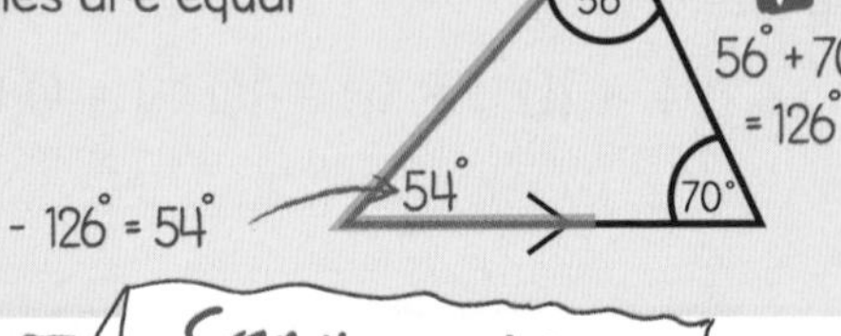

Can you spot the 'F' shape?

Can you spot the 'Z' shape?

Give reasons for all your answers

A. Calculate the value of x.

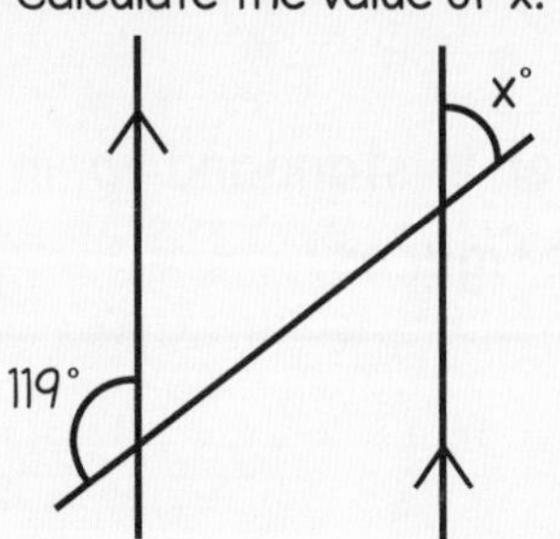

C. Calculate the value of y.

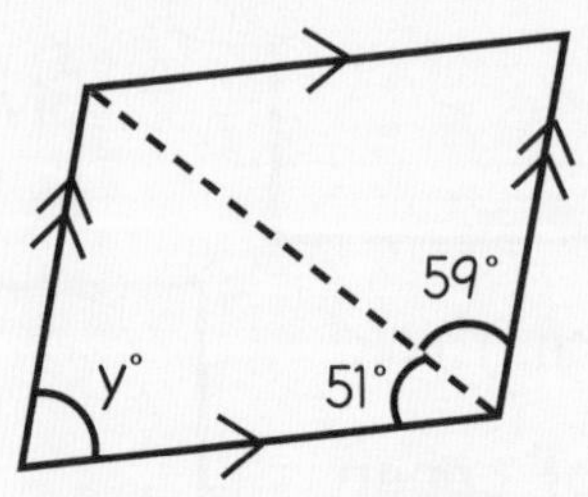

E. Find the value of y.

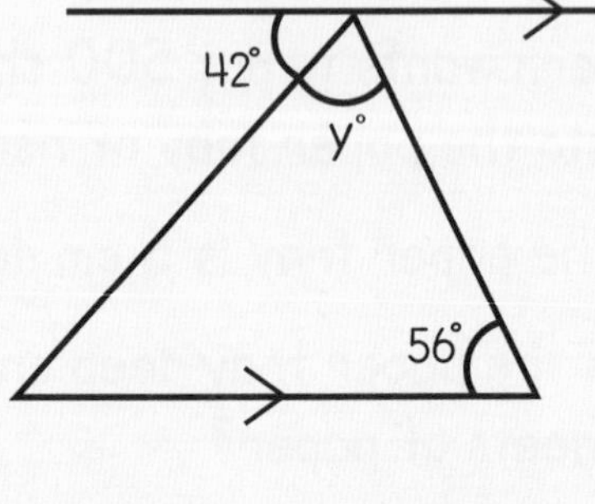

B. Calculate the values of m and n.

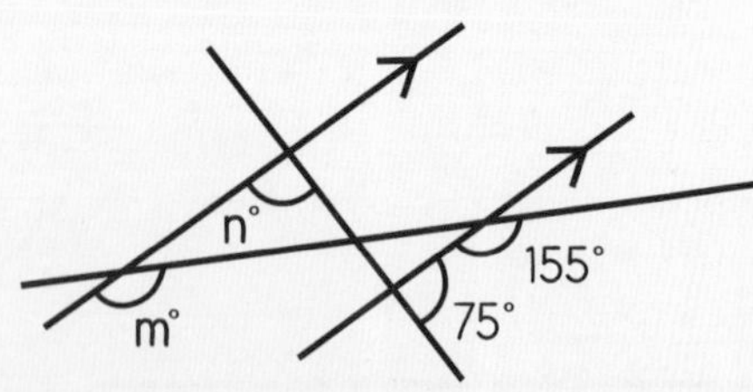

D. Calculate the value of x.

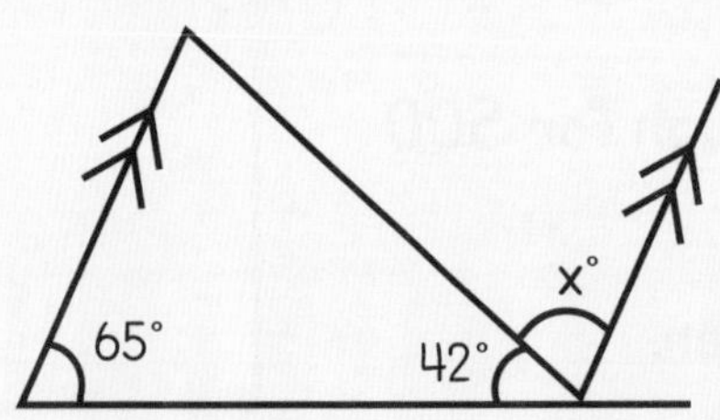

ALTERNATE AND CORRESPONDING ANGLES

Quality!

1. Jane is asked to find angle f, giving reasons for her answer.

Jane says:

"Angle f = 48° because corresponding angles are equal"

Do you agree with Jane?

Explain your answer.

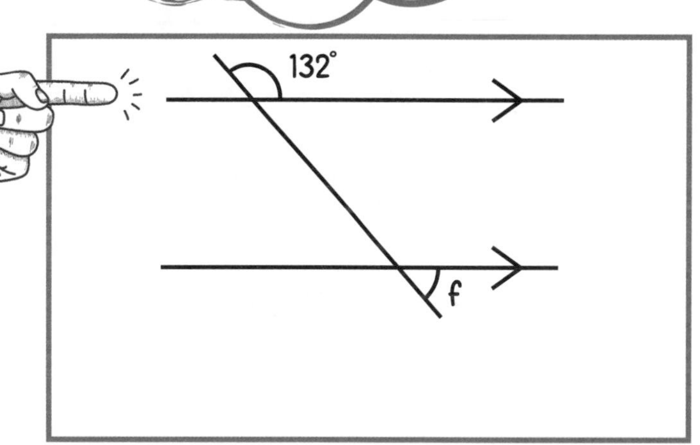

2. Find the value of x, giving reasons for each stage of your working.

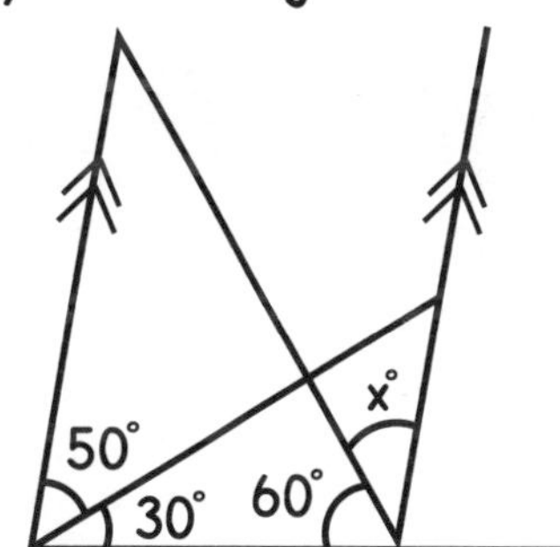

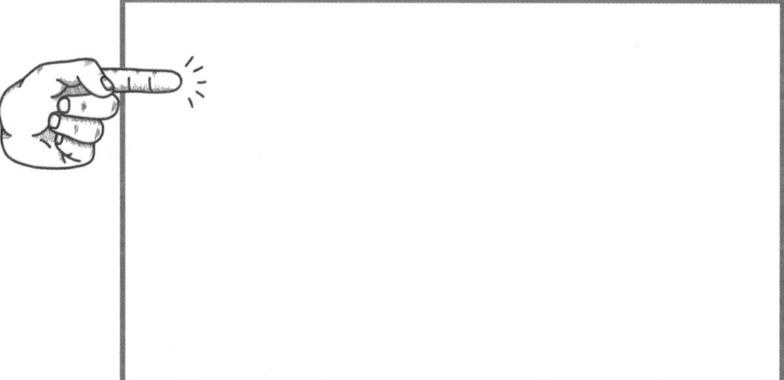

HINT: Try to work out as many angles as possible ... write them on the diagram

3. All angles are in degrees.

Find the value of y.

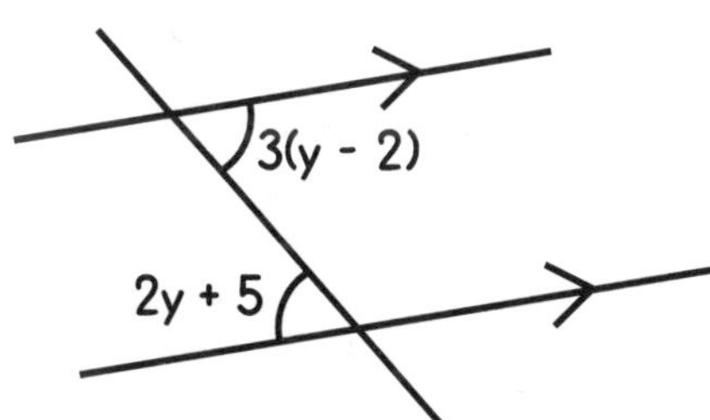

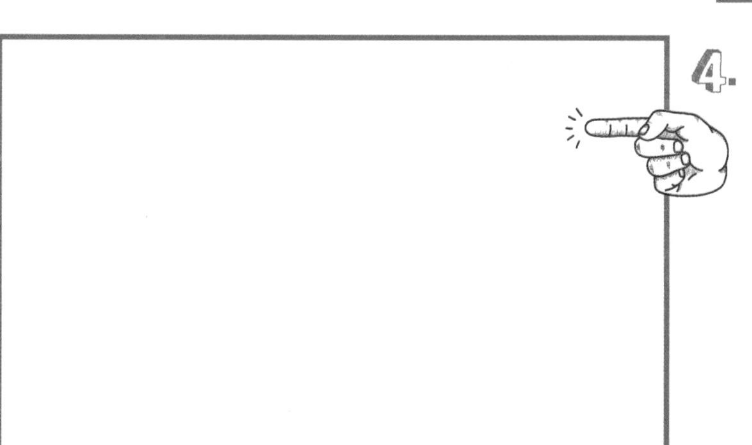

4.

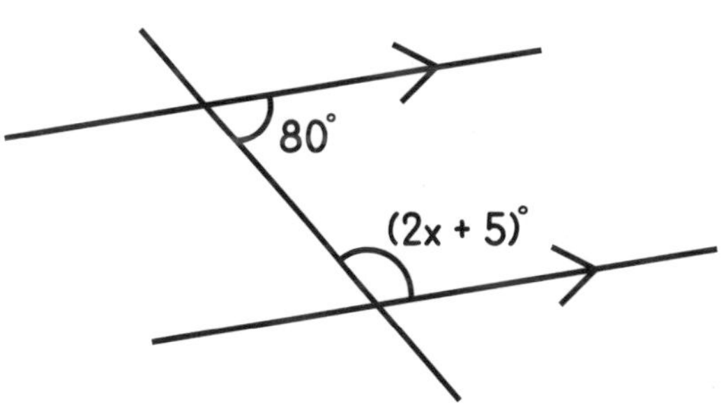

Giving reasons, find the value of x.

READY?

This is not an exterior angle

interior angles

Looking closer

exterior angles

USEFUL STUFF:

* Interior means inside and exterior means outside
* A **regular** polygon is a shape where all the sides are the same length and all the interior angles are the same size
* The sum of angles around a point = 360° & on a straight line = 180°

KEY POINTS:

* The sum of the exterior angles of any polygon is 360°
* Interior angle + exterior angle = 180° (remember)
* The sum of the interior angles increases by 180° as the number of sides of the polygon increases ... like this:

Number of sides	Sum of interior angles
3	180°
4	360°
5	540°
6	720°
7	900°
...	...

+ 180° between each row

e.g. 1 Calculate the size of angle x.

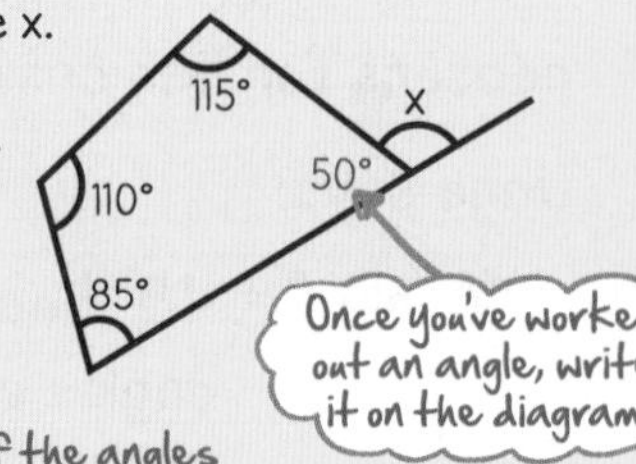

1 Sum of interior angles of a quadrilateral = 360°

85° + 110° + 115° = 310°

360° - 310° = 50°

Once you've worked out an angle, write it on the diagram

2 The sum of the angles on a straight line is 180°

x = 180° - 50° = 130°

e.g. 2 Calculate the size of an interior angle of a regular hexagon. (6 sides)

1 Write a list

sides	sum of interior angles
3	180°
4	360°
5	540°
6	720°

2 Work out the sum of interior angles ÷ number of sides

720° ÷ 6 = 120°

So an interior angle = 120°

1 Work out each exterior angle (360 ÷ number of sides)

360° ÷ 6 = 60°

2 Work out the size of one interior angle

180° - 60° = 120°

e.g. 3 Could this be part of a regular polygon?

144°

36° (180° - 144°)

360° ÷ 36° = 10 (Decagon)

Yes, it's part of a regular 10 sided polygon

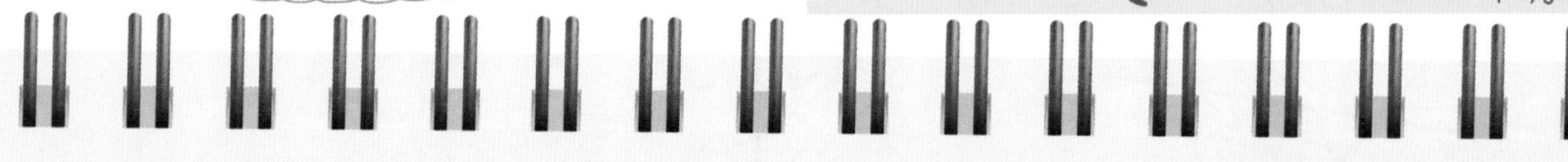

A. Calculate the size of angle m in the kite.
Give a reason for your answer.

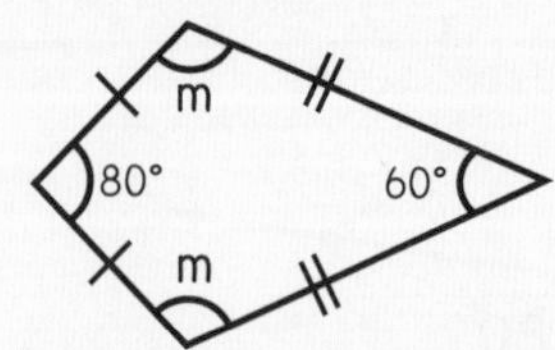

B. Calculate the size of angle a.
Give reasons for your answer.

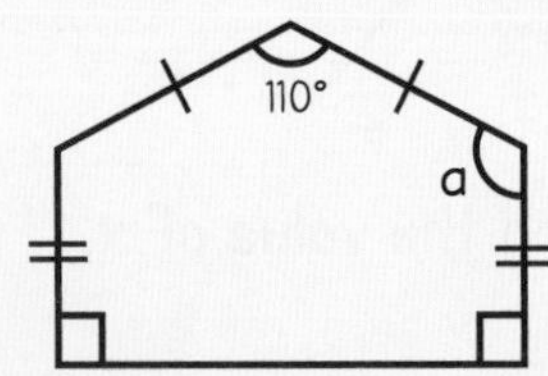

C. The size of each exterior angle of a regular polygon is 40°

Work out the number of sides of the polygon.

D. Find the value of x.

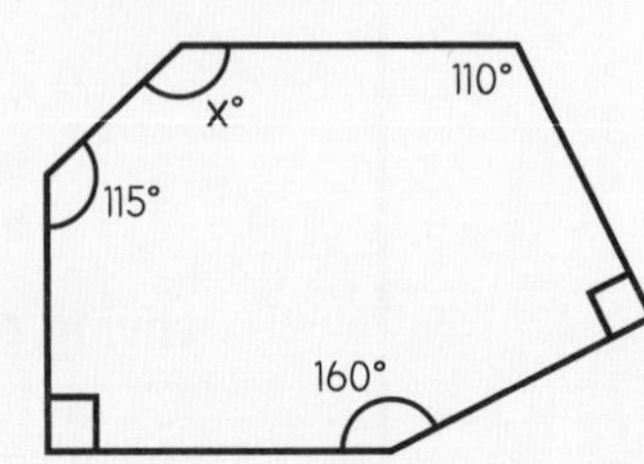

E. Could this be part of a regular polygon? Explain why.

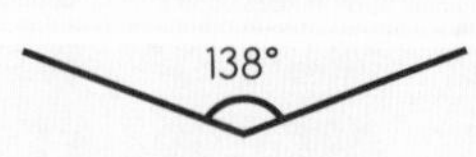

Diagrams not drawn to scale

INTERIOR AND EXTERIOR ANGLES

Belter!

1. Shape A is a regular octagon.
Shape B is a regular pentagon.

Calculate the size of angle x.

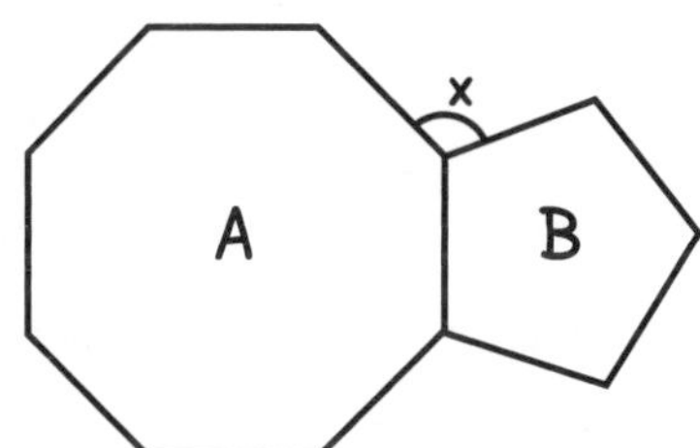

2. ABCDE and EHJKL are regular pentagons.
AEL is an equilateral triangle.
Work out the size of angle DEH.

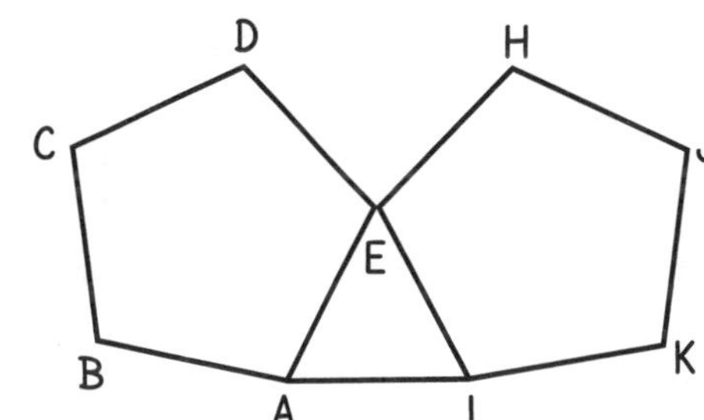

HINT: Move your finger from D to E to H... the angle is in the middle

3. Kenny thinks the exterior angle of a hexagon is 120° because:

$$720° \div 6 = 120°$$

Do you agree with Kenny?

Explain your answer.

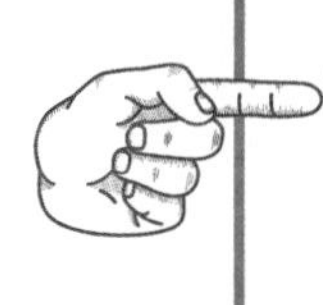

4. The diagram shows a regular hexagon joined to a right-angled triangle.

AC is a straight line.

Find the size of angle x, giving reasons for your answer.

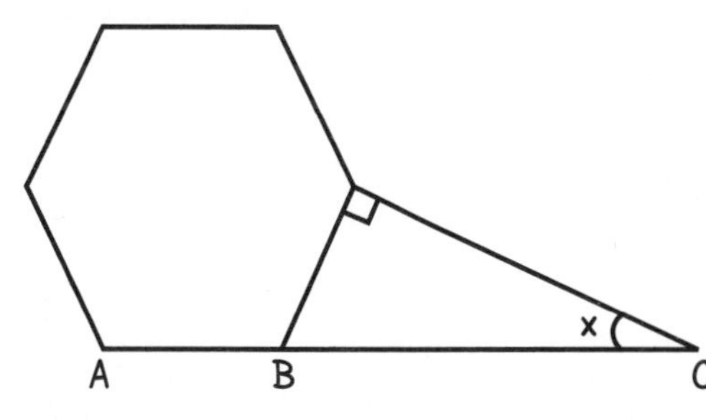

READY?

It is **REALLY USEFUL** to:
* be able to picture 3D shapes in your mind
* draw neatly!

* A **plan** is a 2D drawing showing the view of a 3D shape as if you were looking at the shape from above.
* An **elevation** is a 2D drawing showing the view of a 3D shape as if looking at it (usually) from the **side** or **front**. A sneaky question might throw in a curve ball and ask for a rear elevation (view from the back).
* The different views will usually be labelled with an arrow to indicate where you need to imagine looking at the shape from.

e.g. 1 For the 3D shape shown, draw the:
a) plan view
b) front elevation
c) side elevation

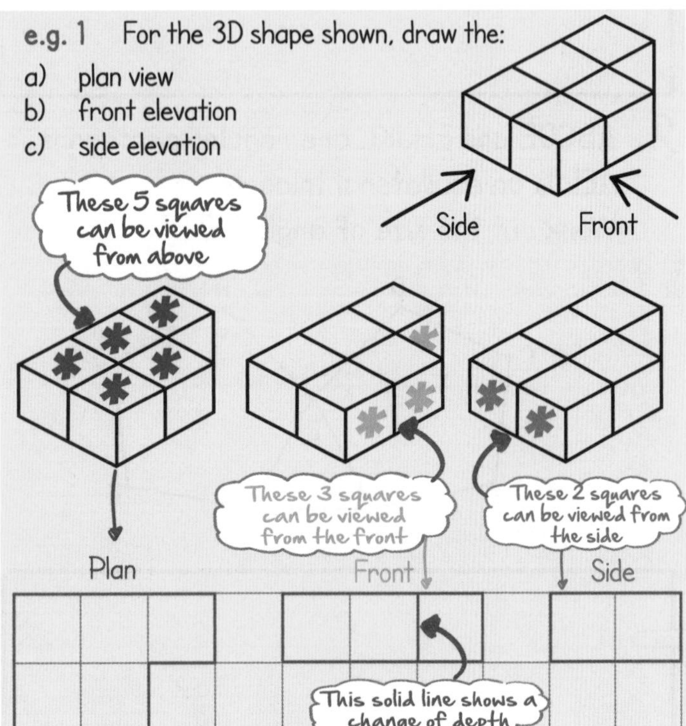

e.g. 2 Here are the plan and front elevation of a solid shape.

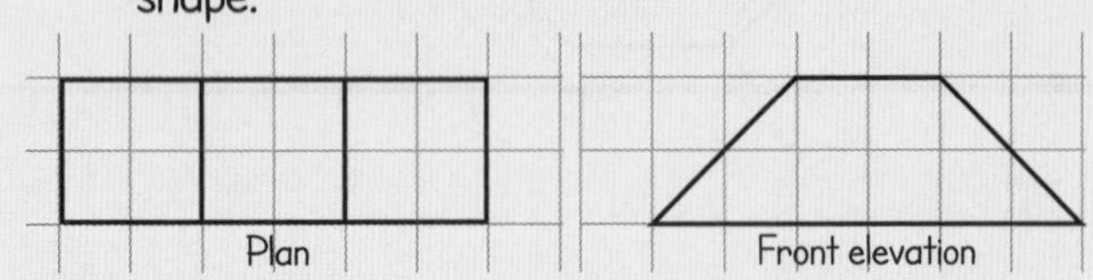

a) On the grid below, draw the side elevation of the solid shape.

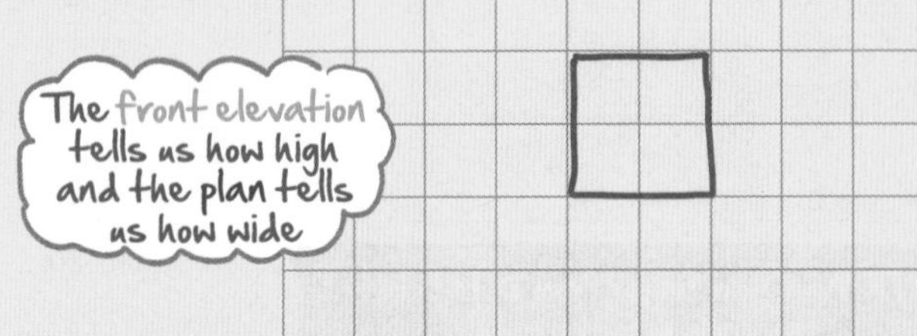

b) Sketch the solid shape.

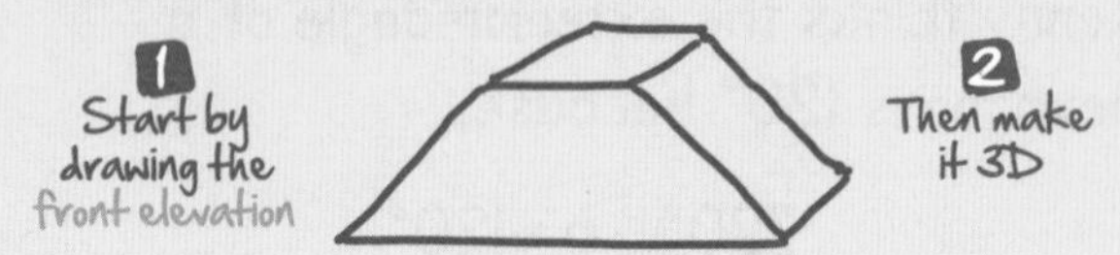

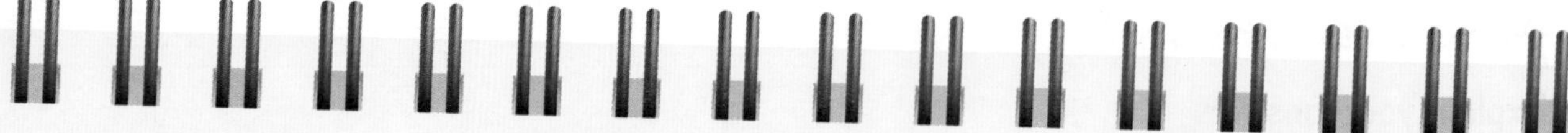

SET?

A. Draw the plan of the square-based pyramid.

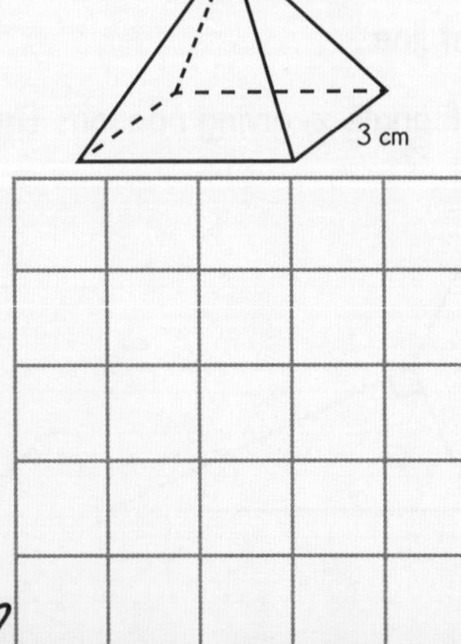

B. A solid is made from cubes.

The plan view, front elevation and side elevation are shown.

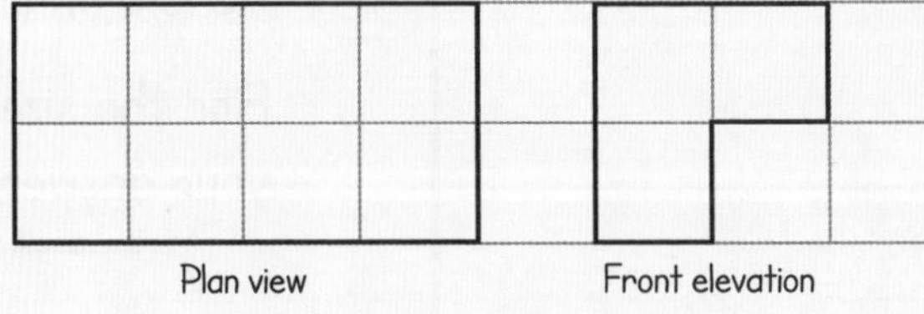

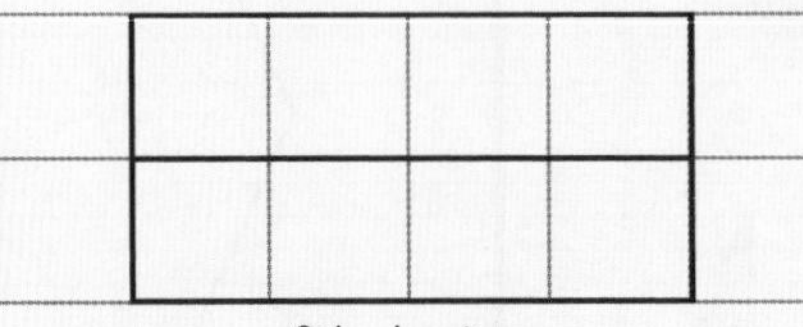

How many cubes were used to make the solid?

C. The diagram represents a solid made from five cubes.

Draw the:
(i) plan view
(ii) front elevation
(iii) side elevation

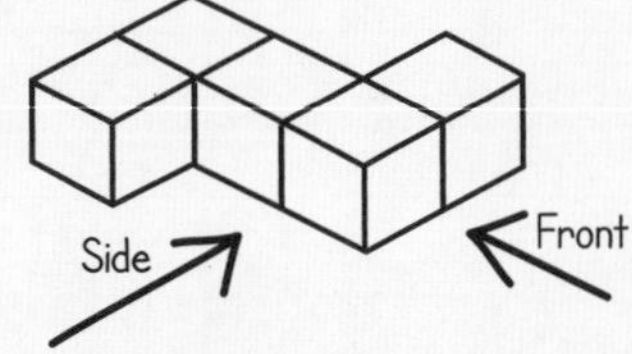

PLANS AND ELEVATIONS

Clever!

1. A solid cuboid is made from 20 centimetre cubes.

a) Sketch a possible solid shape. Label the dimensions.

b) Draw and label the plan, front and side elevations for your solid shape in part a).

2. The diagram represents a solid made from six centimetre cubes.

Draw the:

(i) front elevation,

(ii) side elevation.

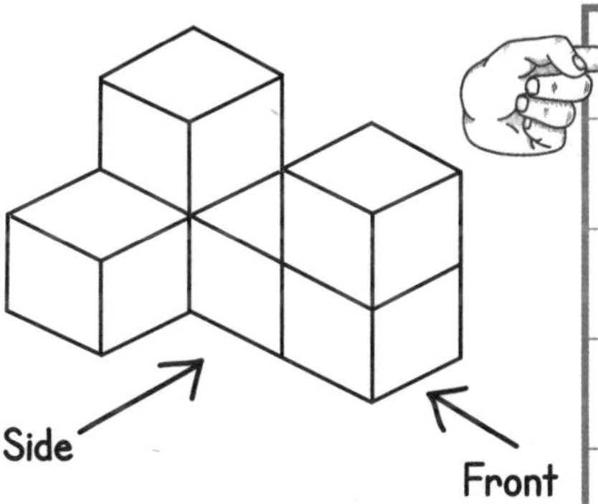

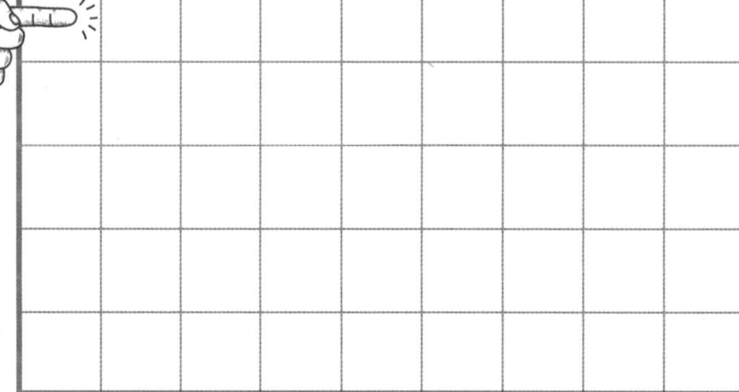

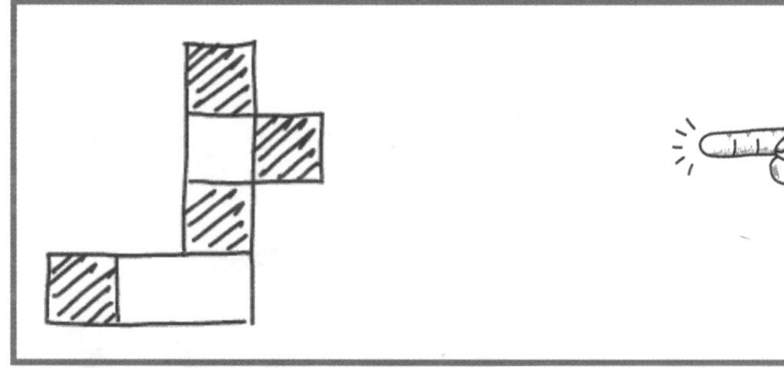

3. Christine is asked to draw the plan of this solid.

She is wrong.

Explain the mistake she has made.

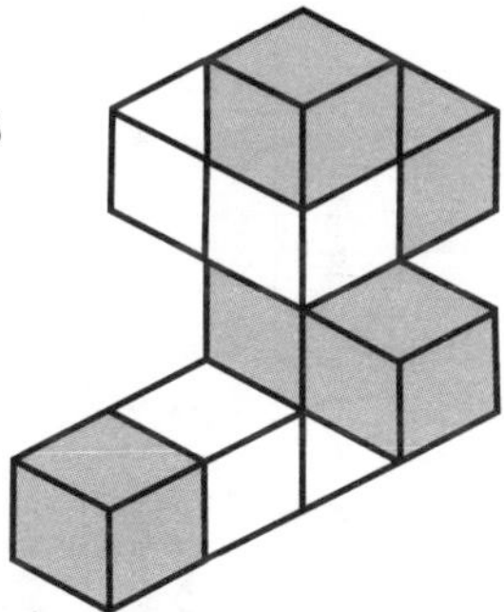

4. Here are the plan, side elevation and front elevation of a solid prism.

Plan

Side elevation

Front elevation

Sketch the prism.

READY?

Lots of geometry problems can be solved by constructing line and angle bisectors using a pair of compasses and a ruler.

You **REALLY NEED** to be able to:
- Draw arcs using a pair of compasses
- Draw straight lines using a ruler
- Make sure your pencil is sharp!

e.g. 1 Use a ruler and a pair of compasses to construct the perpendicular bisector of AB. (90°)

A ——— B

1 Open the compasses to at least half of the length of the line

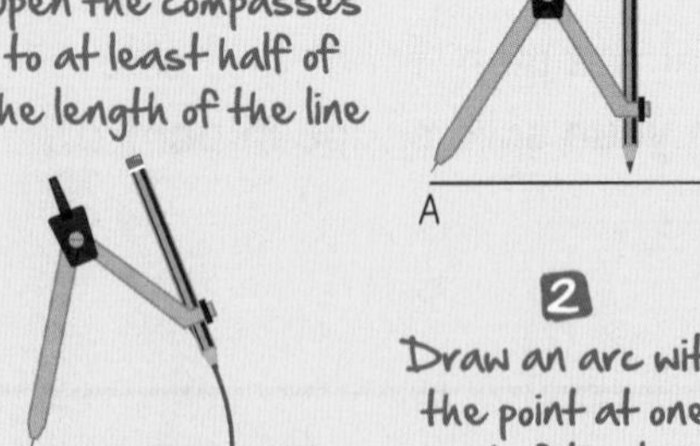

2 Draw an arc with the point at one end of the line

3 Without adjusting the compasses put the point at the other end of the line and draw another arc

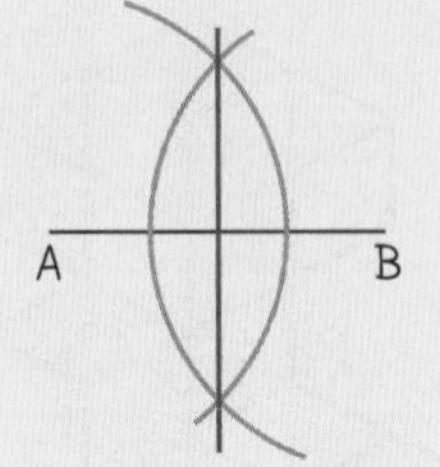

4 Join the points of intersection of the arcs with a straight line using a ruler

e.g. 2 Construct a perpendicular to the line from point P.

P •

1 Draw an arc from P that crosses the line twice

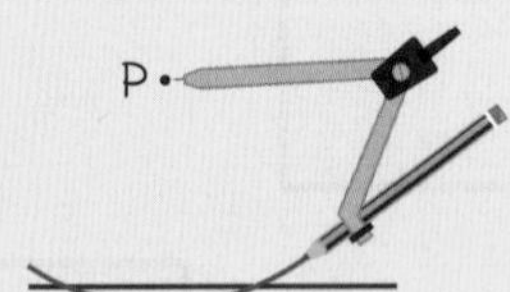

2 Label the points of intersection A and B

3 Construct the perpendicular bisector of AB (like e.g. 1)

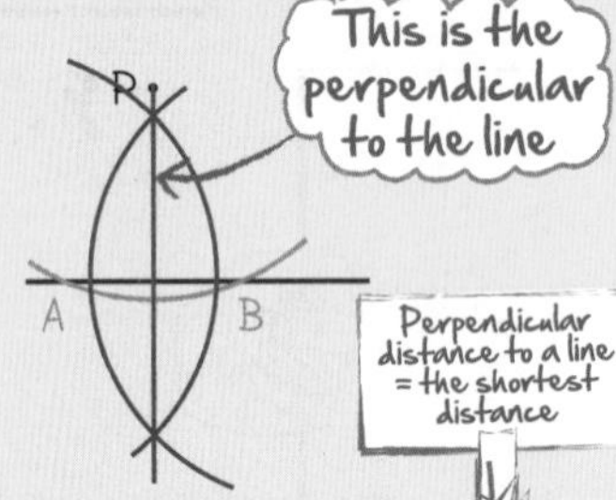

e.g. 3 Bisect the angle LMN.

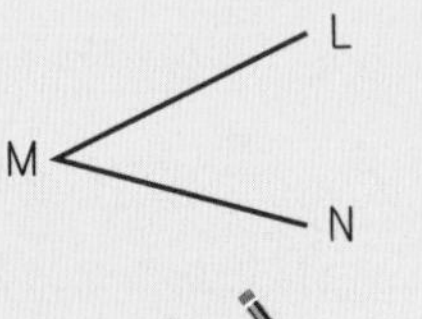

1 With the point at M, draw an arc crossing both lines

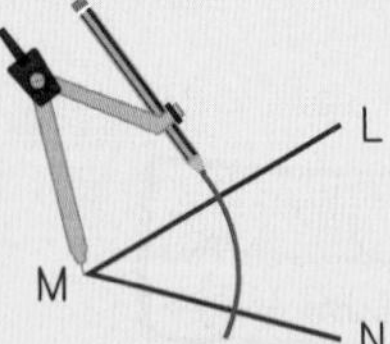

2 From a point of intersection, draw an arc

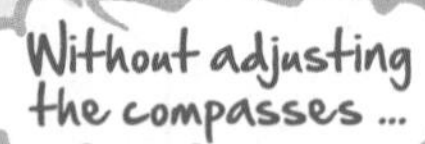

3 From the other point of intersection, draw another arc

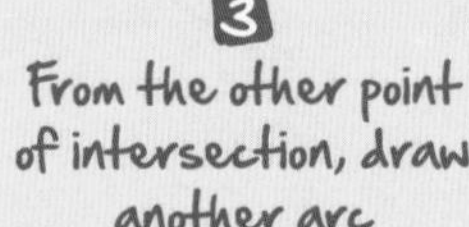

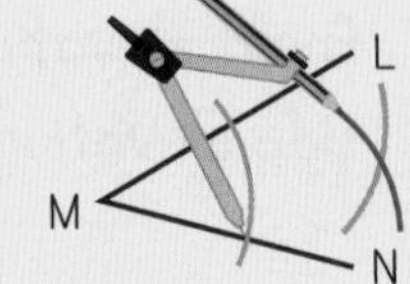

4 Join M to where the two arcs intersect

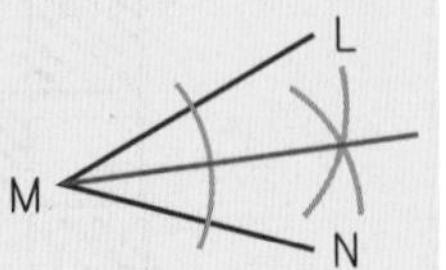

Use a piece of plain paper, a ruler and a pair of compasses

A. Draw a straight line 10 cm long.
Construct a perpendicular bisector of the line.

B. Draw a straight line 78 mm long.
Label the ends of your line A and B.
Construct a perpendicular bisector of the line AB.

C. Use a protractor to construct an angle of 60°.
Bisect the angle.

D. Use a protractor to construct an angle of 110°.
Construct the angle bisector.

E. Construct a perpendicular to the line from the point A.

A •

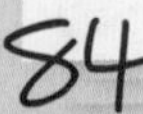

GO! CONSTRUCTIONS

Canny good!

1. Here is the plan of a room drawn to a scale of 1 : 30

   Maddie wants to put a chair in the room.

   The chair has to be:

   - more than 150 cm from B
   - closer to CD than AD

   Construct and shade the region where Maddie can put the chair.

2. By bisecting the angle, construct a rhombus.

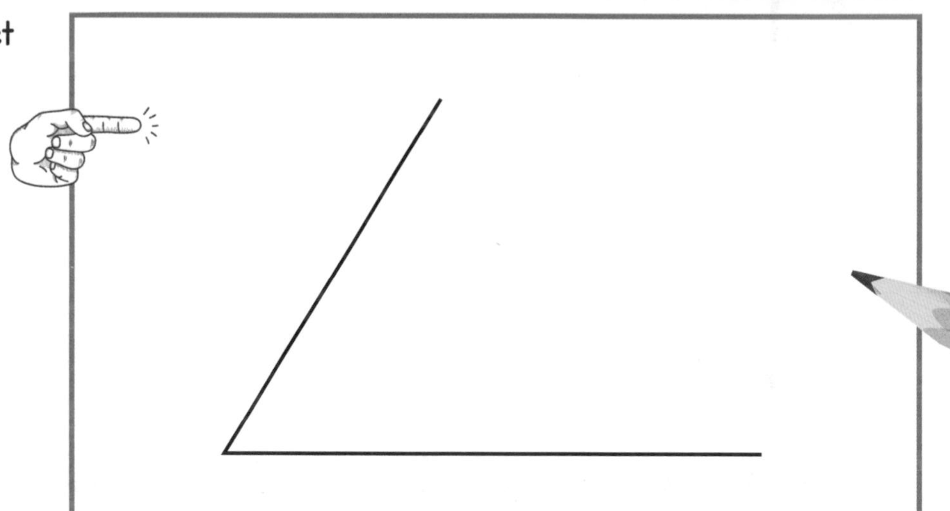

3. The map shows the position of two towns on an island.

   A radio mast is closer to town A than it is to town B.

   The mast is less than 60 km from town B.

   Construct and shade the region where the mast could be.

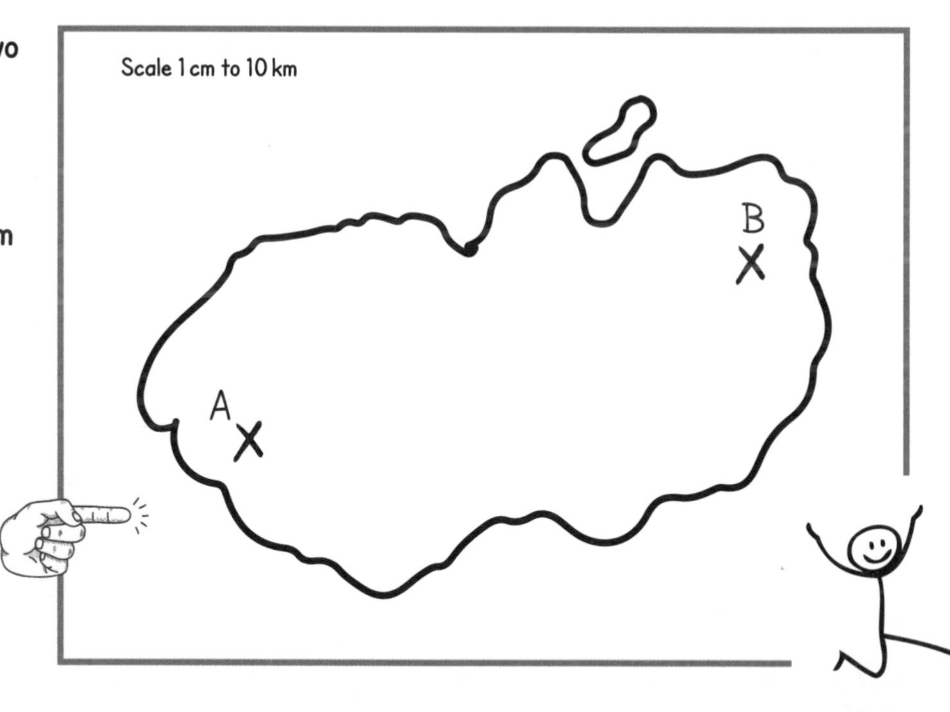

READY?

THE RULES!

1 Bearings are measured from **NORTH**

2 Bearings are measured **CLOCKWISE**

3 Bearings are given as **3 DIGITS**

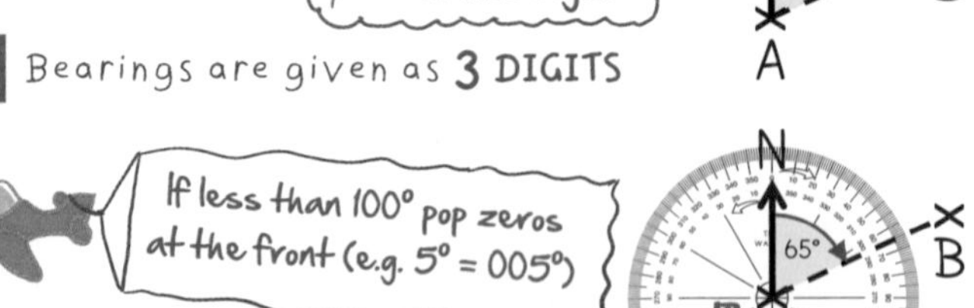

The bearing of B from A is 065°

It is **REALLY USEFUL** to:

* know the sum of the angles at a point is 360° and on a straight line is 180°
* use related angle facts ...
  - Alternate angles are equal
  - Corresponding angles are equal
  - The sum of co-interior (or 'allied') angles is 180°

e.g. 1 Measure the bearing of A from B.

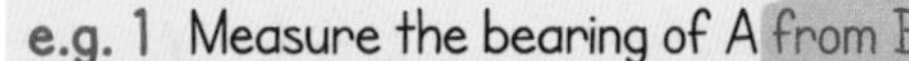

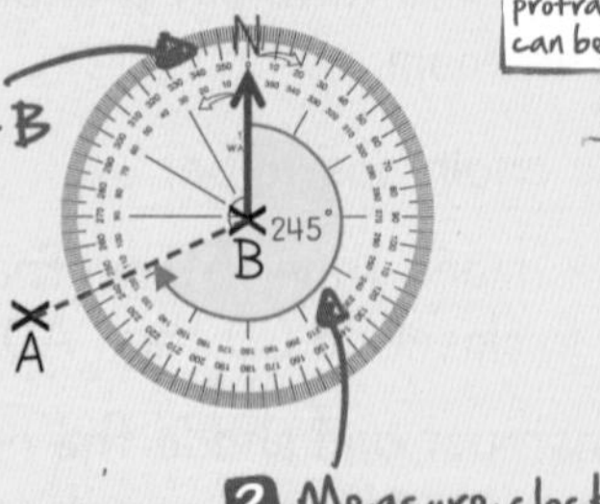

1 Draw a north line at B

2 Measure clockwise

The bearing of A from B is 245°

SOME OTHER STUFF:

* With a question such as "Find the bearing of B FROM A", the word **FROM** tells you where to start: i.e. draw your north line at A.
* Some of the key compass points are also known by their bearings:

Due north is 000°
Due east is 090°
Due south is 180°
Due west is 270°

e.g. 2 The bearing of a ship from a lighthouse is 130°
Work out the bearing of the lighthouse from the ship.

1 Draw a sketch if you're not given one

N
Lighthouse 130°
N
50°
Ship

2 Spot the co-interior angles, they add upto 180°

360° - 50° = 310°

The bearing of the lighthouse from the ship is 310°

Different angle facts can be used to find the missing angles (look out for alternate and corresponding angles)

A. (i) What is the bearing of London from Manchester?

(ii) What is the bearing of Manchester from London?

B. The map shows the position of Sienna (S). Sienna travels 4 km on a bearing of 055° then stops.

Does Sienna enter the Danger Zone shown below? Explain your answer.

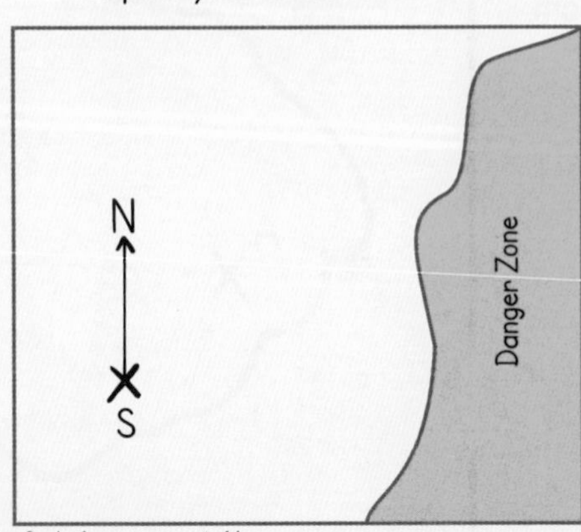

Scale: 1 cm represents 1 km

C. The bearing of a plane from the airport is 070°
Work out the bearing of the airport from the plane.

D. A ship leaves a harbour and sails due west for 5 km. It then sails due south for 10 km.
By drawing a diagram, measure the bearing of the ship from the harbour.
Use a scale of 1 cm = 1 km.

Use a piece of plain paper

BEARINGS

Rocking!

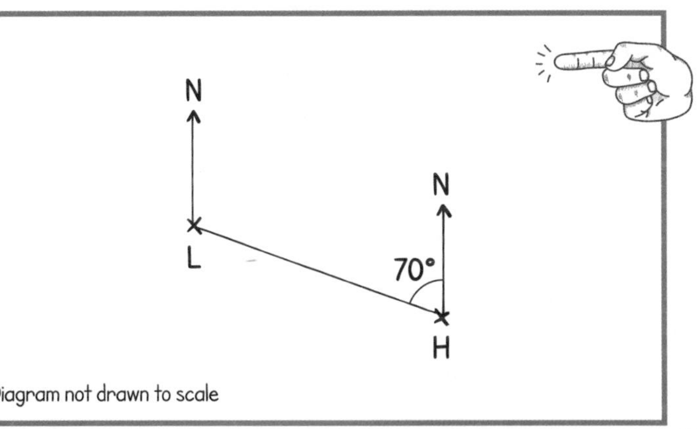

1. Arlo thinks the bearing of L from H is 070°

Do you agree with Arlo?

Explain your answer.

2. Use the map to complete the table:

The bearing of ...	from ...	is ...
Bristol	Birmingham	
		090°
		180°

3. Olivia runs on a bearing of 195° to her friend Grace.

On what bearing must Grace run to return back to the original starting point for Olivia?

N

Oldport

L

1 cm = 100 m

4. A boat leaves Oldport and sails 250 m on a bearing of 120°

The boat then sails due north for 200 m.

The boat then changes direction and travels a further 300 m on a bearing of 030°

The lighthouse (L) will flash if a boat gets closer than 200 m.

Does the lighthouse flash?
Explain your answer.

READY?

Pythagoras' theorem describes the relationship between the sides of a right-angled triangle. It can be used to find missing side lengths. You may have seen it written as:

$$a^2 + b^2 = c^2$$

(a, b and c are the lengths of the sides)

It is **REALLY USEFUL** to remember:

- The longest side of a right-angled triangle is called the hypotenuse and is always opposite the right angle

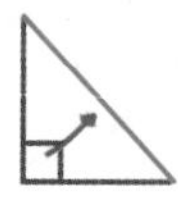

- The first few square numbers are 1 (1 × 1), 4 (2 × 2), 9 (3 × 3) and 16 (4 × 4) ...
- Where the square and square root buttons are on your calculator: x^2 $\sqrt{\ }$

$c^2 = a^2 + b^2$

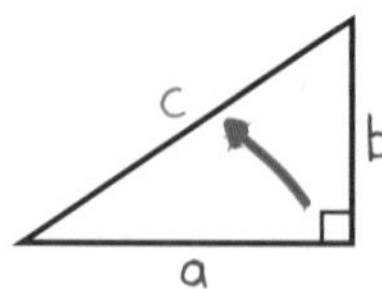

$d^2 = e^2 + f^2$

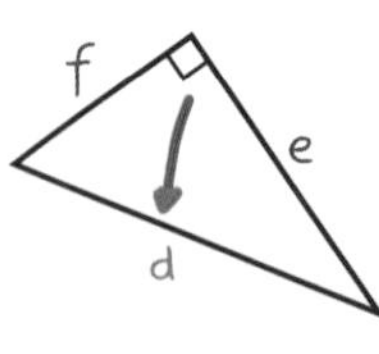

e.g. 1 Calculate the length DE. Give your answer to 1 decimal place.

The line that joins D to E (label it with any letter)

$x^2 = 4^2 + 5^2$

$x^2 = 16 + 25$

$x^2 = 41$

$x = \sqrt{41} = 6.40312 \ldots$

$x = 6.4$ cm (to 1 dp)

Remember to square root

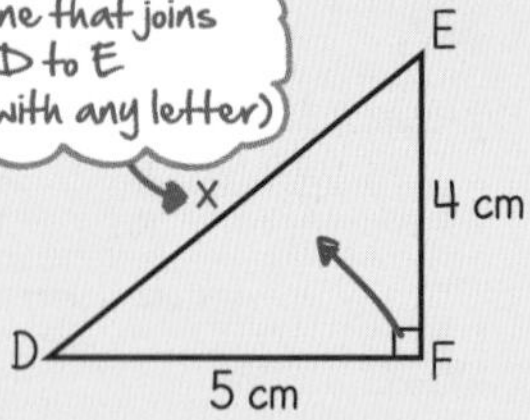

(Triangle DEF: EF = 4 cm, DF = 5 cm, right angle at F, DE = x)

It is not just used for finding the longest side. If we have any two side lengths we can find the third side length.

Subtract if looking for one of the shorter sides

e.g. 2 XYZ is a right-angled triangle, XY = 13 m and YZ = 12 m. Find XZ.

$x^2 = 13^2 - 12^2$

$x^2 = 169 - 144$

$x^2 = 25$

$x = \sqrt{25}$

$x = 5$ m

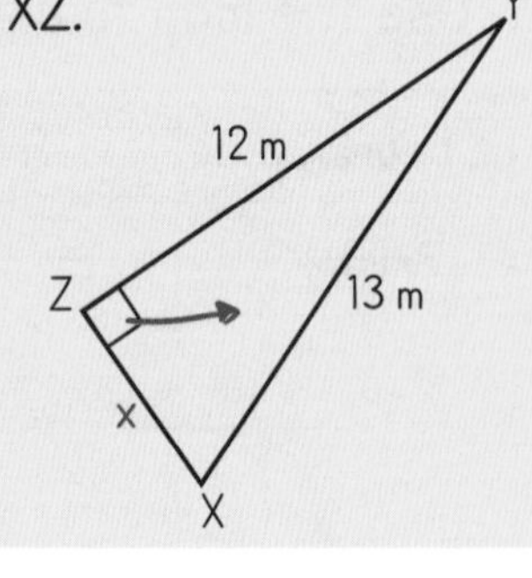

Pythagoras' theorem can only be applied to right-angled triangles

$a^2 = c^2 - b^2$

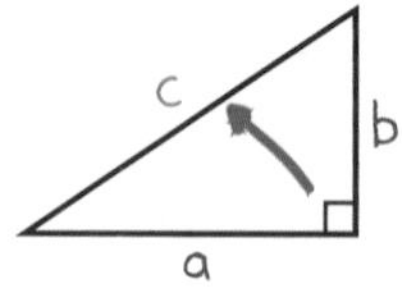

The arrow will remind you which is the longest side and whether we need to add or subtract

$f^2 = d^2 - e^2$

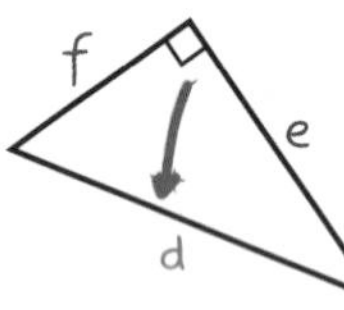

Look out for Pythagorean triples:

These are sets of 3 whole numbers (not decimals) that are the side lengths of a right-angled triangle. The most common ones are:

3, 4 and 5   6, 8 and 10   5, 12 and 13

A. Find the length of PQ.

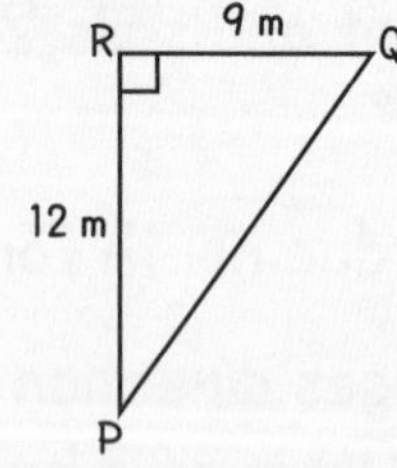

B. Triangle SUT is an isosceles triangle. Calculate the length ST to 1 d.p.

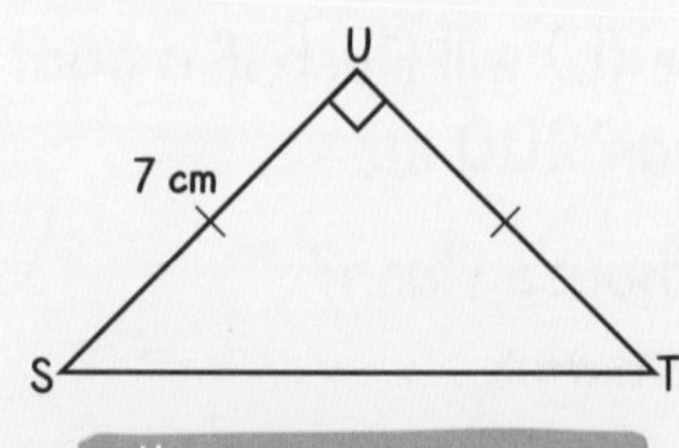

HINT: Isosceles triangles have 2 equal length sides

C. ABC is a right-angled triangle and AC is the longest side.
Given AB = 6 cm and AC = 10 cm, calculate the length of BC.

D. In a right-angled triangle XYZ:
XY = 5 cm
YZ = 12 cm
XZ is the longest side.
Calculate the perimeter of triangle XYZ.

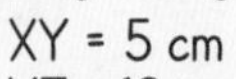

E. Ren's dog is stuck 5 m up a tree.
Ren is using a ladder of length 6 m to try and rescue the dog.
Ren places the ladder 3 m from the base of the tree.
Will Ren be able to reach the dog?
Explain your answer.

GO! PYTHAGORAS' THEOREM 1

Star!

1. E is the centre of rectangle ABCD.
   Work out the length DE.

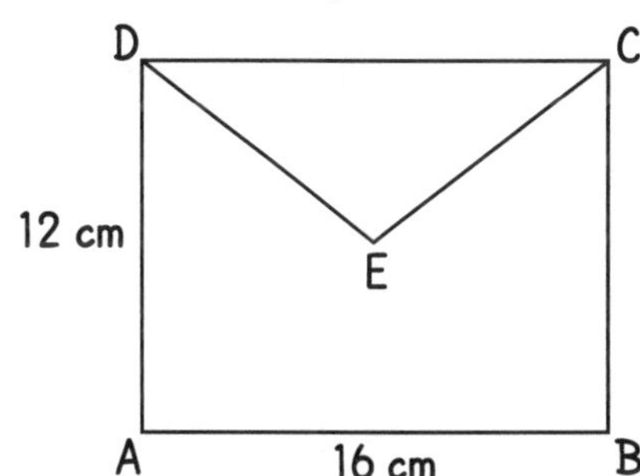

2. The equilateral triangle and the square have the same perimeter.

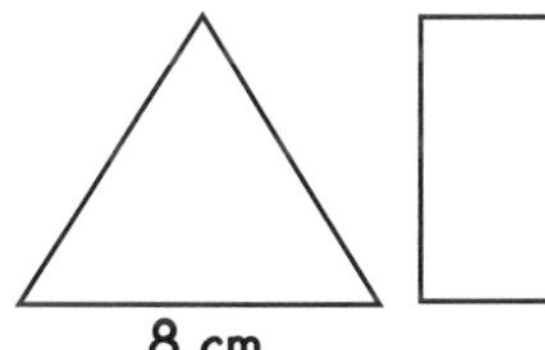

Find the length of the diagonal of the square.
Give your answer to one decimal place.

3. Ship A and ship B set sail from the same port.

   Ship A sails 15 km/h due east
   Ship B sails 22 km/h due south

   After 2 hours, how far away is Ship A from Ship B to the nearest kilometre?

4.

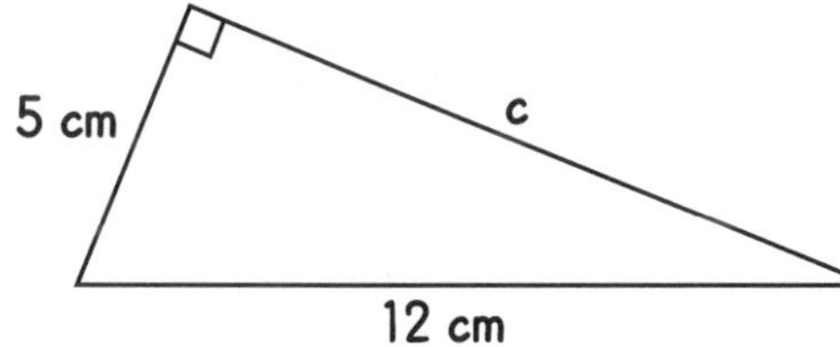

Billy says c = 13 cm because ...

$$a^2 + b^2 = 5^2 + 12^2 = 25 + 144 = 169$$

So $c^2 = 169$

$$c = \sqrt{169} = 13 \text{ cm}$$

Do you agree with Billy? Explain your answer.

READY?

Pythagoras' theorem can be used to solve problems involving right-angled triangles.

e.g. 1 A triangle has sides of length 8 cm, 15 cm and 17 cm. Is this a right-angled triangle? Show how you decide.

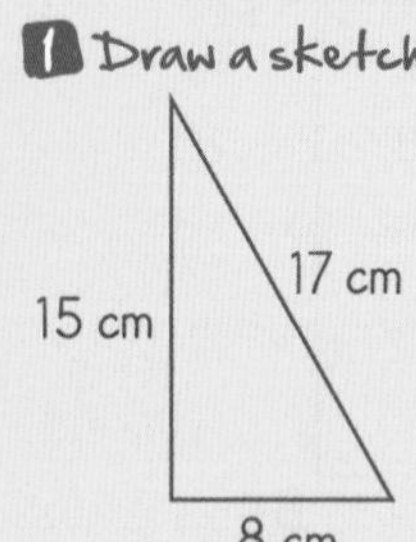

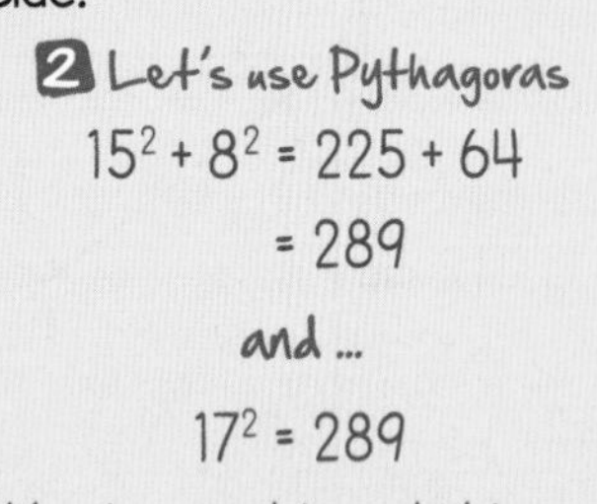

$15^2 + 8^2 = 225 + 64$

$= 289$

and ...

$17^2 = 289$

Yes it is a right-angled triangle (because Pythagoras' theorem works)

Sometimes you will need to be able to apply the process in unfamiliar contexts. It's all about spotting right-angled triangles.

e.g. 2 A triangle has its vertices A at (2,1), B at (5,1) and C at (5,5)

Calculate the length of AC.

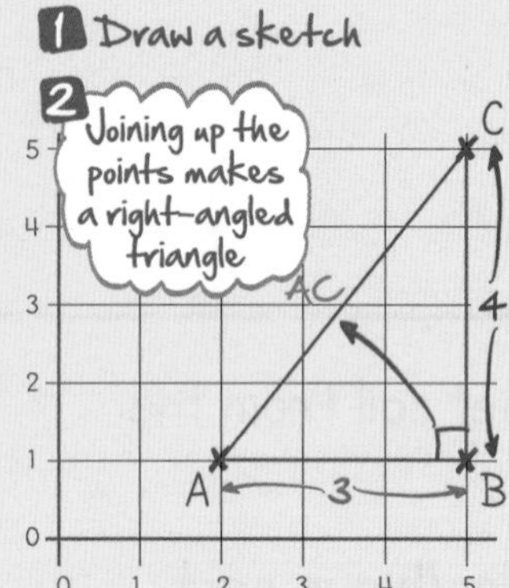

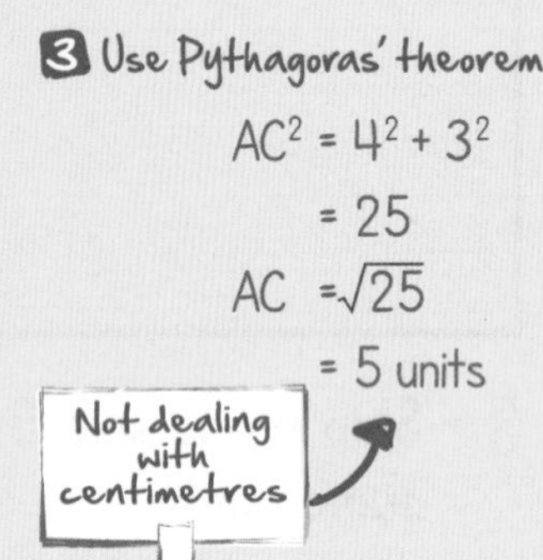

$AC^2 = 4^2 + 3^2$

$= 25$

$AC = \sqrt{25}$

$= 5$ units

Some questions are extra sneaky as they may involve two (or more) triangles.

e.g. 3 Calculate the length of FG.

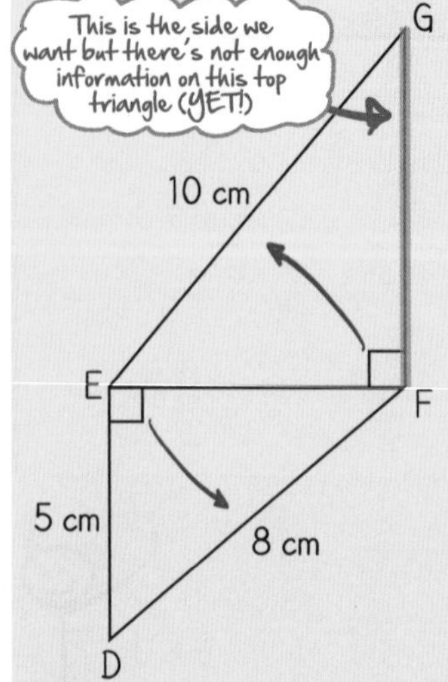

Work out the length of the shared side between the two triangles

$FE^2 = 8^2 - 5^2$

$= 39$

$FE = \sqrt{39} = 6.244...$ cm

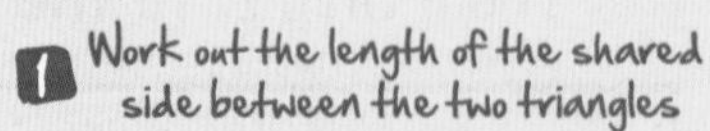

$FG^2 = 10^2 - 6.244...^2$

$= 61$

$FG = \sqrt{61} = 7.810249...$

$= 7.8$ cm (1 d.p.)

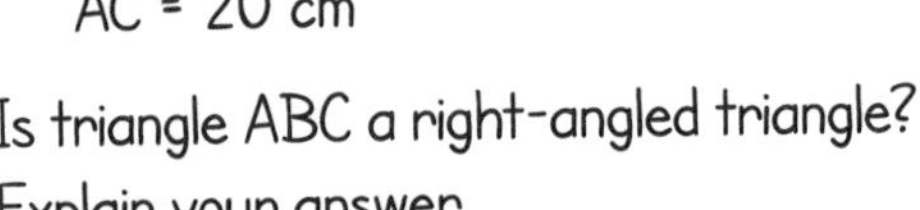

SET?

A. In triangle ABC:

AB = 12 cm

BC = 16 cm

AC = 20 cm

Is triangle ABC a right-angled triangle? Explain your answer.

B. Triangle XYZ has a perimeter of 30 cm.

XY = 8 cm

YZ = 10 cm

Explain why triangle XYZ is not a right-angled triangle.

C. A triangle has its vertices A at (-3, -3), B at (-3, 4) and C at (2, 4)

Calculate the length of AC to one decimal place.

D. Find the perpendicular height of this isosceles triangle to 2 significant figures.

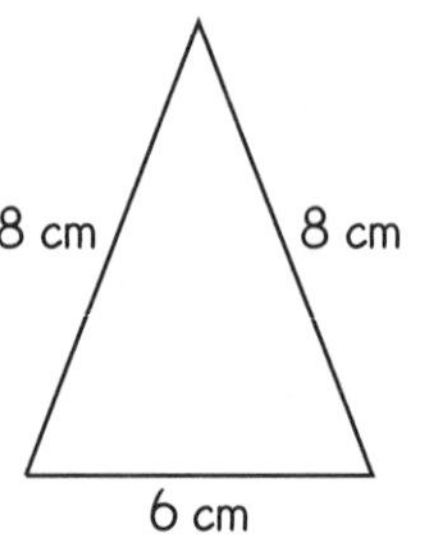

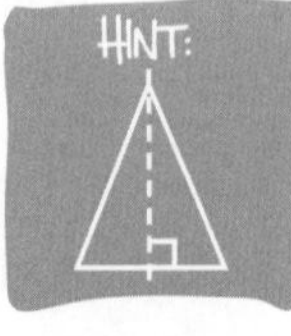

GO! PYTHAGORAS' THEOREM 2

Notable!

1. Point A is at (-7, -2) and point B is at (-2, -6)

Calculate the length of AB to three significant figures.

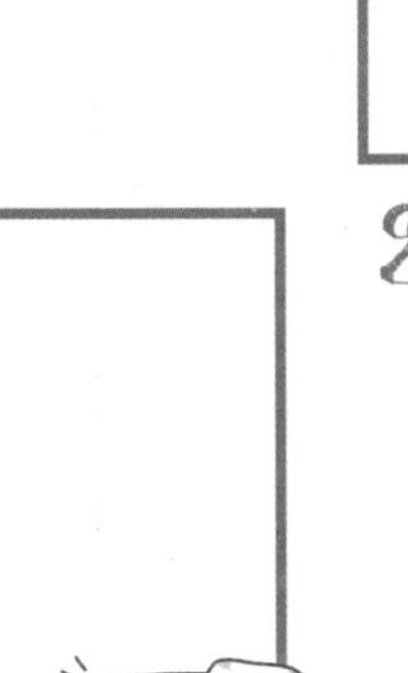

2. Calculate the area of the isosceles trapezium.

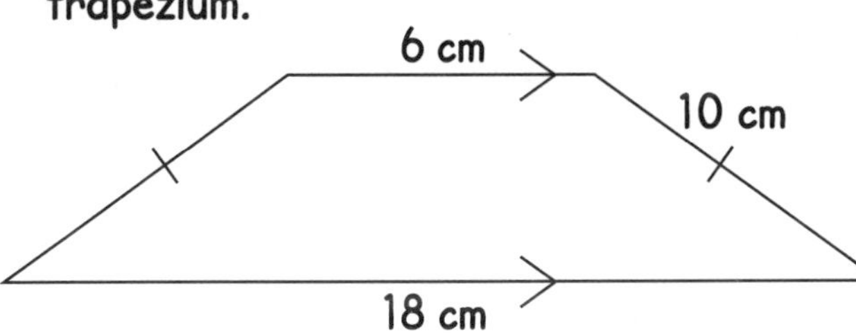

3. An equilateral triangle has sides of length 8 cm.

Find the perpendicular height of the triangle, giving your answer to a sensible degree of accuracy.

4. AD = 8 cm, AB = 8 cm and DC = 5 cm

Angle ABC = Angle BCD = 90°

Calculate the length of AC.

Give your answer correct to 3 significant figures.

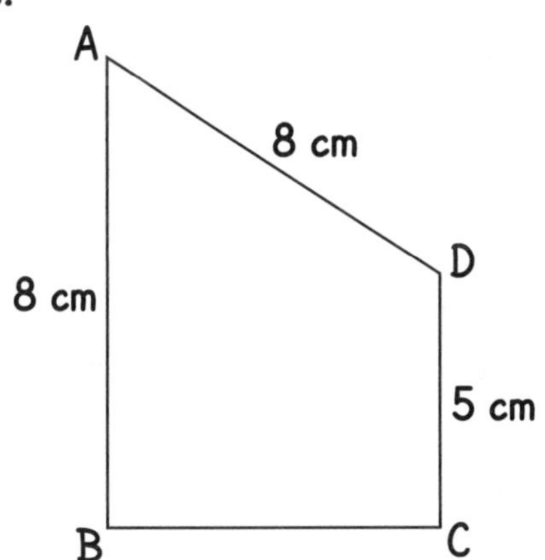

READY?

1. Make sure your calculator is in degrees mode
2. Know where the sin, cos, tan buttons are on your calculator

Trigonometry is the study of the relationship between side lengths and angles of triangles.

The sides of a right-angled triangle have special names. The **hypotenuse** is opposite the right angle. The other two sides are called **opposite** or **adjacent** (next to) depending on which angle is being used:

With a side length and a given angle (not the right angle) we can use trigonometry to find lengths of missing sides using sine (sin), cosine (cos) and tangent (tan).

$\sin\theta = \frac{O}{H}$ $\cos\theta = \frac{A}{H}$ $\tan\theta = \frac{O}{A}$

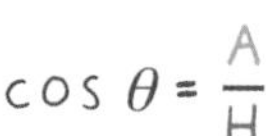
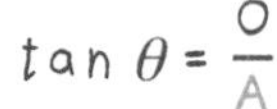
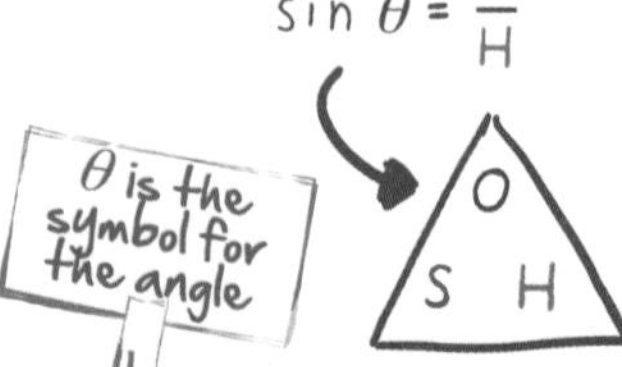

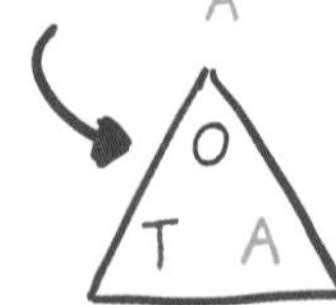

O / T A

e.g. 1 Find the value of y on this triangle to 1 decimal place.

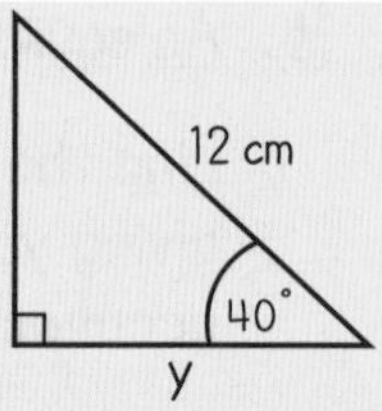

(Triangle: 12 cm, 40°, y)

1 Label the sides

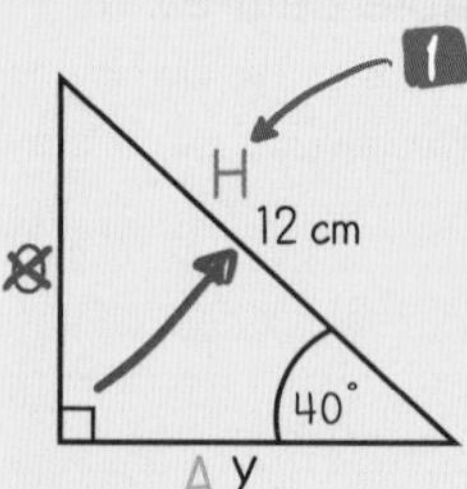

2 Make a decision ... cross off O as it has nothing with it. A and H are in A/C H so we use $\cos\theta = \frac{A}{H}$

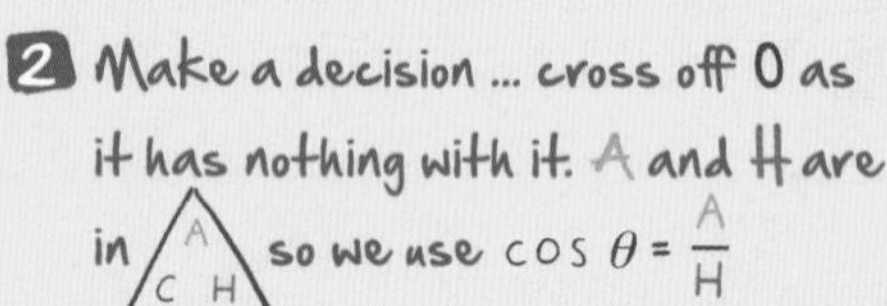

3 Substitute (θ = angle = 40°, A = y, H = 12 cm): $\cos 40 = \frac{y}{12}$

4 Solve:

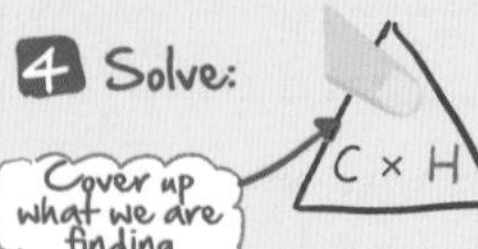

$y = \cos 40 \times 12$

$y = 9.19253...$

so y = 9.2 cm (1 d.p.)

e.g. 2 Find the length of PQ to 2 decimal places.

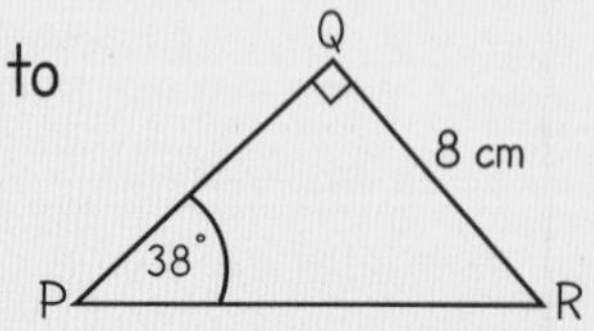

(Triangle PQR: Q right angle, QR = 8 cm, angle P = 38°)

1 Label the sides

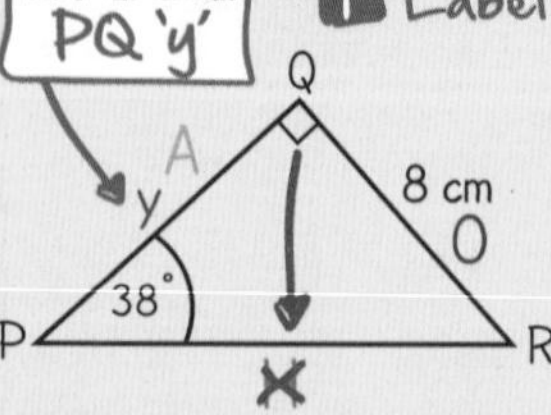

2 Make a decision ... cross off H as it has nothing with it. O and A are in O/T A so we use $\tan\theta = \frac{O}{A}$

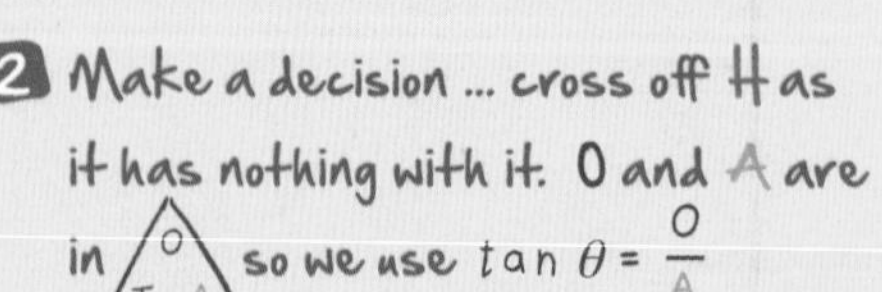

3 Substitute (θ = angle = 38°, O = 8 cm, A = y): $\tan 38 = \frac{8}{y}$

4 Solve:

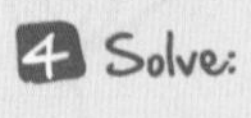
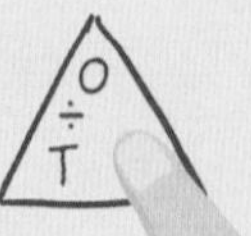

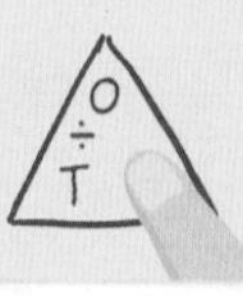

$y = \frac{8}{\tan 38}$

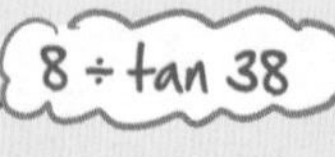

y = 10.2395... so PQ = 10.24 cm (2 d.p.)

SET?

A. Label each of the below triangles with opposite, adjacent and hypotenuse.

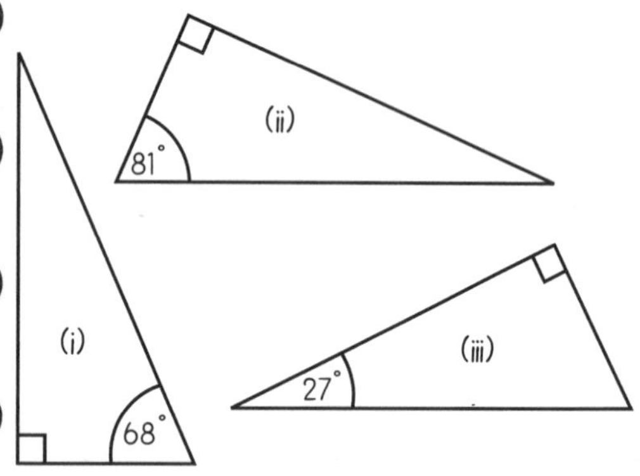

B. Each of these triangles has a side labelled x. Decide whether you would use sin, cos or tan to find this length.

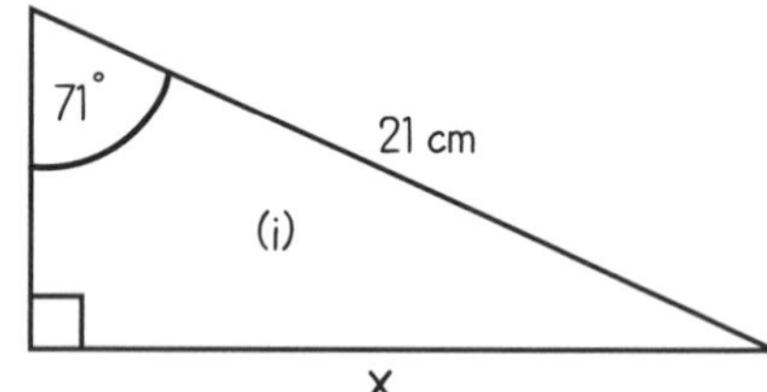

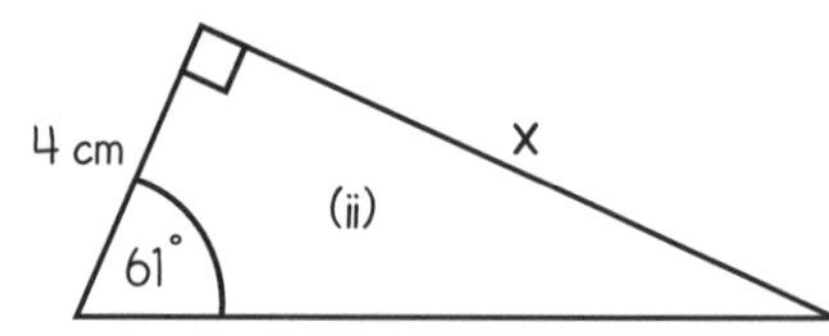

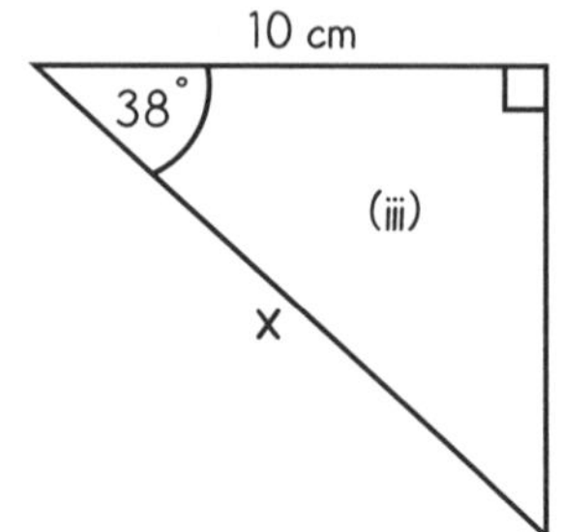

C. Find the value of x in each triangle in question B. Give your answers to one decimal place.

TRIGONOMETRY 1

Smokin'!

1. Mackenzie is finding the value of k in this triangle. Here is his working.

$\tan 48 = \frac{8}{k}$

$\tan 48 \times 8 = 8.884900119$

$k = 8.9$ cm (1 d.p.)

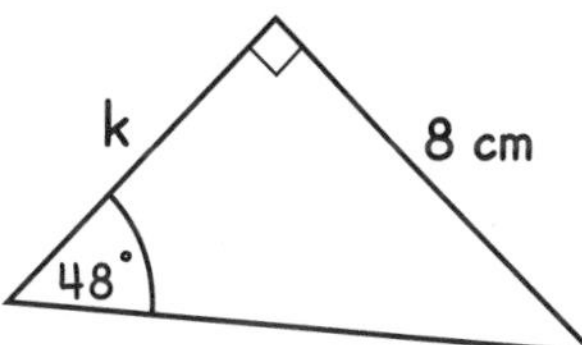

Mackenzie is wrong. Explain why.

2. The diagram shows two right-angled triangles.

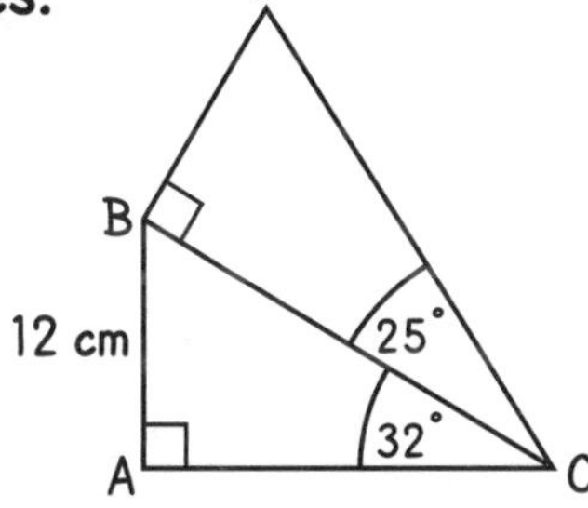

Find the length of DC to a suitable degree of accuracy.

3. Find the length of k in this triangle.

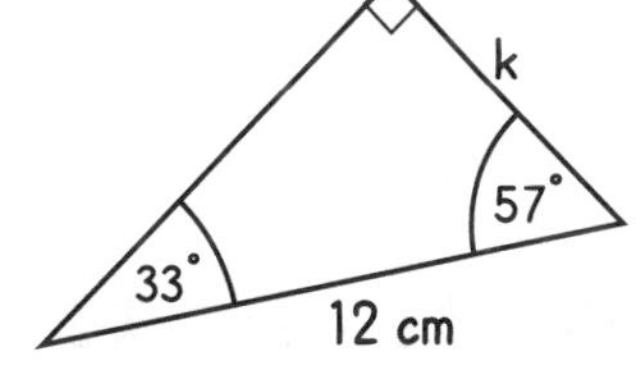

4. Newtown is 16 kilometres from Oldtown on a bearing of 075°

How far east of Oldtown is Newtown? Give your answer to three significant figures.

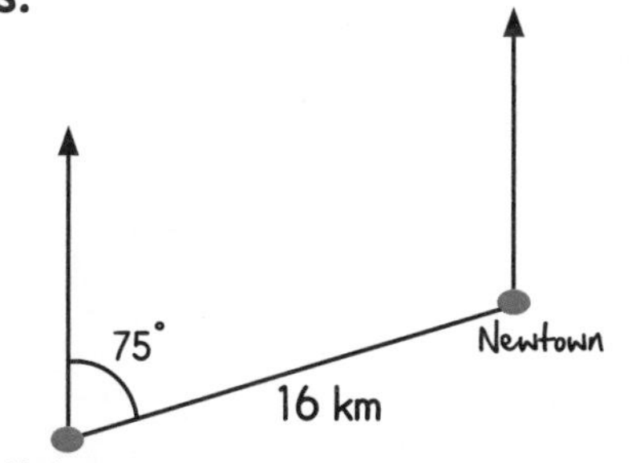

READY?

Trigonometry can also be used to find a missing angle of a right-angled triangle if we know two sides. REMEMBER:

1. Label: opposite, adjacent, hypotenuse
2. Make a decision: choose sin, cos or tan
3. Substitute: the numbers you know
4. Solve: the equation you have just made

e.g. 1 Find the size of angle x in this triangle. Give your answer to 1 decimal place.

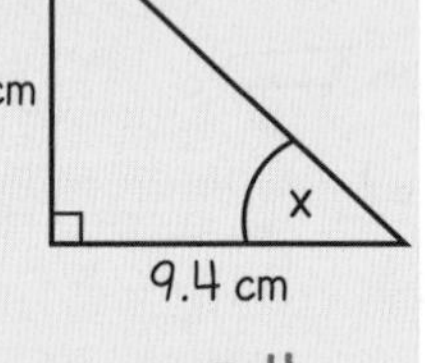

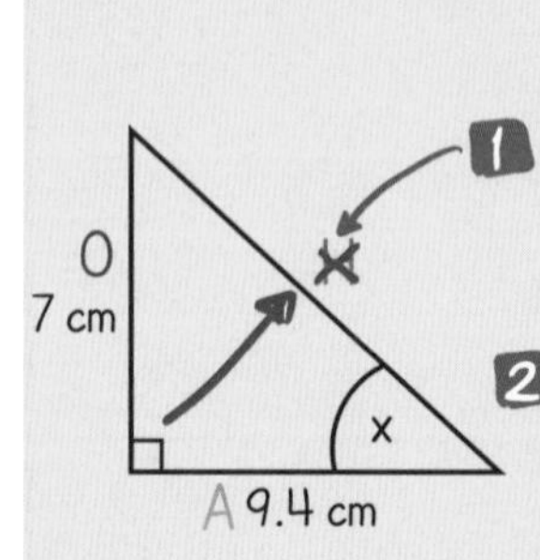

1 Label the sides

2 Make a decision ... cross off H as it has nothing with it. O and A are in $\frac{O}{T\ A}$ so we use $\tan\theta = \frac{O}{A}$

3 Substitute (θ = angle = x, O = 7 cm, A = 9.4 cm):

$$\tan x = \frac{7}{9.4}$$

7 ÷ 9.4

4 Solve: $\tan x = 0.7446...$

So $x = \tan^{-1} 0.7446... = 36.6743...$

$x = 36.7^\circ$ (1 d.p.)

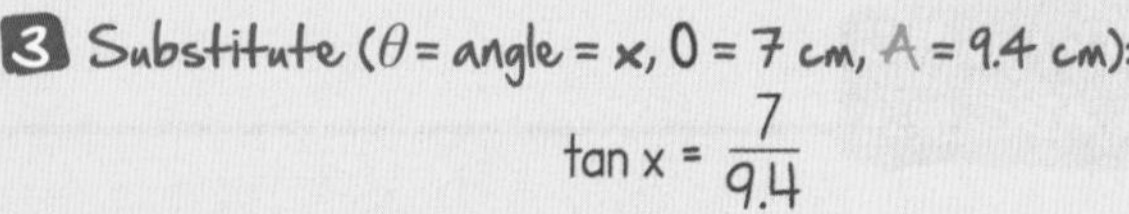

e.g. 2 Find the value of angle PRQ. Give your answer correct to 2 significant figures.

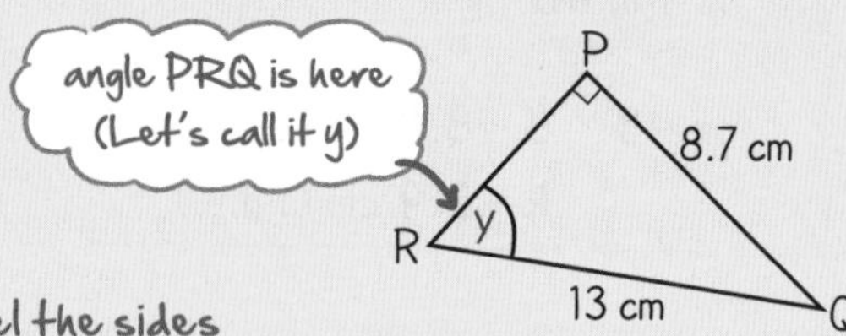

1 Label the sides

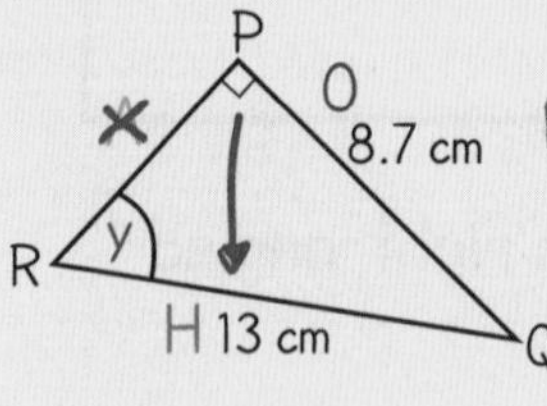

2 Make a decision ... cross off A as it has nothing with it. O and H are in $\frac{O}{S\ H}$ so we use $\sin\theta = \frac{O}{H}$

3 Substitute (θ = angle = y, O = 8.7 cm, H = 13 cm):

$$\sin y = \frac{8.7}{13}$$

8.7 ÷ 13

4 Solve: $\sin y = 0.6692...$

So $y = \sin^{-1} 0.6692... = 42.007722...$

angle PRQ = 42° (2 s.f.)

Ways to remember SOHCAHTOA:
Some Of Harry's Cats Are Heavier Than Other Animals
(can you make up your own?)

SET?

Find the size of the angle labelled y in each of the following right-angled triangles. Give your answers to three significant figures.

A. 12 cm, 5 cm, y

C. 7 cm, 15 cm, y

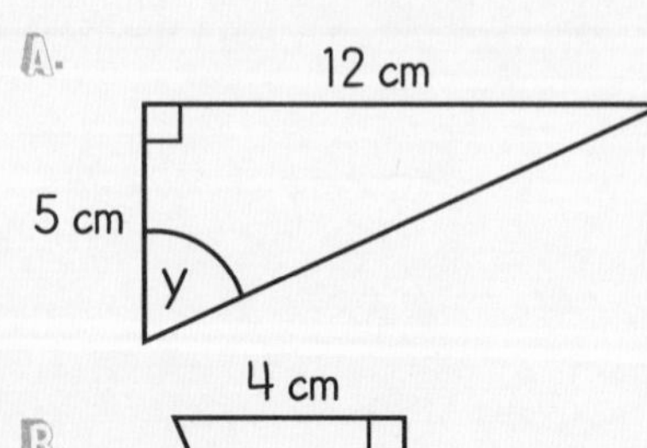

B.

D.

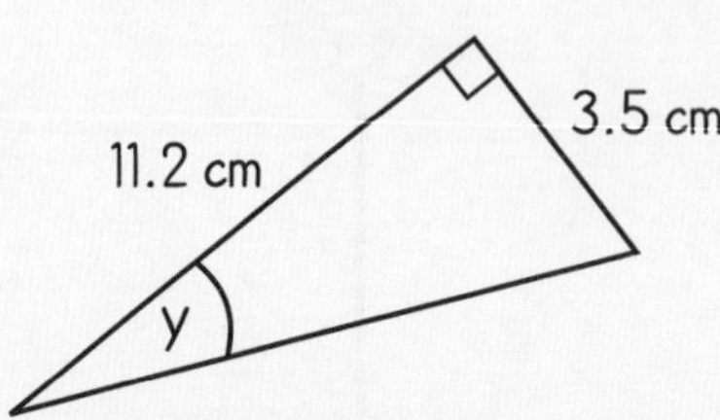

E. 8.2 cm, 10.5 cm, y

Some Old Hamsters Can Attack Horses, Tigers Or Anteaters

GO! TRIGONOMETRY 2

Top!

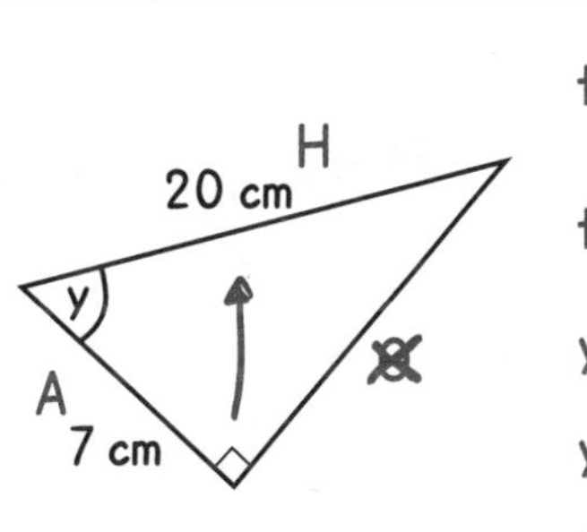

$\tan y = \frac{O}{A}$

$\tan y = \frac{20}{7} = 2.857...$

$y = \tan^{-1} 2.857...$

$y = 70.71...$

$y = 70.7^\circ$ (1d.p.)

1. Harvey is finding the value of y in this triangle.

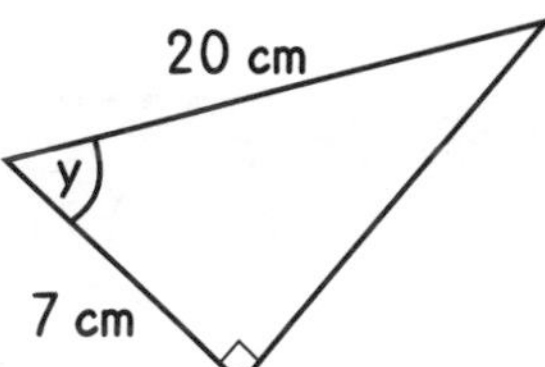

Do you agree with Harvey's workings? Explain why.

2. Here is a kite.

Work out the size of angle m.

Give your answer to three significant figures.

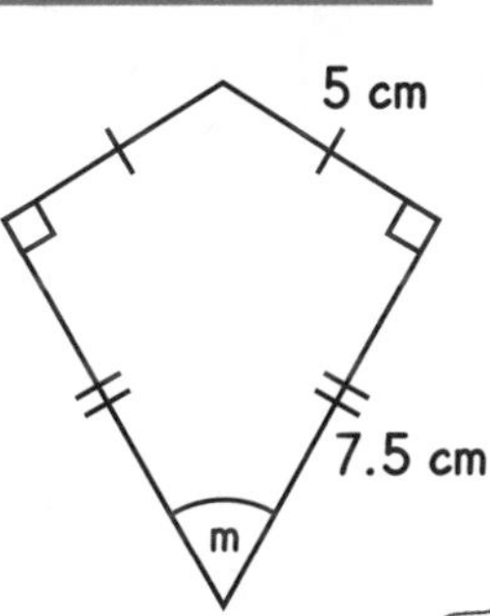

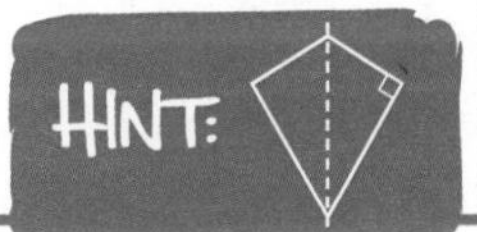

3. Find the missing angles in this triangle.

Give your answers correct to one decimal place.

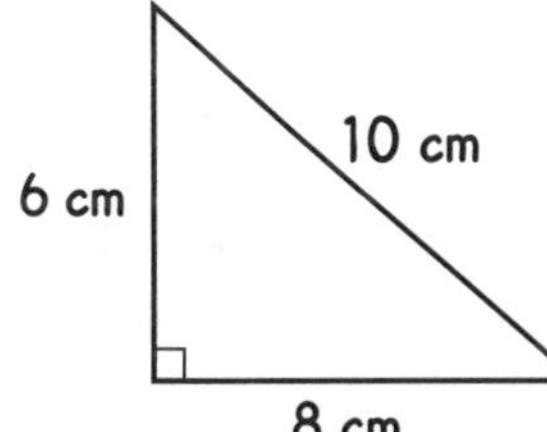

4. A boat is 250 metres from a lighthouse.

The lighthouse is 41 metres tall.

Calculate the angle of elevation from the boat to the top of the lighthouse.

Give your answer to two significant figures.

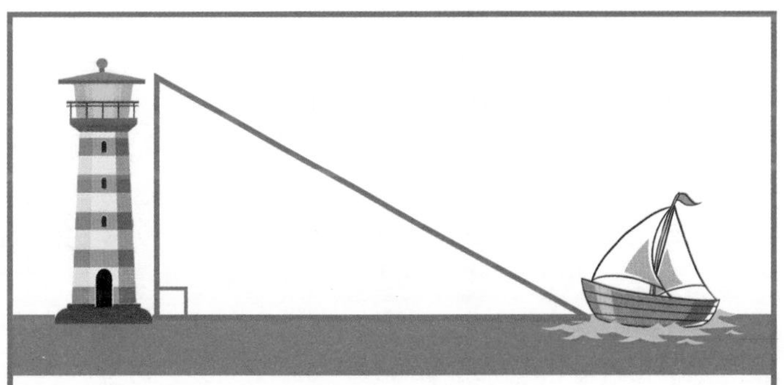

Elevation means 'up' from the starting position

READY?

Some trigonometry questions can be tackled without a calculator. You need to know the exact "trig" values for sin, cos and tan of the angles shown in this table:

($\frac{\sqrt{2}}{2}$ can be written as $\frac{1}{\sqrt{2}}$)

θ	0°	30°	45°	60°	90°
$\sin\theta$	0	$\frac{1}{2}$	$\frac{\sqrt{2}}{2}$	$\frac{\sqrt{3}}{2}$	1
$\cos\theta$	1	$\frac{\sqrt{3}}{2}$	$\frac{\sqrt{2}}{2}$	$\frac{1}{2}$	0
$\tan\theta$	0	$\frac{\sqrt{3}}{3}$	1	$\sqrt{3}$	Doesn't exist

SOHCAHTOA

$\sin\theta = \frac{O}{H}$ $\cos\theta = \frac{A}{H}$ $\tan\theta = \frac{O}{A}$

e.g. 1 Show that PR = 4 cm

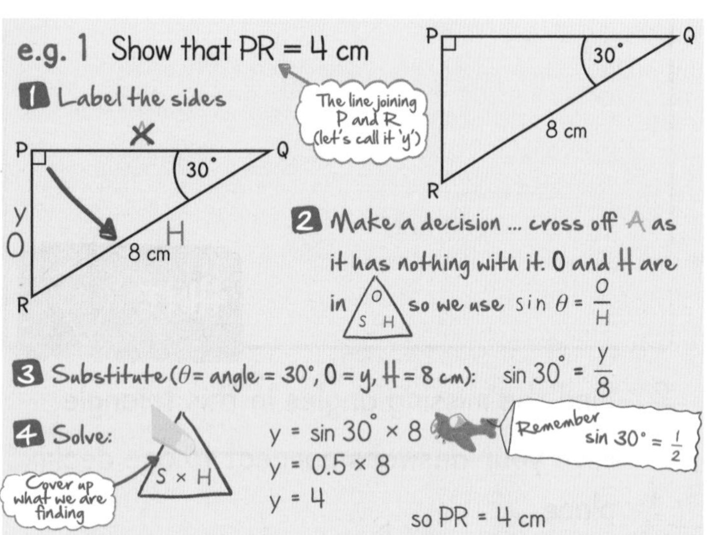

1 Label the sides

2 Make a decision ... cross off A as it has nothing with it. O and H are in (O / S H) so we use $\sin\theta = \frac{O}{H}$

3 Substitute (θ = angle = 30°, O = y, H = 8 cm): $\sin 30° = \frac{y}{8}$

4 Solve:

$y = \sin 30° \times 8$

$y = 0.5 \times 8$

$y = 4$

so PR = 4 cm

e.g. 2 A vertical flagpole AC is supported by a wire AB at an angle of 60° to the horizontal ground.

The base of the wire is 2.4 m from the base of the pole. Show that the length of the wire is 4.8 m.

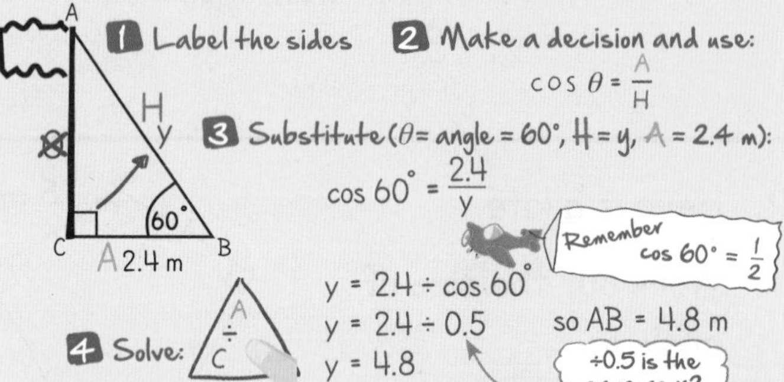

1 Label the sides **2** Make a decision and use: $\cos\theta = \frac{A}{H}$

3 Substitute (θ = angle = 60°, H = y, A = 2.4 m): $\cos 60° = \frac{2.4}{y}$

4 Solve:

$y = 2.4 \div \cos 60°$

$y = 2.4 \div 0.5$

$y = 4.8$

so AB = 4.8 m

e.g. 3 Triangle ABC has a right angle at B.
Angle BAC = 60°, AB = 14 cm.
Calculate the length of BC.

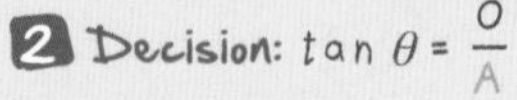

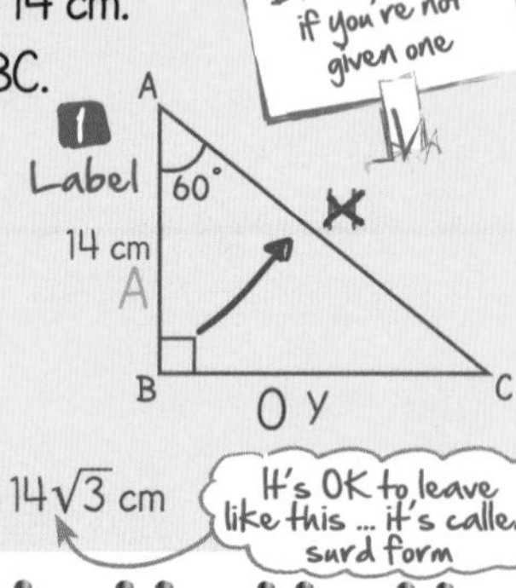

2 Decision: $\tan\theta = \frac{O}{A}$

3 Substitute: $\tan 60° = \frac{y}{14}$

4 Solve: $y = \tan 60° \times 14$

$y = \sqrt{3} \times 14$

so BC = $14\sqrt{3}$ cm

Remember $\tan 60° = \sqrt{3}$

It's OK to leave like this ... it's called surd form

Cover up the table above!

A. (i) Circle the exact value of cos 60°

0 $\frac{\sqrt{2}}{2}$ $\frac{1}{2}$ $\frac{\sqrt{3}}{2}$ 1

(ii) Circle the exact value of sin 90°

0 $\frac{\sqrt{2}}{2}$ $\frac{1}{2}$ $\frac{\sqrt{3}}{2}$ 1

(iii) Circle the exact value of tan 0°

0 $\frac{\sqrt{2}}{2}$ $\frac{1}{2}$ $\frac{\sqrt{3}}{2}$ 1

(iv) Circle the exact value of cos 90°

0 $\frac{\sqrt{2}}{2}$ $\frac{1}{2}$ $\frac{\sqrt{3}}{2}$ 1

(v) Circle the exact value of sin 45°

0 $\frac{\sqrt{2}}{2}$ $\frac{1}{2}$ $\frac{\sqrt{3}}{2}$ 1

B. Show that BC = 16 cm.

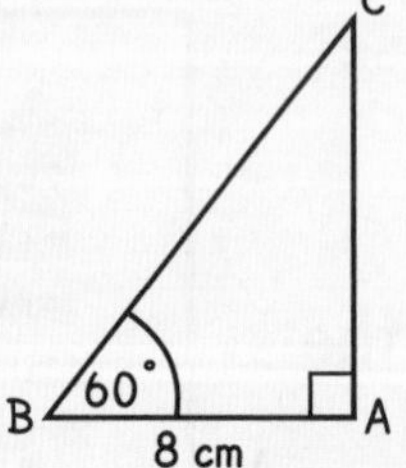

C. A vertical flagpole is supported by a rope of length 18 m.

The rope makes an angle of 30° to the ground.

How tall is the flagpole?

D. The base of a ladder is placed 1.5 m from the base of a wall.

The ladder makes an angle of 30° with the wall.

Show that the ladder is 3 m long.

TRIGONOMETRY 3
(WITHOUT A CALCULATOR)

Tekkers!

1. Find the exact length and width of the rectangle.

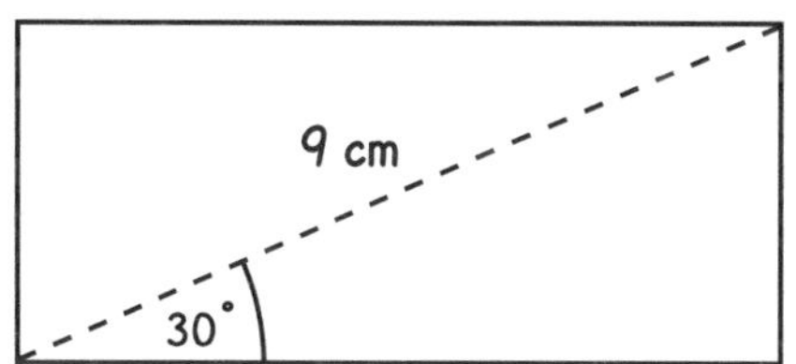

2. An equilateral triangle has side lengths of 4 cm.

Use trigonometry to show that the perpendicular height of the triangle is $2\sqrt{3}$ cm.

3. Mick thinks there are no acute angles for which sine and cosine have the same value.

Do you agree with Mick? Explain your answer.

4. AB = 8cm
$\angle DAB = 30^\circ$
$\angle DBC = 45^\circ$

Find the length DC.

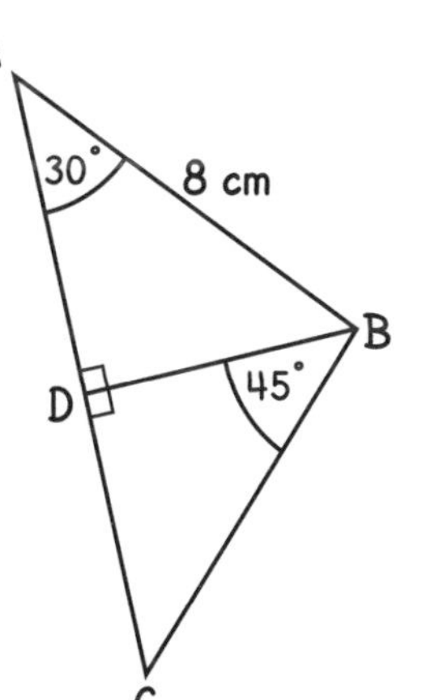

READY?

We often need to be able to combine skills from different areas of maths ... a common combination is Pythagoras with trigonometry!

REMEMBER:
Pythagoras' theorem is used to calculate missing sides in right-angled triangles ... but only if you have two sides already.
Trigonometry is used to calculate missing sides and angles in right-angled triangles.

e.g. 1 AB = 4 cm
CD = 12 cm
DE = 13 cm
Angle EBC = 60°
Angles ABE = ECD = BEC = 90°
Calculate the length of AE to 1 d.p.

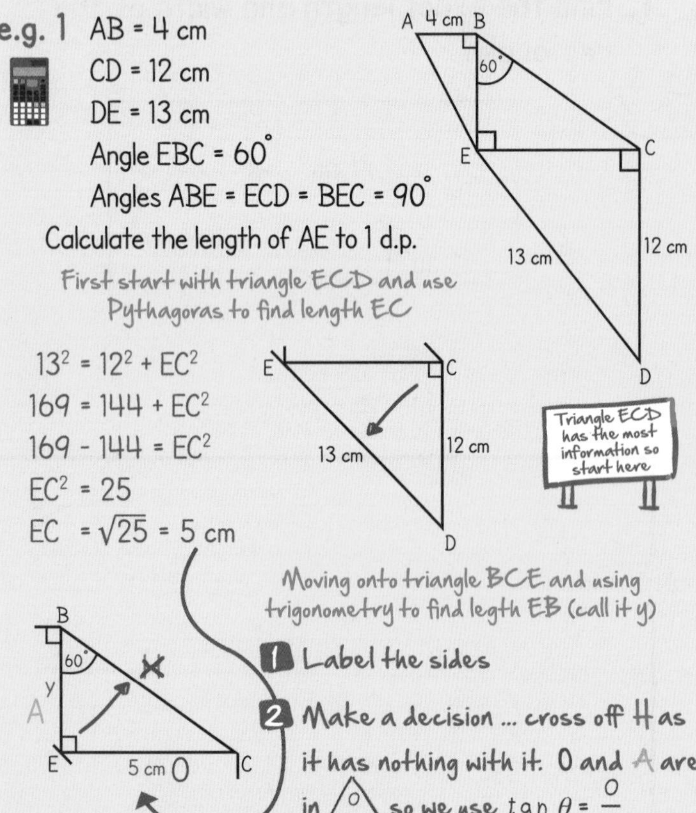

First start with triangle ECD and use Pythagoras to find length EC

$13^2 = 12^2 + EC^2$
$169 = 144 + EC^2$
$169 - 144 = EC^2$
$EC^2 = 25$
$EC = \sqrt{25} = 5$ cm

Moving onto triangle BCE and using trigonometry to find legth EB (call it y)

1 Label the sides

2 Make a decision ... cross off H as it has nothing with it. O and A are in OTA so we use $\tan\theta = \frac{O}{A}$

3 Substitute (θ = angle = 60°, O = 5 cm, A = y): $\tan 60 = \frac{5}{y}$

4 Solve:

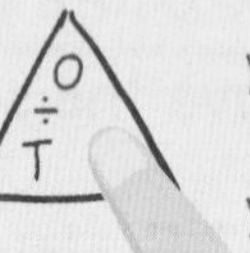

$y = \frac{5}{\tan 60}$

y (EB) = 2.886751... cm

Don't round here ... we're not finished yet

e.g. 2 A vertical flagpole is supported by two ropes. One rope of length 5 m is secured to the ground and is 3 m from the base of the flag pole. The second rope is 8 m long.
What angle does the second rope make with the ground?

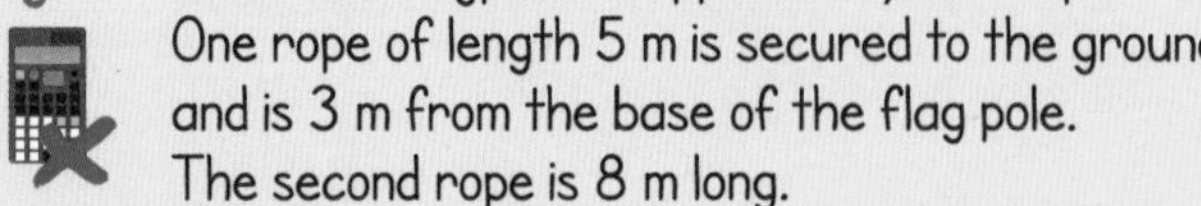

First find height of flag pole using Pythagoras

$5^2 - 3^2 = 16$
$\sqrt{16} = 4$

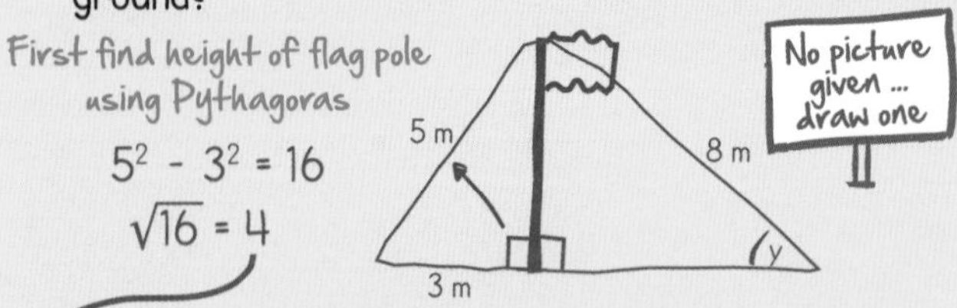

Moving onto the right hand triangle and using trigonometry to find angle y

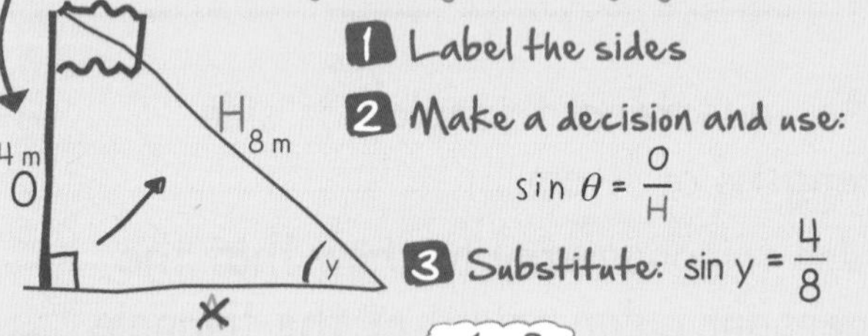

1 Label the sides

2 Make a decision and use: $\sin\theta = \frac{O}{H}$

3 Substitute: $\sin y = \frac{4}{8}$

4 Solve: sin y = 0.5 ← 4 ÷ 8

So y = 30°

The rope makes an angle of 30° with the ground

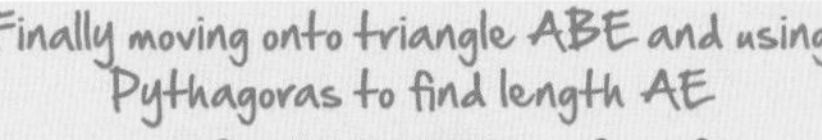

Finally moving onto triangle ABE and using Pythagoras to find length AE

$AE^2 = (2.886751...)^2 + 4^2$
$AE^2 = 24.33333...$
$AE = \sqrt{24.333...} = 4.9329...$
AE = 4.9 (to 1 d.p.)

SET?

A. Angle BAD = 50°
Angle ADB = Angle DBC = 90°
AB = 16 cm CD = 18 cm

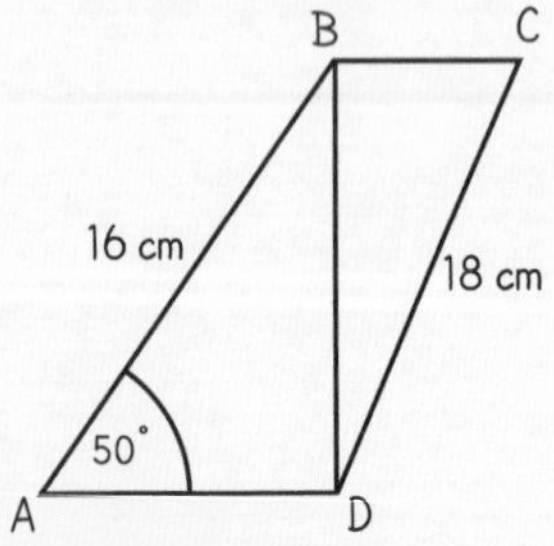

a) Calculate the length of:
(i) BD
(ii) AD
(iii) BC
Give your answers correct to 1 d.p.

b) Calculate the size of angle BCD to one decimal place.

B. BC = 15 cm CD = 9 cm
Angle BAD = 30°
Calculate the length of AD.

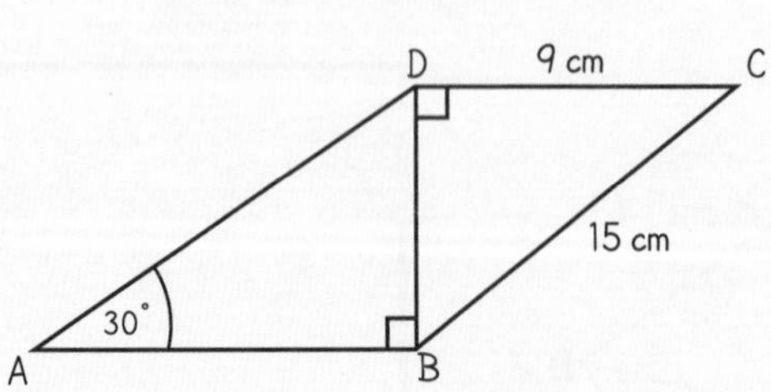

C. Triangle PQR is an equilateral triangle.
Angle QTR = 90°
QT = 5 cm
TR = 8 cm

Calculate the perpendicular height of triangle PQR correct to 1 d.p.

HINT: Perpendicular height is the height straight up through the middle

PYTHAGORAS WITH TRIGONOMETRY

Top notch!

1. AB = 8 cm and BC = 11 cm
∠ABD = 70°
∠ADB = ∠BDC = 90°

Calculate the length of AC to 1 d.p.

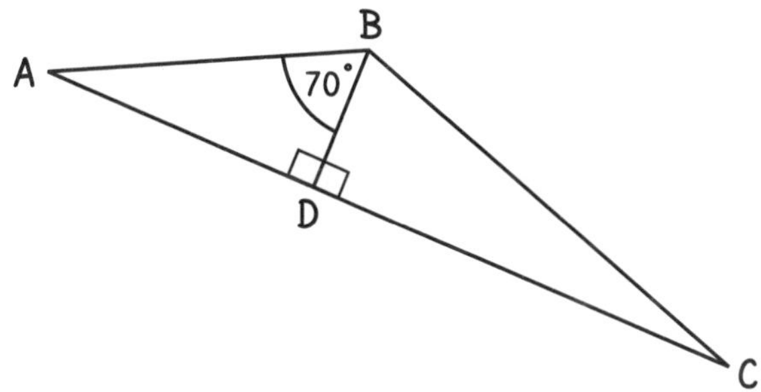

2. The diagram is made from two right-angled triangles and an isosceles triangle.

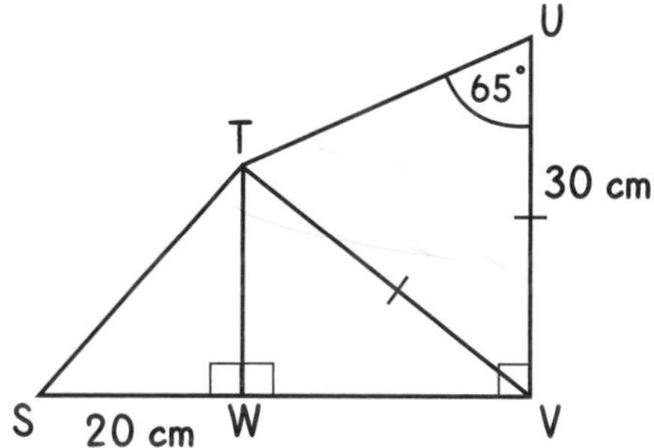

Omar calculates that ST = 18 cm.

a) Explain why he cannot be correct.

b) Calculate the correct length of ST.
Give your answer correct to 1 d.p.

3. STUVW is a regular pentagon
VX = XW, WY = 20 cm, XY = 12 cm

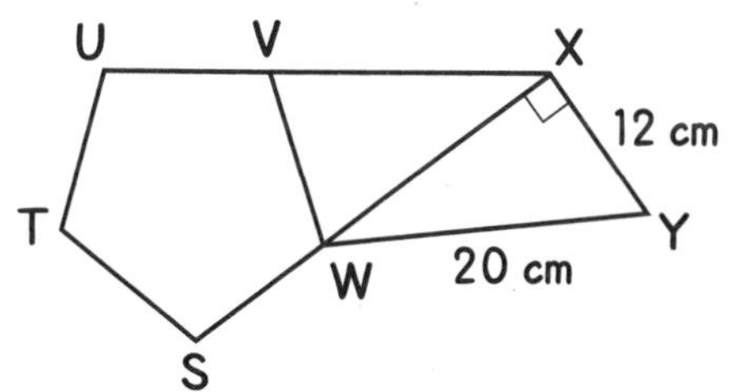

Find the length of a side of the pentagon to 2 d.p.

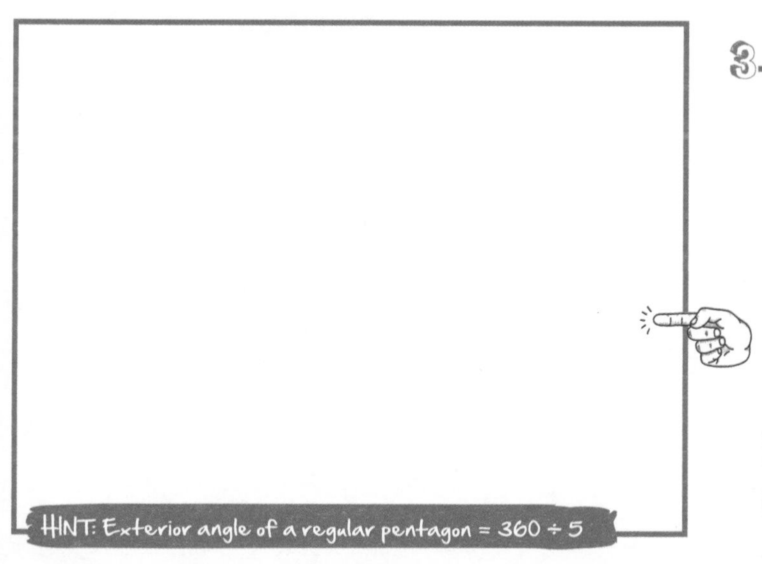

READY?

π = pi (pronounced pie) and is a special number (3.14...) that is the same for any circle (it is the circumference ÷ diameter).

The formula circumference = π × diameter can be used to find the circumference of a circle when you know its diameter (or radius).

You **REALLY NEED** to:

* know where π is on your calculator
* remember two formulae:

$C = \pi \times d$ and $A = \pi \times r^2$

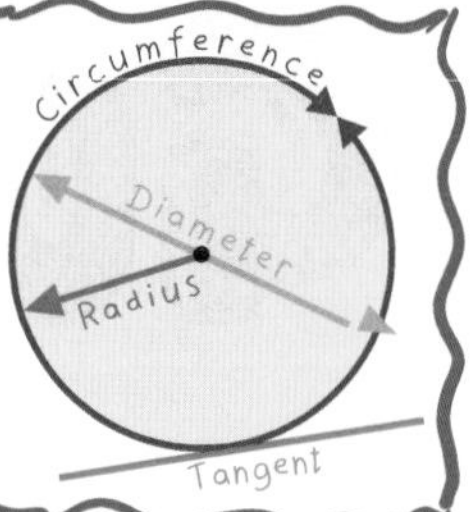

The formula area = π × radius² is used to find the area of a circle when you know its radius (or diameter).

e.g. 1 Find the circumference of this circle.

Give your answer correct to one decimal place.

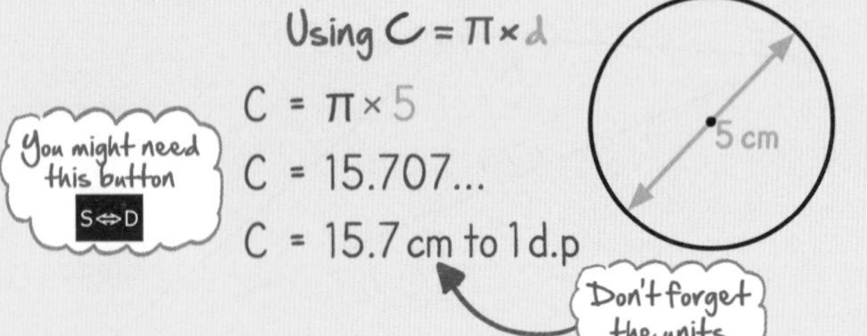

Using $C = \pi \times d$

$C = \pi \times 5$

$C = 15.707...$

$C = 15.7$ cm to 1 d.p

e.g. 2 The radius of a circle is 18.3 mm.

Find the circumference of the circle correct to three significant figures.

Using $C = \pi \times d$

$C = \pi \times 36.6$

$C = 114.982...$

$C = 115$ mm to 3 s.f

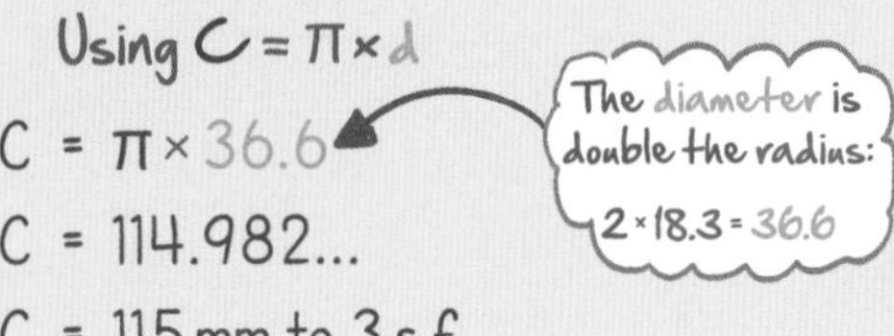

e.g. 3 Find the area of this circle.

Give your answer correct to three significant figures.

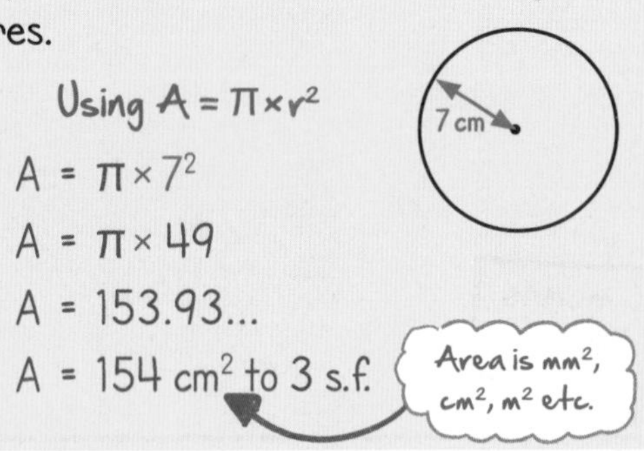

Using $A = \pi \times r^2$

$A = \pi \times 7^2$

$A = \pi \times 49$

$A = 153.93...$

$A = 154\ \text{cm}^2$ to 3 s.f.

e.g. 4 Find the area of this circle.

Leave your answer in terms of π.

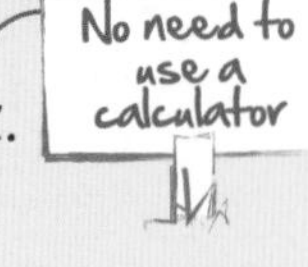

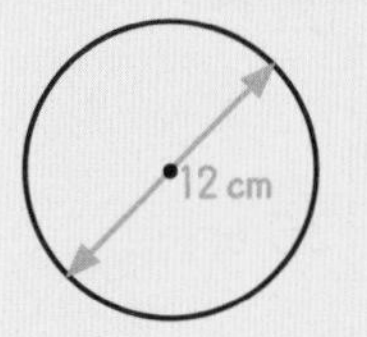

Using $A = \pi \times r^2$

$A = \pi \times 6^2$

$A = \pi \times 36$

$A = 36\pi\ \text{cm}^2$

The radius is half the diameter:
12 ÷ 2 = 6

Circumference can be used to solve circle problems involving length or distance, such as the number of turns of a wheel or space to sit at a circular table.

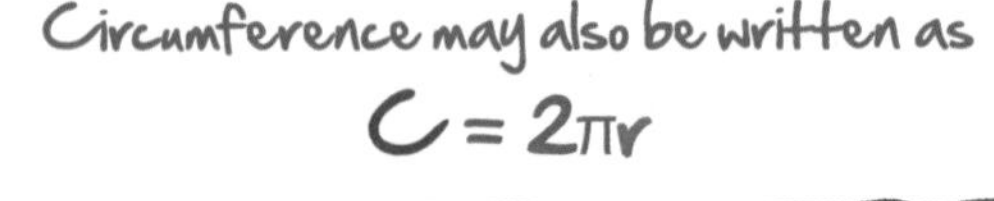

Find the area and circumference of each of these circles.
Give your solutions to one decimal place.

A.

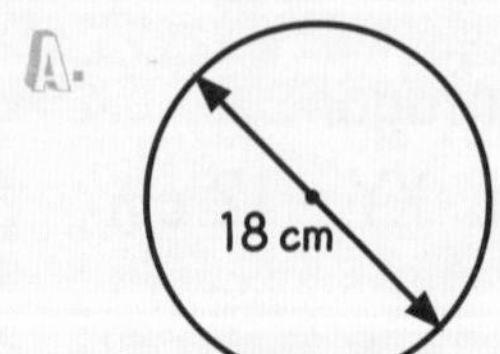

C.

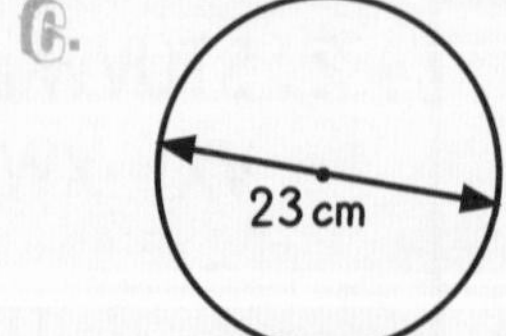
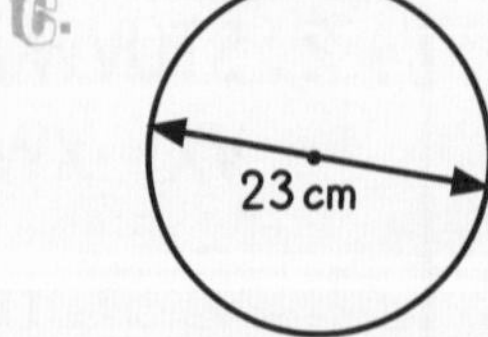

B.

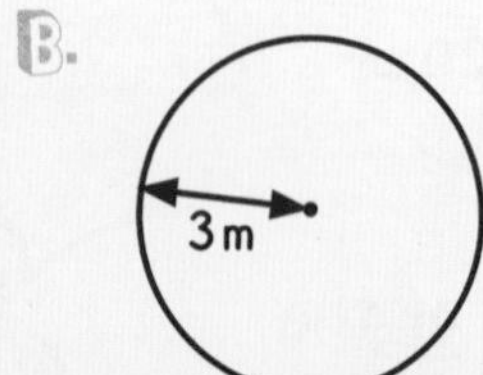

D.

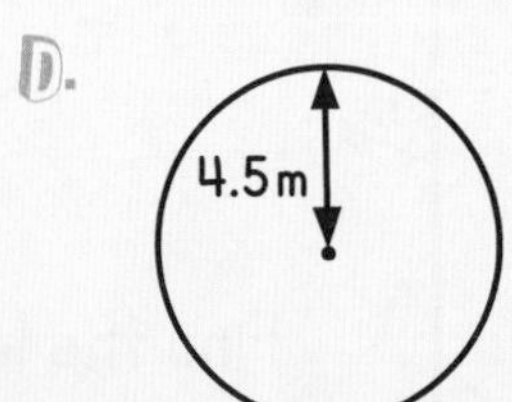

E. Find the circumference and area of this circle.
Give your answer in terms of π.

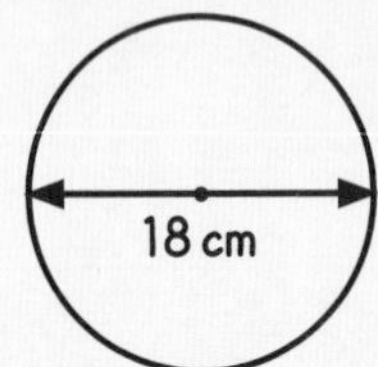

CIRCLES 1

Cool beans!

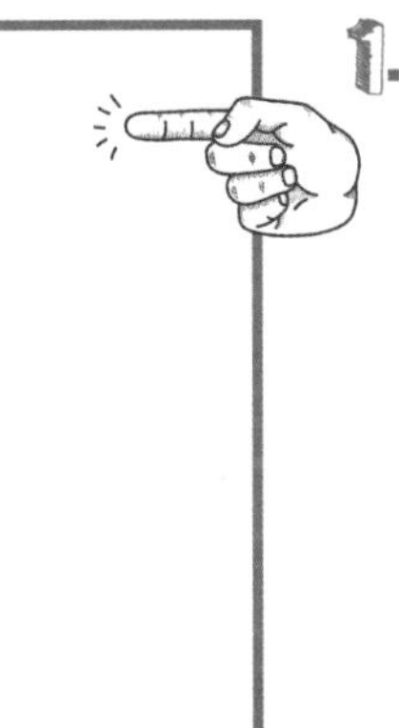

1. Martyn is asked to work out the area of this circle and to give his answer in terms of π. Here is his working:

$A = \pi r^2$

$A = \pi \times 14^2$

$A = 196\pi \text{ cm}^2$

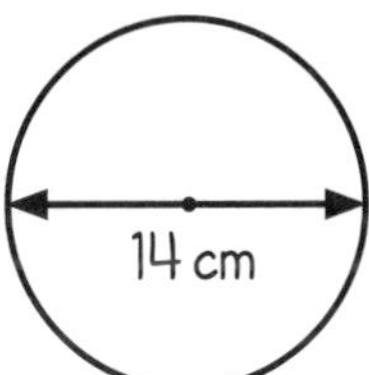

Martyn is wrong.

Explain the mistake he has made.

2. Dani is organising a conference.

The people attending will sit around circular tables.

Each person needs a length of 75 centimetres around the circumference of a table.

Each table has a radius of 0.65 metres.

60 people are attending the conference.

How many tables are needed?

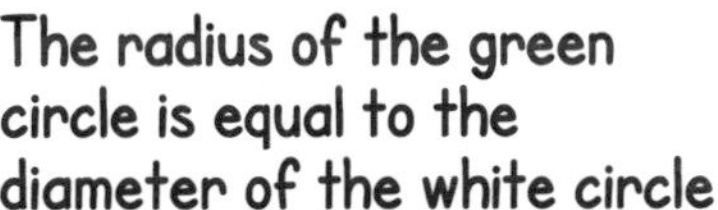

3. A logo design is based on two circles.

The radius of the green circle is equal to the diameter of the white circle.

The diameter of the white circle is 18 mm.

Calculate the area of the logo that is green, give your answer to a sensible degree of accuracy.

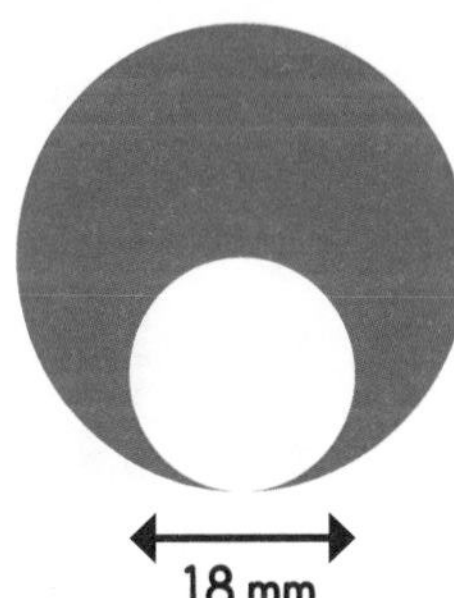

4. Iain's bike wheels have a diameter of 29 inches.

Iain cycles exactly one kilometre. How many full turns does each wheel make?

Use 1 inch = 2.54 cm.

100 cm = 1 m, 1000 m = 1 km

READY?

We can use circle formulae to solve problems where we are given the area or circumference, and need to work ꓷɹɐʍʞɔɐq*. (*backwards)

REMEMBER:
Circumference = π × **diameter**
Area = π × **radius**^{2}

Using these formulae, we can also solve problems involving parts of a circle such as a semicircle.

e.g. 1 The circumference of a circle is 400 cm.
Find the radius of the circle.
Give your answer correct to one decimal place.

Using $C = \pi \times d$

$400 = \pi \times d$

$\div \pi \quad \div \pi$

$127.323... = d$

$63.661... = r$

radius = 63.7 cm to 1 d.p.

The radius is half the diameter

e.g. 2 The area of a circle is 81π cm^2.
Find the diameter of the circle.

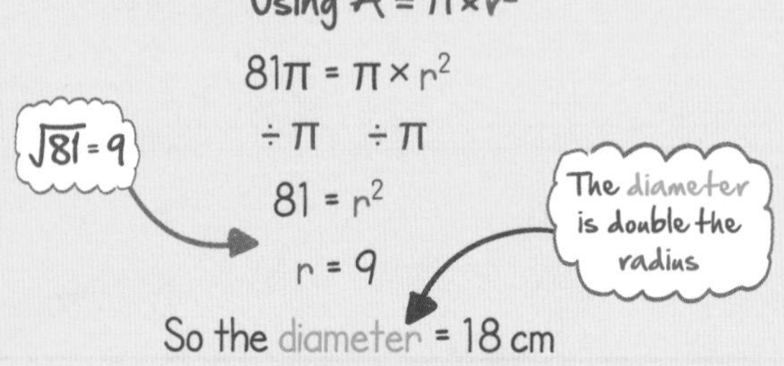

Using $A = \pi \times r^2$

$81\pi = \pi \times r^2$

$\div \pi \quad \div \pi$

$81 = r^2$

$r = 9$

So the diameter = 18 cm

$\sqrt{81} = 9$

The diameter is double the radius

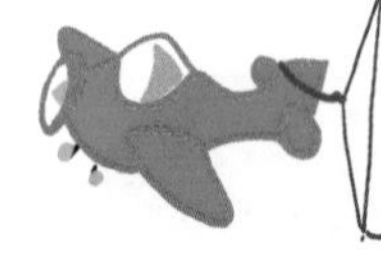

REMEMBER:
Always state the correct units with your answer

e.g. 3 Find the perimeter of this semicircle.
Give your answer correct to three significant figures.

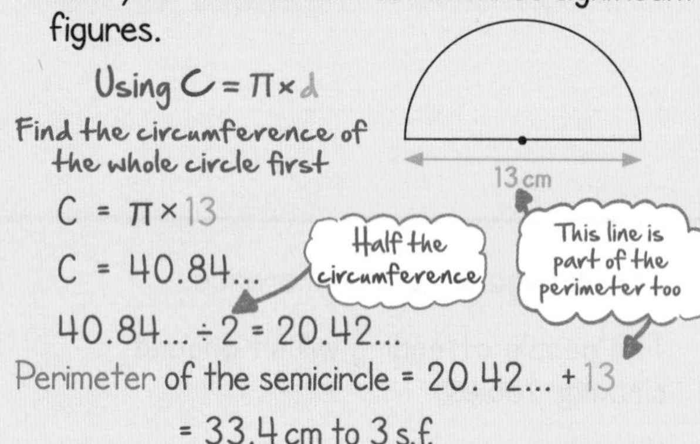

Using $C = \pi \times d$

Find the circumference of the whole circle first

$C = \pi \times 13$

$C = 40.84...$

$40.84... \div 2 = 20.42...$

Half the circumference

This line is part of the perimeter too

Perimeter of the semicircle = 20.42... + 13

= 33.4 cm to 3 s.f.

e.g. 4 Find the shaded area. Leave your answer in terms of π.

12 cm

1 Find area of square → $12 \times 12 = 144$ cm^2

2 Find area of circle → $\pi \times 6^2 = 36\pi$ cm^2

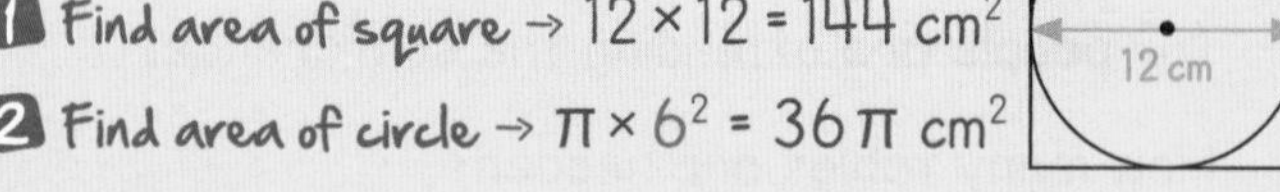

Area of square − area of circle = $(144 - 36\pi)$ cm^2

3 Shaded area → $\frac{1}{4}$ of this

Shaded area = $\dfrac{144 - 36\pi}{4}$

= $(36 - 9\pi)$ cm^2

$144 \div 4 = 36$
$36 \div 4 = 9$

If rounding is needed in these questions, give answers to 3 significant figures

A. The circumference of a circle is 25 cm.
Find the diameter of the circle.

B. The circumference of a circle is 34 m.
Find the radius of the circle.

C. The area of a circle is 40 mm^2.
Find the radius of the circle.

D. The area of a circle is 64π cm^2.
Find the diameter of the circle.

E. Find the area and perimeter of the semicircle.

18 cm

F. A shape is made by removing a semicircle from a square.

The square has side length of 10 cm.
Work out the shaded area.

GO! CIRCLES 2

Blinding!

1. Holly is asked to find the radius of a circle with area 90 cm^2. Here is her working:

$$90 = \pi r^2$$

$$\sqrt{90} = \pi r$$

$$9.486... = \pi r$$

$$r = 3.019...$$

so $r = 3.02$ cm to 3 s.f.

Holly is wrong. Explain her mistake.

2. A shape is made by removing a circle from a larger circle. The two circles have the same centre.

Calculate the shaded area.

Give your answer to three significant figures.

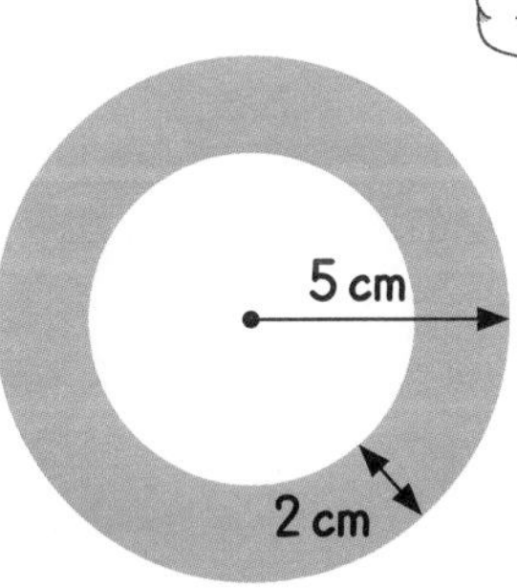

3. A Penny Farthing bicycle has a front wheel with a circumference of 166.5 inches.

The rider of the bicycle is 1.62 metres tall.

Is the rider taller than the front wheel of her bicycle? Explain your answer.

Use 1 inch = 2.54 cm.

4. The diagram is made from a large semicircle and two identical smaller semicircles.

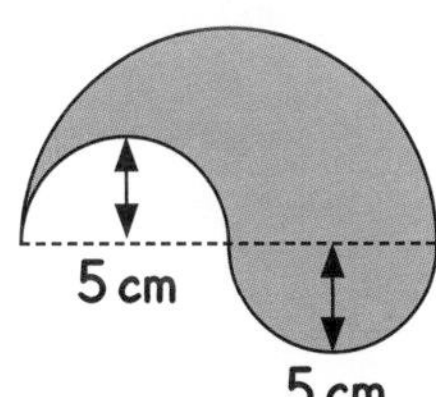

Giving your answers in terms of π, find the:

a) area of the shape.

b) perimeter of the shape.

We can use the area of the full circle to find the area of a sector.

e.g. 1 Find the area of the sector.

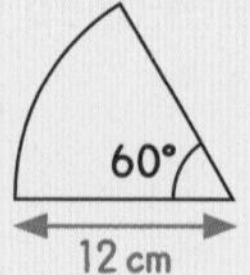

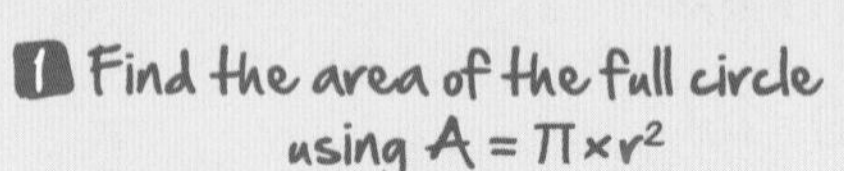

$A = \pi \times 12^2$

$A = \pi \times 144$

$A = 452.3... \text{ cm}^2$

The sector is $\frac{60°}{360°}$ (or $\frac{1}{6}$) of the circle

(Angle of the sector) (Full circle)

2 Calculate the area of the sector

$$\text{Area of sector} = \frac{60}{360} \times 452.3...$$

$$= 75.4 \text{ cm}^2 \text{ to 1 d.p.}$$

e.g. 2 Find the exact value of the area of the sector.

6 cm, 240°

$$\text{Area of the sector} = \frac{240}{360} \times \pi \times 6^2$$

$$= \frac{2}{3} \times \pi \times 36$$

$$= 24\pi \text{ cm}^2$$

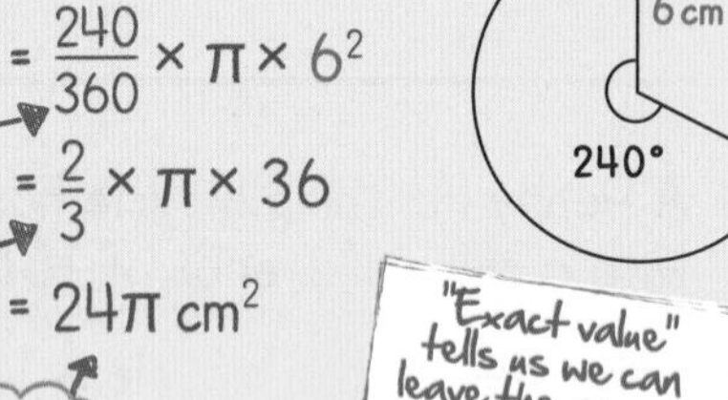

"Exact value" tells us we can leave the answer in terms of π

We need to know the difference between: a chord, an arc, a sector and a segment.

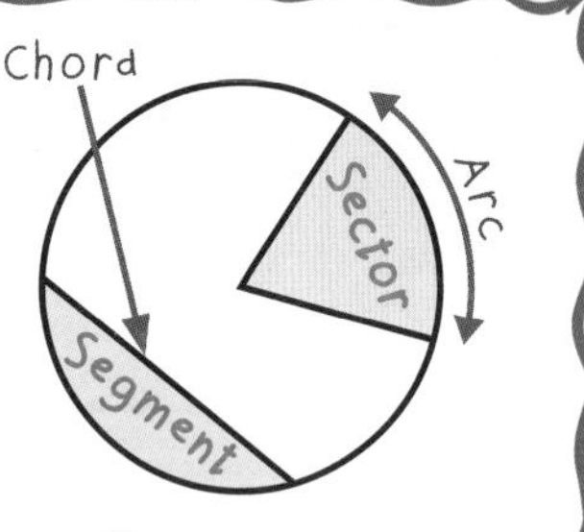

We can use the circumference of the full circle to find an arc length.

e.g. 3 a) Find the length of the arc.

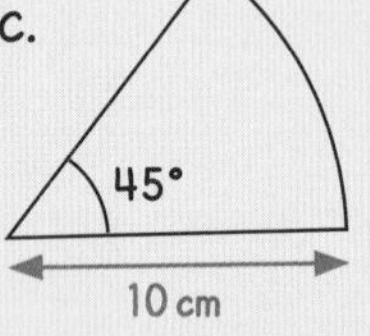

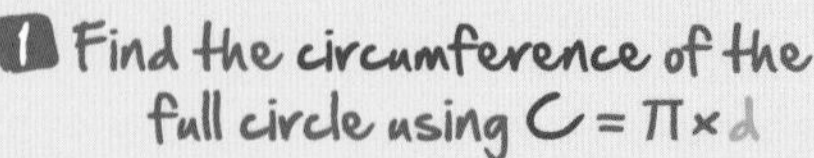

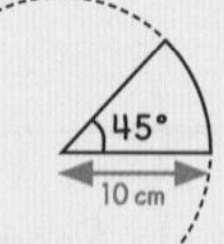

$C = \pi \times 20$

$C = 62.8... \text{ cm}$

The arc is $\frac{45°}{360°}$ (or $\frac{1}{8}$) of the circumference

(Angle of the sector) (Full circle)

2 Calculate the length of the arc

$$\text{Length of arc} = \frac{45}{360} \times 62.8...$$

$$= 7.9 \text{ cm to 1 d.p.}$$

b) Find the perimeter of the sector.

Perimeter = arc length from a) PLUS the two radii

Perimeter = 7.9 + 10 + 10

= 27.9 cm (1 d.p.)

The perimeter is the distance all the way around the shape

If rounding is needed in these questions, give answers to 3 significant figures

A. Find the area of the sector.

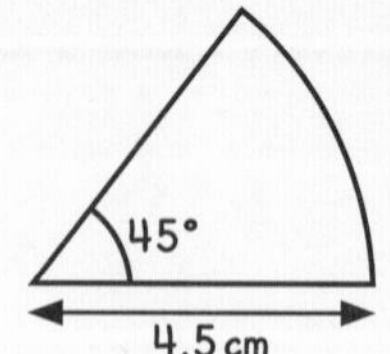

B. Find the length of the arc.

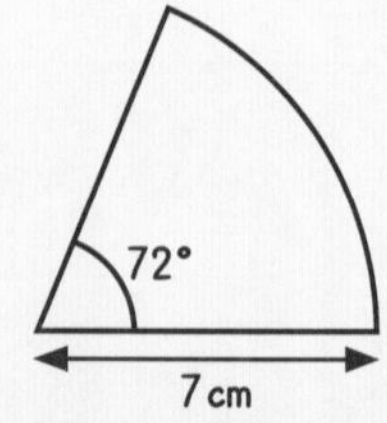

C. Find the exact value of the area of the sector.

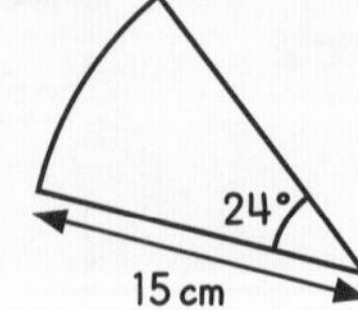

D. Find the area of the sector.

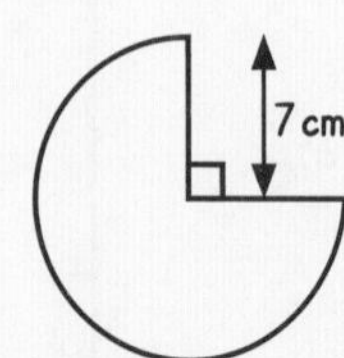

E. Find the perimeter of the sector.

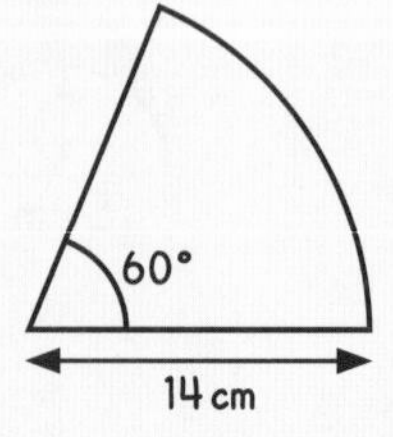

ARCS AND SECTORS

Electric!

1. Richard works out the perimeter of this sector.

Here is his working:

$(\pi \times 30) \div 4 = 23.56...$

$23.56... + 30 + 30 = 83.56...$

Perimeter = 83.6 cm to 1 d.p.

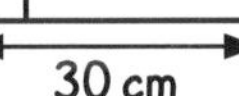

Richard is wrong. Explain why.

2. The diagram shows two circular arcs with centre O.

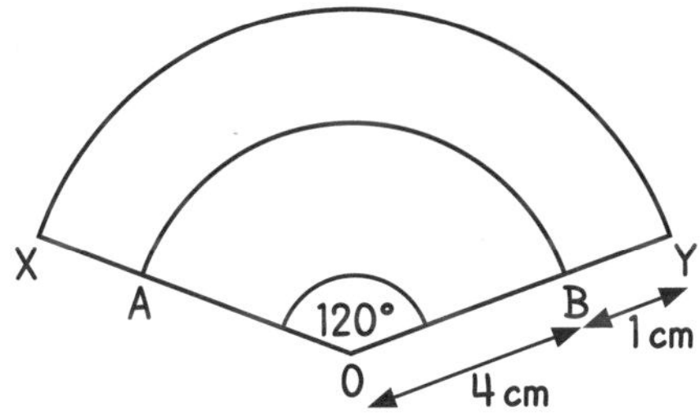

How much longer is arc XY than arc AB?

Give your answer correct to 1 decimal place.

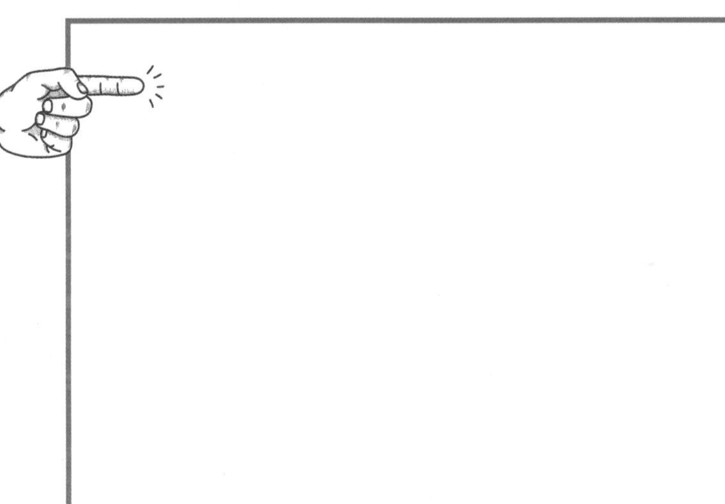

3. The shape is made from four identical sectors.

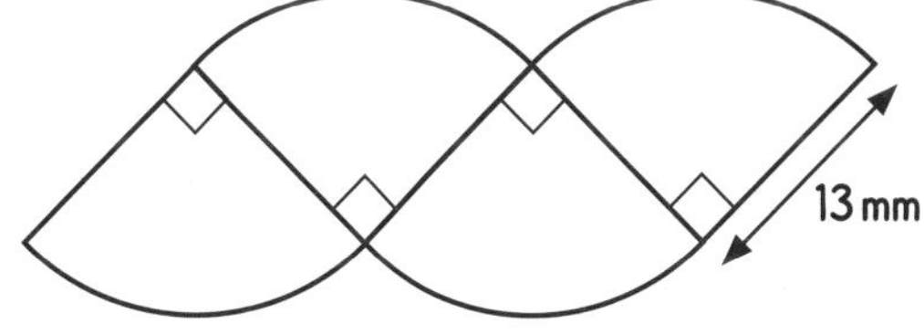

a) Find the exact value of the area of the shape.

b) Find the perimeter of the shape in terms of π.

4. The sector and the rectangle have the same area.

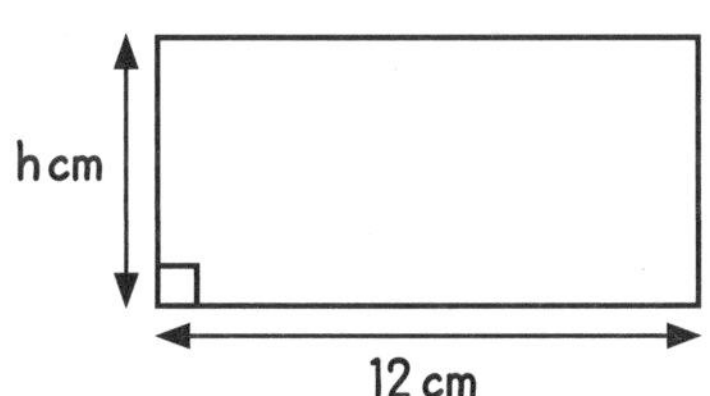

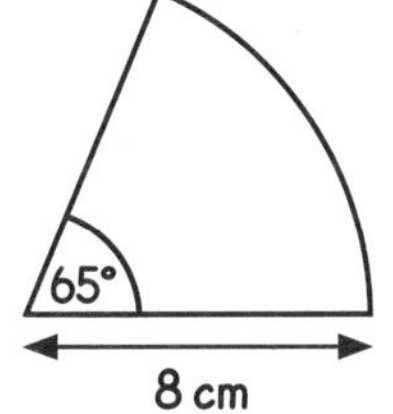

a) Find the area of the sector to 1 d.p.

b) Find the value of h to the nearest whole number.

A prism is a 3D shape with the same cross section running through it:

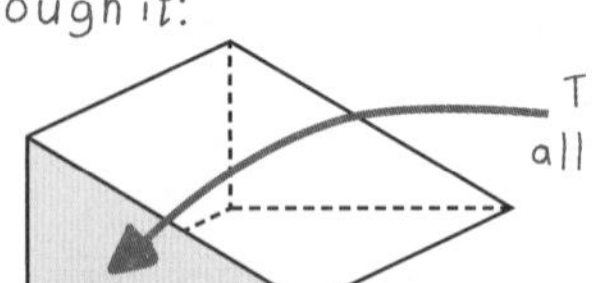

The **surface area** of a prism is calculated by finding the area of each of the faces and then adding them all together.

The **volume** of a prism = area of cross section × length.

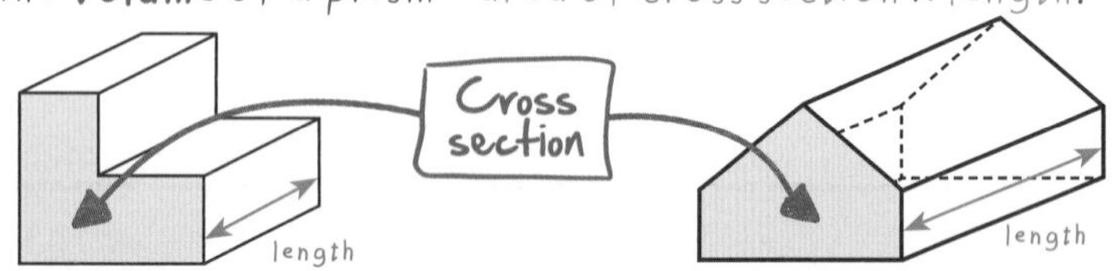

It is **REALLY USEFUL** to be able to ...

Calculate the circumference of a circle using $C = \pi d$ and calculate the area of a:

* Rectangle (length × width) & triangle (base × height ÷ 2)
* Trapezium (half the sum of the parallel sides × height)
* Parallelogram (base × perpendicular height)
* Circle using the formula $A = \pi r^2$

This height

e.g. 1 For the cube, calculate the:

a) surface area.

All 6 faces are the same size on a cube

One face → $3 \times 3 = 9\text{ cm}^2$

Total surface area = $6 \times 9 = 54\text{ cm}^2$

b) volume.

Using volume = area of cross section × length

Area of cross section = $3 \times 3 = 9\text{ cm}^2$

Volume = $9 \times 3 = 27\text{ cm}^3$

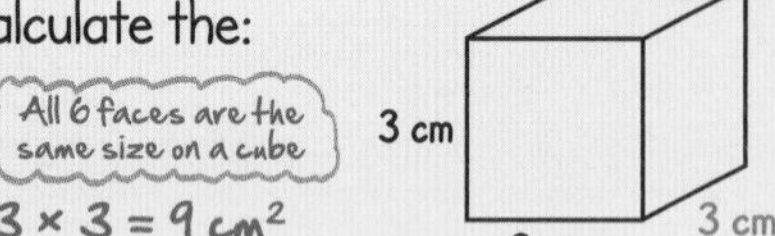

Use the correct units

e.g. 2 For the triangular prism, calculate the:

a) volume.

It's a triangle

Area of cross section = $3 \times 4 \div 2 = 6\text{ m}^2$

Volume = $6 \times 10 = 60\text{ m}^3$

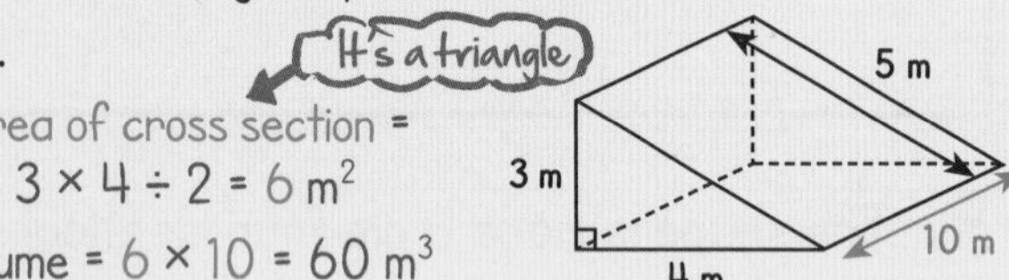

b) surface area.

Front and back face → $3 \times 4 \div 2 = 6\text{ m}^2$ ← 2 of these

Base → $4 \times 10 = 40\text{ m}^2$

Sloping face → $5 \times 10 = 50\text{ m}^2$

Side face → $3 \times 10 = 30\text{ m}^2$

These are rectangles

Total surface area = $6 + 6 + 40 + 50 + 30 = 132\text{ m}^2$

Remember that the cross section of a cylinder is a circle.

e.g. 3 For the cylinder, calculate the:

a) volume.

It's a circle

Area of cross section = $\pi \times 5^2 = 78.5...\text{ cm}^2$

Volume = $78.5... \times 25 = 1963.495...\text{ cm}^3$

$= 1963\text{ cm}^3$ (to nearest whole number)

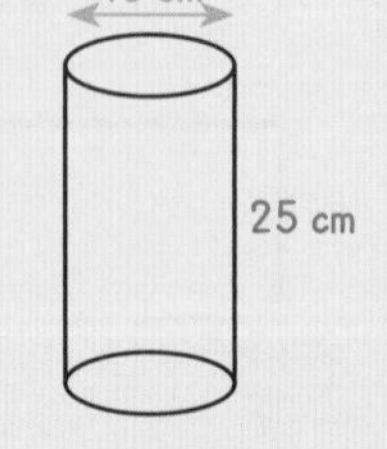

b) surface area.

Top and bottom → 78.5... ← 2 of these

Area of curved face → $\pi \times 10 \times 25 = 785.3...$

Total surface area = $(2 \times 78.5...) + 785.3...$

$= 942\text{ cm}^2$ (to nearest whole number)

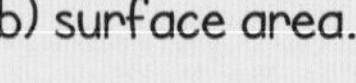

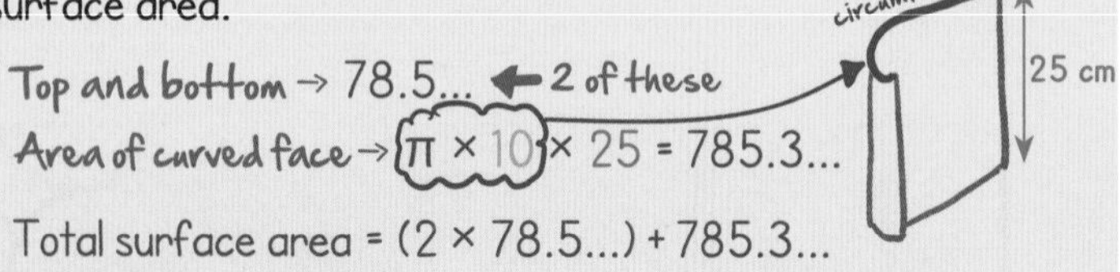

The curved surface of a cylinder is a rectangle (think about the label of a baked beans tin)

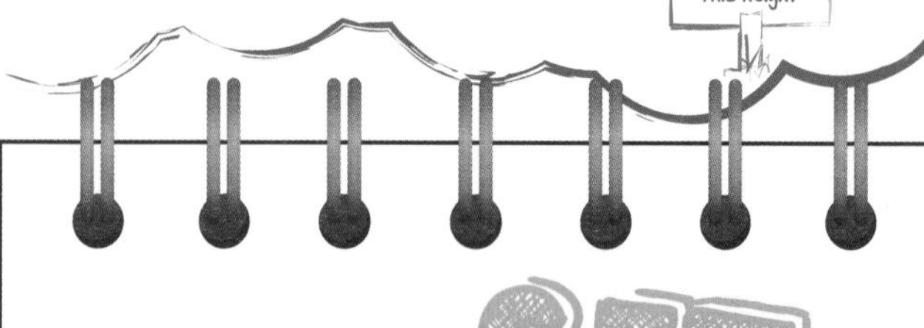

Calculate the surface area and volume of each of the below 3D prisms:

A.

B.

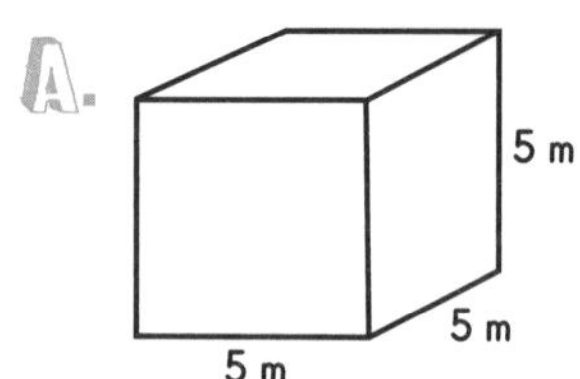

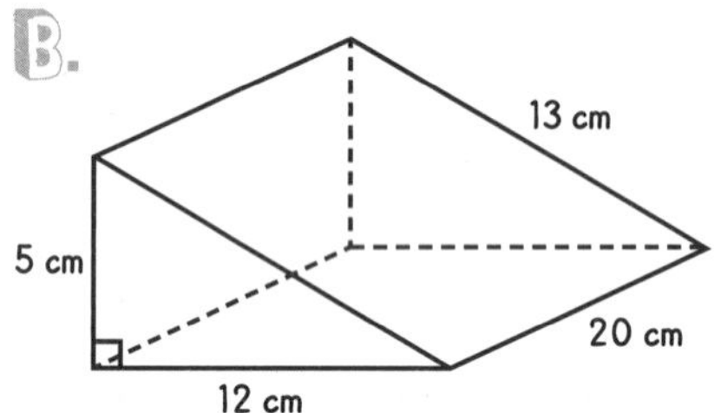

C.

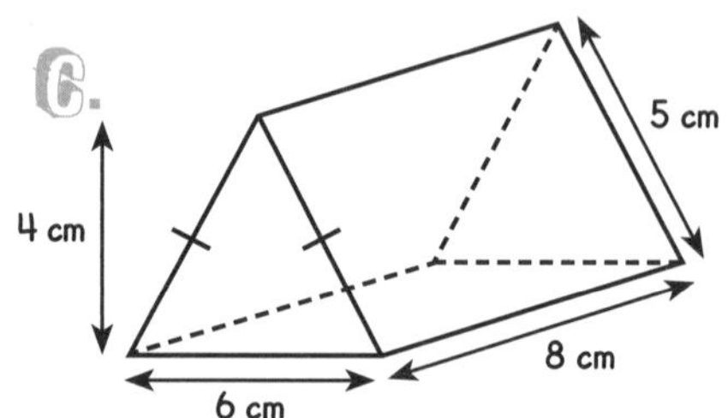

D. Calculate the volume and surface area of the cylinder. Give your answers to 1 decimal place.

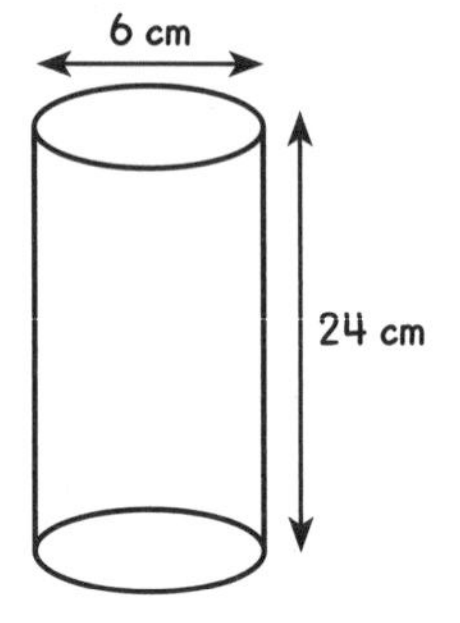

GO! SURFACE AREA AND VOLUME 1

Great!!

1. Luke paints all the faces of this water tank.
   It is a cylinder with:
   diameter 120 cm
   height 2.4 m
   One tin of paint covers 6 m^2
   How many tins of paint are needed to paint the tank?

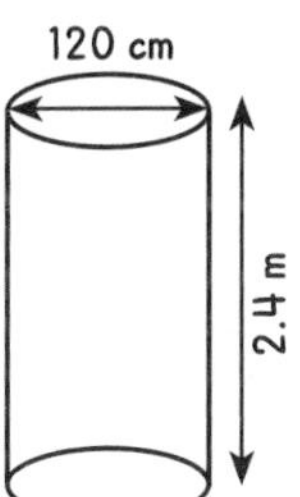

2. The triangular prism is filled with water.

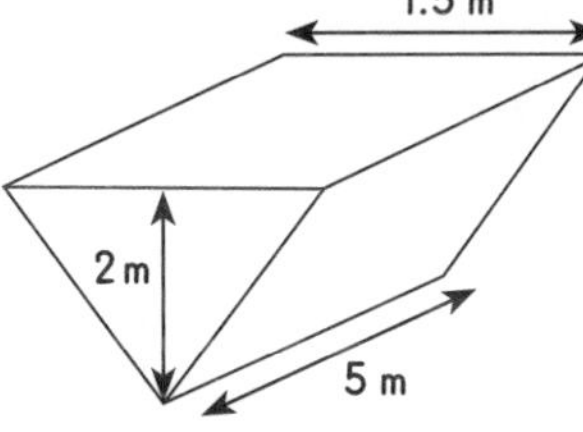

The water is then poured into this cuboid.

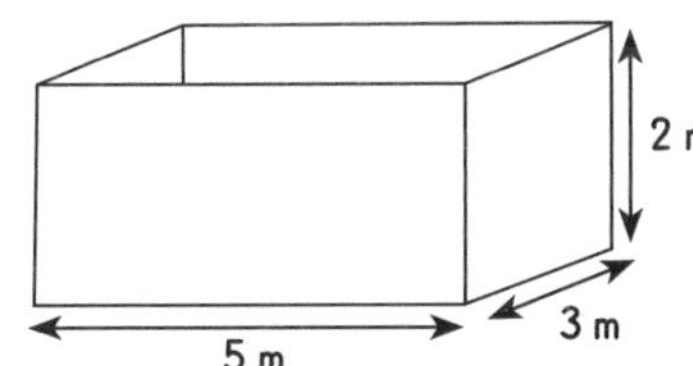

Find the height of the water in the cuboid.

3. The triangular prism has a volume of 24 cm^3 where x, y and z are different integers.

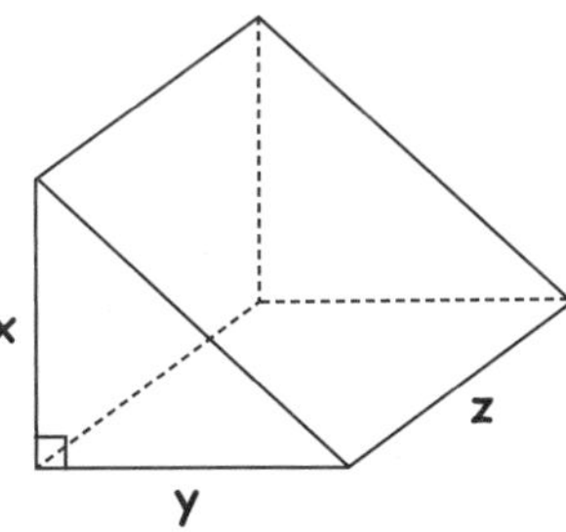

Work out possible values for x, y and z.

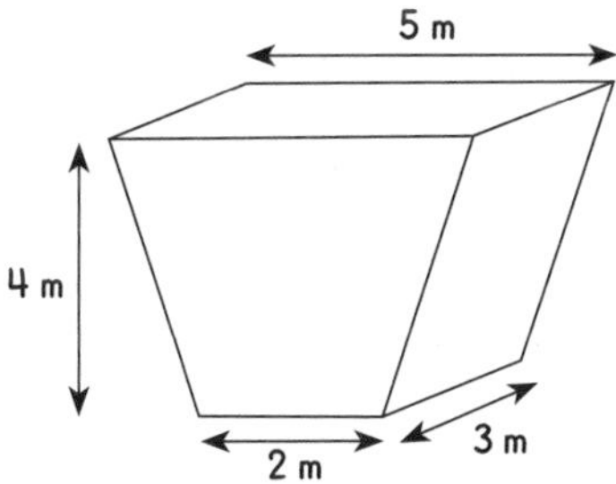

Melios says the volume is 120 m^3 because:

$$5 \times 2 \times 4 \times 3 = 10 \times 4 \times 3 = 40 \times 3 = 120$$

Do you agree with Melios? Explain your answer.

READY?

It is **REALLY USEFUL** to know how to use the following buttons on your calculator:

* square x^2 and cube x^3
* square root $\sqrt{\blacksquare}$ and cube root $\sqrt[3]{\blacksquare}$ 
* pi (π) SHIFT $\times 10^x$

There are several useful formulae that you need to use to find the:

* Volume and curved surface area of a cone 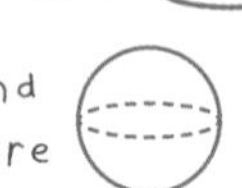
* Surface area and volume of a sphere
* Volume of a pyramid

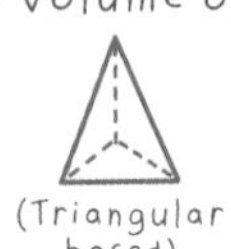

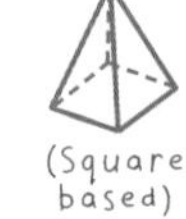

e.g. 1 a) Find the volume of the sphere. Give your answer to 3 significant figures.

Using volume of a sphere $= \frac{4}{3}\pi r^3$
(diameter = 10 cm, so radius = 5 cm)

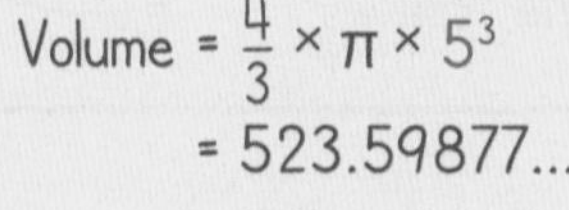

Volume $= \frac{4}{3} \times \pi \times 5^3$
$= 523.59877...$
$= 524\text{ cm}^3$ (3 s.f.)

* Volume of a sphere $= \frac{4}{3}\pi r^3$

b) Find the surface area of the sphere to 3 s.f.

Using surface area $= 4\pi r^2$

Surface area $= 4 \times \pi \times 5^2$
$= 4 \times \pi \times 25$
$= 314.15926... = 314\text{ cm}^2$ (3 s.f.)

Left in terms of π this would be $100\pi\text{ cm}^2$

* Surface area of a sphere $= 4\pi r^2$

e.g. 3 Giving your answers to 3 s.f. find the:

a) volume of the cone.

The slant height (l) 10 cm; 8 cm; 6 cm; The perpendicular height (h)

Using volume of a cone $= \frac{1}{3}\pi r^2 h$
(height = 8 cm and radius = 6 cm)

Volume $= \frac{1}{3} \times \pi \times 6^2 \times 8$
$= 301.59289$
$= 302\text{ cm}^3$ (3 s.f.)

* Volume of a cone $= \frac{1}{3}\pi r^2 h$

b) surface area of the cone.

Surface area = Curved surface area + area of base
(curved surface area $= \pi rl$, area of base $= \pi r^2$)

Surface area $= \pi \times 6 \times 10 + \pi \times 6^2$
$= 188.49... + 113.09...$
$= 301.59289...$
$= 302\text{ cm}^2$ (3 s.f.)

The base is a circle

* Curved surface area $= \pi rl$

e.g. 2 Find the volume of the square based pyramid with a perpendicular height of 6 cm:

6 cm; 4 cm

1. Find the base area (it's a square) → $4 \times 4 = 16\text{ cm}^2$
2. Using volume of a pyramid $= \frac{1}{3} \times$ base area $\times$ height

Volume $= \frac{1}{3} \times 16 \times 6$
$= 32\text{ cm}^3$

* Volume of a pyramid $= \frac{1}{3} \times$ base area $\times$ height

This is the perpendicular height

* Some formulae may be provided in the exam

A. Here is a square based pyramid.

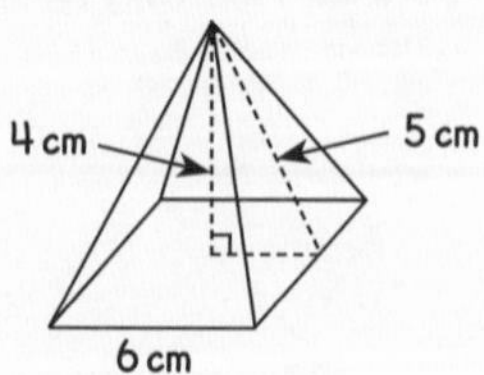

(i) Calculate the volume.

(ii) Calculate the surface area.

B. Here is a cone.

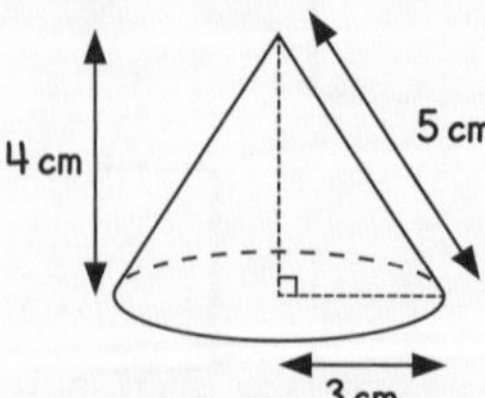

(i) Calculate the volume. Give your answer to one decimal place.

(ii) Calculate the surface area. Give your answer to one decimal place.

C. Calculate the surface area and volume of a sphere with radius 6 cm. Leave your answers in terms of π.

SURFACE AREA & VOLUME 2

Smart!

Surface area of a sphere = $4\pi r^2$

1. Find the surface area of a hemisphere of radius 10 cm.

   Leave your answer in terms of π.

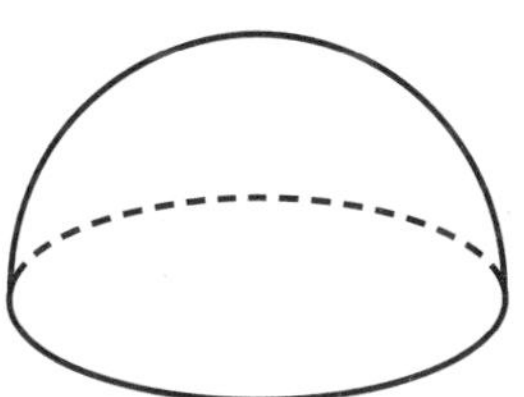

2. Table tennis balls have a diameter of 4 cm.

   8 balls are stored in a box.

   The box is a cube with side length of 8 cm.

   Calculate the volume of unused space in the box, giving your answer to 3 significant figures.

3. Find the volume of the toy rocket.

   Give your answer:

   a) in terms of π.

   b) to 3 s.f.

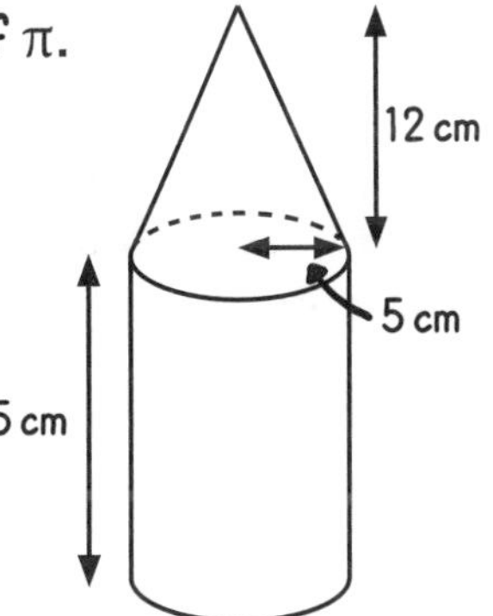

4. Find the surface area of the cone. Give your answer to 1 d.p.

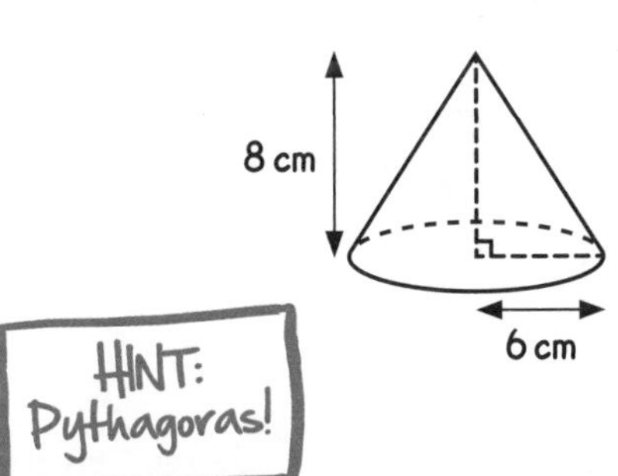

A population is the whole group of people or items. A sample is a smaller part of a population (normally being chosen to take part in a survey). If an entire population is doing a survey, it's called a census.

You **REALLY NEED** to know:

- The larger the sample, the more reliable the results (but not too large as it needs to be manageable)
- In a random sample each member of a population has an equal chance of being selected

ADVANTAGES OF USING A SAMPLE INCLUDE:

- Quick to carry out
- Inexpensive
- Less data to analyse

DISADVANTAGES OF USING A SAMPLE INCLUDE:

- May be biased because not everyone is represented
- Sample size may be too small for results to be reliable

e.g. 1 Mrs Jobbo wants to find out how often students use the school library at lunchtime. She gives a questionnaire to the first 10 students she meets in the library on a Wednesday lunchtime.

Give two possible reasons why this is not a suitable sample.

Reason 1 10 is not many students to ask, the sample size is too small.

Reason 2 She is only asking students in the library on a Wednesday lunchtime.

Needs to be at different locations, different days and different times

e.g. 2 Which of these methods will produce a random sample of 10 people from a class of 30 people? Explain your answer.

A. Asking the first 10 people on the register. ✗

B. Start with the 1st person on the register and ask every 3rd person. ✗

C. Asking the first 10 people you are friends with. ✗

D. Each name is put on the same size piece of paper and put into a hat. 10 pieces of paper are pulled out. ✓

E. Assigning a number to each person and using a random number generator to pick 10 numbers. ✓

D and E because each person has the same chance of being selected and there is no control over who is included.

A sample is biased (unfair) if some members of the population are more likely to be included than others

Pulling names out of a hat is a simple way of selecting randomly

A. A headteacher wants to change the school uniform. She is planning to survey a random sample of 100 students.

(i) Explain what is meant by the term random sample.

(ii) Describe a method the headteacher could use to select a random sample.

(iii) Describe the population from which she is taking her random sample for the survey.

B. Place the number of the statement in the correct position in the table:

	Census	Sample
Advantages		
Disadvantages		

1. Cheap to carry out
2. Less data to analyse
3. Everyone is represented
4. Not everyone is represented
5. Takes a long time
6. Results are reliable
7. Could be biased

C. Mr Topman wants to select 10 students as a sample. He closes his eyes and points at 10 desks.

Is the sample biased? Explain your answer.

SAMPLING

Groovy!

-8	31%
6	69%

64 votes

1. Based on the results of a poll, Alfie says:

   'over a quarter of all people think the answer to the calculation 3 - 4 + 7 is -8 (the wrong answer!)'

   Explain why Alfie's statement could be incorrect.

2. Naomi is keen to investigate for how long students use social media each day.

   She is planning to sample 50 students from her school.

a) Explain what is meant by the term 'sample'.

   Naomi asks 50 students in the sixth form to complete a questionnaire.

b) How could Naomi improve her method of sampling?

3. Anna and Fred are collecting information about Year 11 opinions on a prom.

   Anna decides to ask everyone in Year 11

   Fred decides to use a sample of Year 11

   State one advantage and one disadvantage for each of their methods.

	Anna	Fred
Advantage		
Disadvantage		

4. A chef in a school wants to find out what students think of the school canteen.

   She gives a questionnaire to the first 10 students leaving the canteen on a Friday lunchtime.

   Her sample is biased.

   Give three possible reasons for this.

Reason 1

Reason 2

Reason 3

READY?

1. The Mode is the most common item in a set of data. There can be no mode, and there can be more than one mode.

e.g. 1 20 students record their eye colour. What is the modal eye colour?

This still means mode

Blue	Blue	Grey	Green
Brown	Brown	Blue	Green
Grey	Blue	Brown	Blue
Green	Brown	Blue	Brown
Grey	Blue	Brown	Blue

Blue is listed 8 times, brown is listed 6 times, and green and grey are listed 3 times each

Blue is the mode of the data

2. The Mean is found by dividing the sum of the numbers by the number of items in the set of data.

e.g. 2 Find the mean of 15, 12, 8, 16, 8

The sum of the numbers is:

$$15 + 12 + 8 + 16 + 8 = 59$$

There are five numbers, so:

$$59 \div 5 = 11.8$$

The mean is 11.8

Don't round unless asked to in the question

There are three types of average and NO MATTER what anyone else tells you ... the range is not one of them! However, the range can be useful ... it is the largest value subtract the smallest value and it measures the spread of data.

3. The Median is the middle number when the data is placed in order from smallest to largest.

e.g. 3 Find the median of 15, 12, 8, 16, 8

Step 1: 8, 8, 12, 15, 16 ← Write the numbers in size order

Step 2: ~~8~~, 8, 12, 15, ~~16~~

~~8~~, ~~8~~, (12) ~~15~~, ~~16~~ ← Cross off the first and last ... and then again

The median is 12

Sometimes there will be two numbers in the middle ... find the middle of these two numbers for the median.

e.g. 4 Find the median of 4, 5, 7, 9, 11, 1

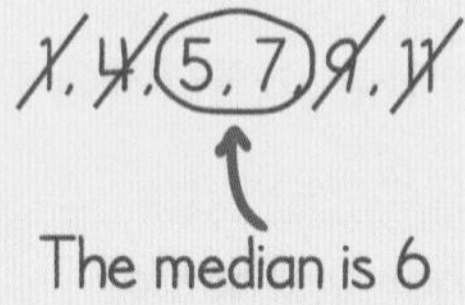

The median is 6

To find the midpoint between two numbers, add them then divide by 2; i.e. 5 + 7 = 12
12 ÷ 2 = 6

What would the median be for 2, 3, 7, 7, 9, 10? Answer = 7

SOME OTHER STUFF:

* The mode is useful with non-numerical (wordy) data
* The mean can be affected by extreme values:

e.g. 1, 4, 2, 85 ← 85 ... Extreme!

* The median is NOT affected by extreme values

SET?

A. Find the modal cycle helmet size from the list here:

M	M	L	S	L
XL	M	M	S	M
L	L	XS	XL	S
M	L	M	S	XS
XS	M	M	L	M
L	XL	M	S	XL

B. Find the median of these two sets of data:

(i) 92, 65, 66, 75, 102, 68, 72

(ii) 92, 65, 66, 75, 102, 68, 72, 77

C. Calculate the mean of this list:

17, 24, 30, 19, 25, 26, 18, 17

D. Calculate the mean of the set of data. Give your answer to 2 decimal places.

23, 22, 32, 18, 24, 31, 13

E. Two cricketers score runs in 6 games of cricket:

Player A: 3, 28, 112, 75, 34, 1

Player B: 17, 158, 0, 23, 20, 2

Which player has the higher average? Show all your working.

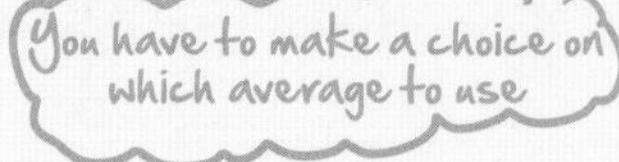

AVERAGES

Splendid!

1. Here are the salaries of eight people in a company:

£18,000	£19,500	£23,000
£23,000	£24,000	£25,000
£32,000	£58,000	

a) Write down the modal salary.

b) Work out the median salary.

c) Calculate the mean salary.

d) The manager of the company says:

"Workers here generally earn over £27,000"

Do you think this is a fair statement?
Use averages to explain your answer.

2. Theo is working out the mean of some numbers:

97, 85, 102, 79, 110

Using his calculator to help, he writes down:

97 + 85 + 102 + 79 + 110 ÷ 5 = 385

Theo is wrong. Explain the mistake he has made.

3. A set of 6 integers has:

- a median of 13
- a mean of 12.5
- no mode

Four of the integers are 8, 9, 15 and 17

Find the other two integers.

HINT: Find the total of the 6 values

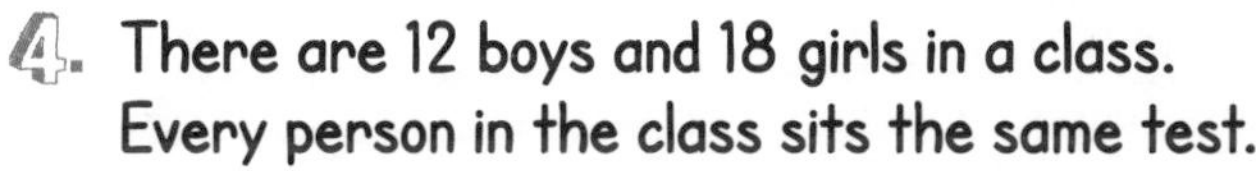

4. There are 12 boys and 18 girls in a class. Every person in the class sits the same test.

The mean score for the whole class is 60%.

The mean score for the boys is 54%.

What is the mean score for the girls in the class?

READY?

1. The Mode

e.g. 1 James keeps a record of the types of bird he observed in a month. Which bird is the mode?

Bird	Frequency
Sparrow ←	(17)
Magpie	4
Starling	7
Pigeon	12
Buzzard	5

Look for the largest number in the frequency column

Mode = Sparrow

2. The Mean

To find the mean from a table, the subtotals are needed first.

e.g. 2 Find the mean number of sweets. Give your answer to one decimal place.

Sweets in bag	Frequency	Subtotals
16	3	16 × 3 = 48
17	5	17 × 5 = 85
18	8	18 × 8 = 144
19	6	19 × 6 = 114
20	1	20 × 1 = 20
TOTALS →	23	411

The mean is not 411 ÷ 5

Mean = 411 ÷ 23 = 17.869... = 17.9 (to 1 d.p.)

3. The Median

To find the middle position, add 1 to the total frequency then divide by 2

e.g. 3 The table shows the marks scored in a test by 19 students. Find the median mark achieved.

1 $\frac{19+1}{2} = 10$ ← Look for the 10th person

Mark	Frequency
4	3
5	1
6	4
7 ←	(9)
8	2
	19

2 Keep adding until we get to or past the 10th person

3 + 1 = 4

4 + 4 = 8

8 + 9 = 17

The median must be in here

Median = 7 marks

A. The table shows holiday destinations for students in a class. Write down the modal destination.

Destination	Frequency
UK	8
Europe	9
Americas	3
Africa	1
No holiday	5

B. The data here shows the number of bedrooms in some houses on a new development.

Bedrooms	Frequency
1	2
2	4
3	8
4	14
5	3

(i) Write down the modal number of bedrooms.

(ii) Find the median number of bedrooms.

(iii) Calculate the mean number of bedrooms to 1 d.p.

(iv) Work out the range of the data.

C. The table shows the number of cats owned by a group of friends.

Number of cats	Frequency
0	7
1	11
2	7
3	6
4	3

(i) Find the median number of cats.

(ii) Calculate the mean number of cats to 1 d.p.

(iii) What is the modal number of cats?

AVERAGES FROM A TABLE

Pro!

1. Jack surveys the students in his class and records the number of children in each family.

a) Show that the mean number of children in a family is 3.1 to 1 decimal place.

b) Jack says:

"therefore the average number of children in a family in the UK is 3.1"

Give a reason why Jack's conclusion may be wrong.

Children	Frequency
1	2
2	6
3	11
4	6
5	3

2. The table shows the number of goals scored by a football team over 24 matches.

a) Work out the mean number of goals scored.

b) The team play a 25th match. The mean number of goals scored is now 1.84. How many goals were scored in the 25th match?

Goals	Frequency
0	3
1	6
2	8
3	5
4	2

3. Look at the information about the number of errors recorded in an experiment.

Which one of the following statements is definitely true?

* The modal number of errors is 15
* The median number of errors is 3
* The mean number of errors is 2.4 to two significant figures
* The range is 4

Number of errors	Frequency
0	2
1	7
2	11
3	15
4 or more	6

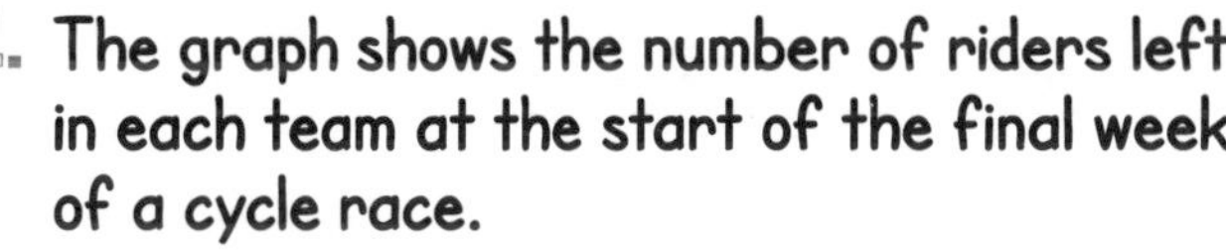

4. The graph shows the number of riders left in each team at the start of the final week of a cycle race.

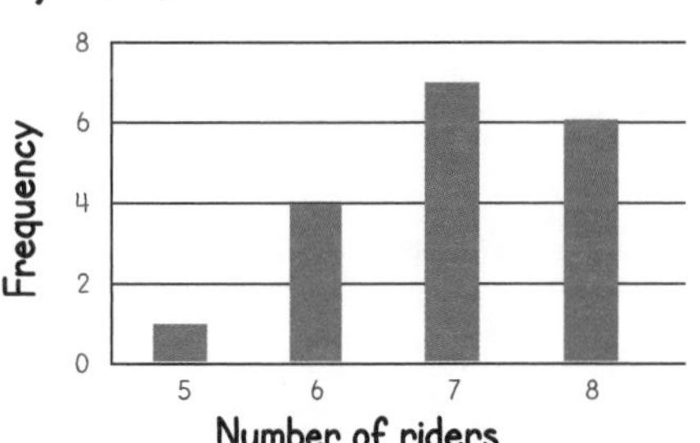

True or false?

mean = median = mode

You must show all your working.

When the spread of the data is large, it can be represented as grouped data. The groups are sometimes called class intervals.

1. The Modal Class

e.g. The table shows information about the heights of students in a class, rounded to the nearest centimetre. Write down the modal class.

Height (h cm)	Frequency
$120 \le h < 130$	1
$130 \le h < 140$	7
$140 \le h < 150$	(12)
$150 \le h < 160$	7
$160 \le h < 170$	5

Look for the largest number in the frequency column

The modal class is $140 \le h < 150$ as it has the highest frequency

2. The Median

e.g. Find the class interval containing the median.
continued

32 students → $\frac{32+1}{2} = \frac{33}{2} = 16.5$

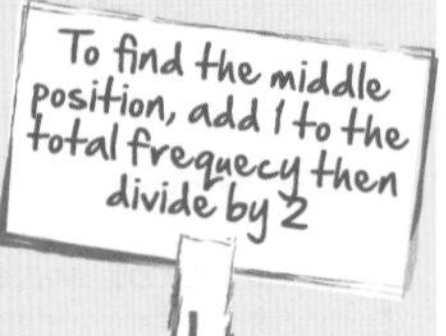

The median must be between the 16th and 17th students ...

1 + 7 = 8 and 1 + 7 + 12 = 20, so the 16th and 17th students are in the third group down

The median is in the class interval $140 \le h < 150$

3. Estimate for the Mean

When the data is grouped, we cannot find the exact mean. We use the midpoints of the class intervals to estimate the mean.

e.g. Calculate an estimate for the mean.
continued

As it is an estimate for the mean, we need to find the midpoint of each class interval and then multiply by the frequency to get the subtotals

Height (h cm)	Frequency		Midpoint		Subtotals
$120 \le h < 130$	1	×	125	=	125
$130 \le h < 140$	7	×	135	=	945
$140 \le h < 150$	12	×	145	=	1740
$150 \le h < 160$	7	×	155	=	1085
$160 \le h < 170$	5	×	165	=	825
TOTALS →	32				4720

Estimate for the mean = 4720 ÷ 32
= 147.5 cm

A. The data here show distances that Luma runs during a month.

Distance (d km)	Frequency
$0 \le d < 5$	7
$5 \le d < 10$	9
$10 \le d < 15$	11
$15 \le d < 20$	3

(i) Write down the modal class for Luma's runs.

(ii) Find the interval that contains the median distance.

(iii) Calculate an estimate for the mean distance. Give your answer to one decimal place.

B. Vanda keeps a record of the distances she cycles in a month. The table shows the information.

Distance (d km)	Frequency
$0 \le d < 10$	12
$10 \le d < 20$	3
$20 \le d < 50$	6
$50 \le d < 150$	4

(i) Write down the modal class for the data.

(ii) Find the interval that contains the median distance.

(iii) Calculate an estimate for the mean distance.

(iv) Vanda thinks that the range for her data is 140 km. Explain why Vanda might not be correct.

AVERAGES FROM GROUPED DATA

Terrific!

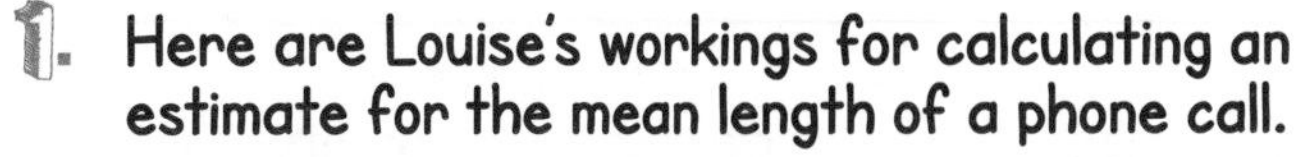

1. Here are Louise's workings for calculating an estimate for the mean length of a phone call.

Time (t seconds)	Frequency		Midpoint	Subtotals
$0 \le t < 30$	12	×	15	= 180
$30 \le t < 60$	19	×	45	= 855
$60 \le t < 90$	7	×	75	= 525
$90 \le t < 120$	3	×	105	= 315
			Total	1875

Estimate for the mean = 1875 ÷ 4 = 468.75 seconds

Louise is wrong. Explain the mistake she has made.

2. The table shows information about the handspans of a group of people.

Cassie says:

"the modal class is the same as the class interval containing the median"

Do you agree with Cassie?

Explain why.

Handspan (h cm)	Frequency
$16 \le h < 18$	3
$18 \le h < 20$	4
$20 \le h < 22$	13
$22 \le h < 24$	7
$24 \le h < 26$	2

Height (h m)	Frequency
$600 \le h < 700$	224
$700 \le h < 800$	126
$800 \le h < 900$	68
$900 \le h < 1000$	22
$1000 \le h < 1100$	5

3. Here is some data about the height, in metres, of mountains in England and Wales.

a) How many mountains are there?

b) Calculate an estimate for the mean height of a mountain in England and Wales to 1 d.p.

c) The actual mean height is 725 metres. Give a reason for the difference between this and your answer in part b).

4. The table shows information about the mass, in grams, of some eggs.

The estimated mean for the 25 eggs is 61.6 grams.

What is the upper limit for the mass of an XL egg?

Size	Mass (m grams)	Frequency
S	$33 \le m < 53$	5
M	$53 \le m < 63$	8
L	$63 \le m < 73$	9
XL	$73 \le m <$	3

READY?

It is **REALLY USEFUL** to know how to calculate the midpoint of a class interval:
e.g. Midpoint of $10 < x \leq 20$ is 15 because $\frac{(10 + 20)}{2} = \frac{30}{2} = 15$

A **frequency polygon** is a type of **frequency diagram**. They are constructed by plotting the midpoints of class intervals and joining the points with straight lines.

e.g. 1 The table shows the marks some students scored in a test. Draw a frequency polygon for this data.

Mark (m)	Frequency	Midpoint
$0 \leq m < 10$	8	5
$10 \leq m < 20$	12	15
$20 \leq m < 30$	4	25
$30 \leq m < 40$	2	35

1 Find the midpoint for each class interval

2 Plot the midpoint with the frequency

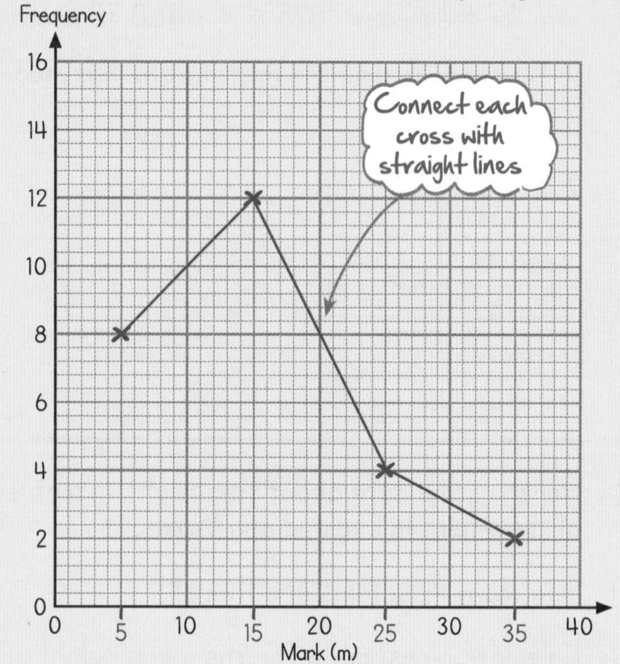

e.g. 2 The frequency polygon shows how long it took 20 people to run one mile. Complete the table.

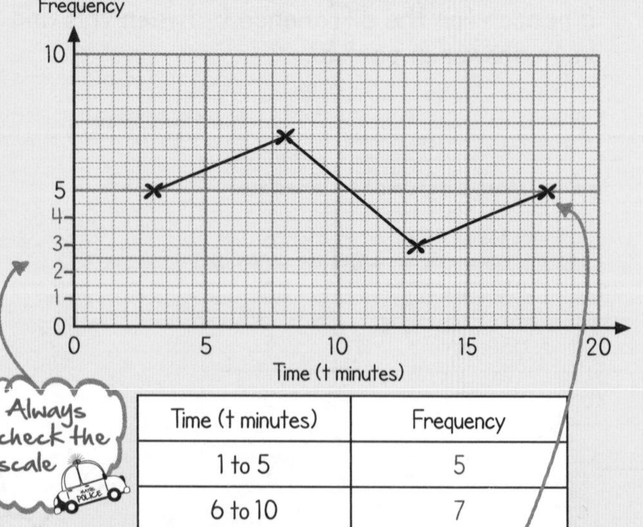

Time (t minutes)	Frequency
1 to 5	5
6 to 10	7
11 to 15	3
16 to 20	5

A. Work out midpoint of the class intervals:

Time (t seconds)	Midpoint
$0 < t \leq 4$	
$4 < t \leq 8$	
$8 < t \leq 20$	
$20 < t \leq 40$	
$40 < t \leq 60$	
$60 < t \leq 80$	

B. The table and frequency diagram show the time to complete a maths test.

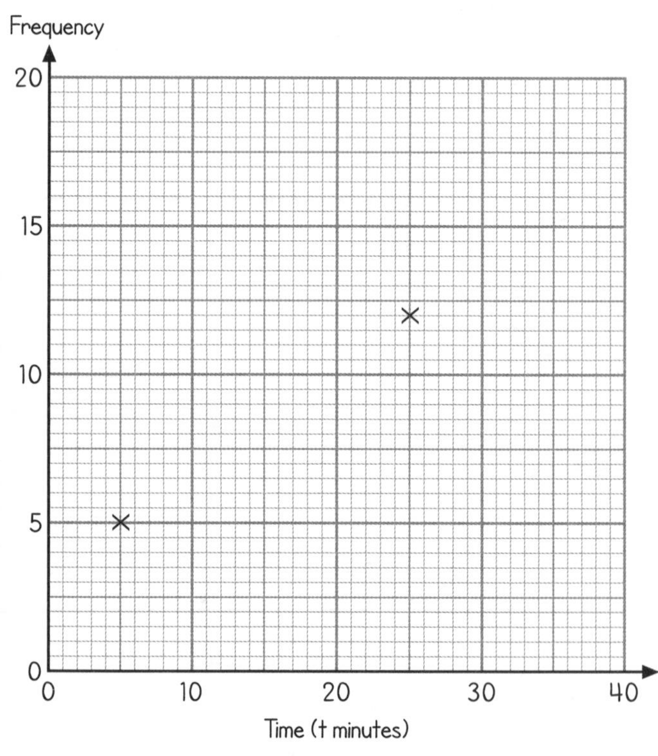

(i) Use the diagram to complete the table.

Time (t minutes)	Frequency
$0 < t \leq 10$	....
$10 < t \leq 20$	15
.... $< t \leq$	....
$30 < t \leq 40$	3

(ii) Complete the frequency diagram.

GO! FREQUENCY DIAGRAMS

Marvellous!

1. The frequency polygons show the test scores for Class A and Class B.

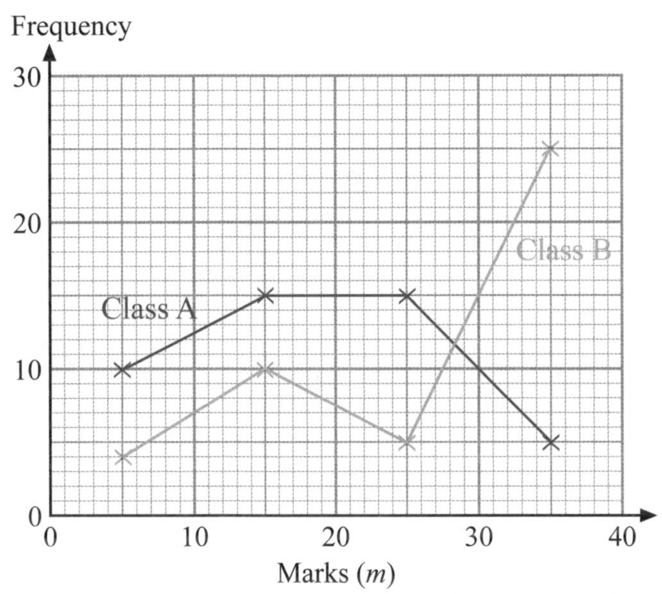

Compare and contrast the performances of the two classes.

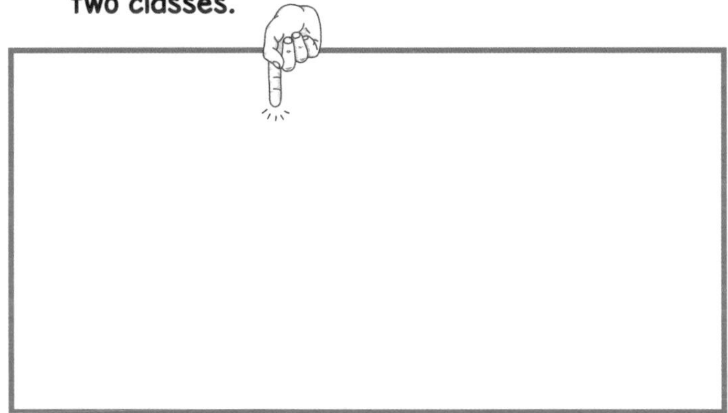

2. Use the information to complete the frequency diagram and table.

Time (minutes)	Frequency
1 - 5	....
6 -	12
.... -	8
16 - 20	10

Frequency

15

10

5

0

0 5 10 15 20

Time (minutes)

3. Debbie has drawn a frequency polygon to represent this information. Find the three mistakes.

Time (t seconds)	Frequency
$0 < t \leq 100$	6
$100 < t \leq 200$	15
$200 < t \leq 300$	20
$300 < t \leq 400$	4

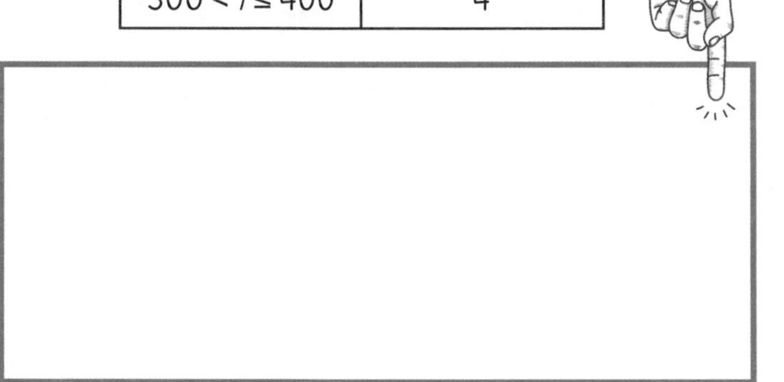

Frequency

30

20

10

0

0 100 200 300 400

Time (t seconds)

READY?

In maths, **lines of best fit** are:
* straight lines that follow the trend (pattern) of the points
* straight lines with roughly the same number of crosses either side of the line

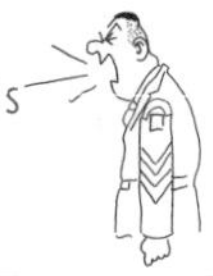

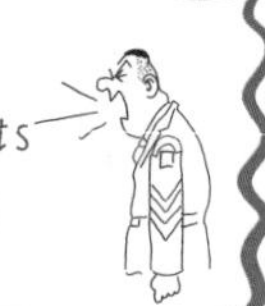

Scatter graphs (also called scatter diagrams) are used for data that contains pairs of values. They illustrate whether there is a relationship between these values - this relationship is called the correlation.

e.g. Dom collects information about the maximum temperature and the number of visitors to an outside splash pool over ten days. He shows this information on a scatter graph.

One of the points is an outlier.

a) Circle this outlier. *It's the cross away from the trend*

b) Give a possible reason for this outlier.

It may have been a rainy day. *There are other possible reasons*

c) For all the other points write down the type of correlation shown by the graph.

Positive correlation. *The trend is bottom left to top right*

d) Draw a line of best fit. *In the direction of the crosses*

e) On the 11th day the maximum temperature was 21°C. Estimate the number of visitors to the pool on this day.

46 visitors. *Read up from 21°C to the line of best fit, then ... read across (always check the scale of the axes)*

f) Explain why it would not be sensible to use the scatter graph to predict the number of visitors on a day when the maximum temperature was 16°C.

16°C is outside the range of the given data. *16°C is away from the group of crosses*

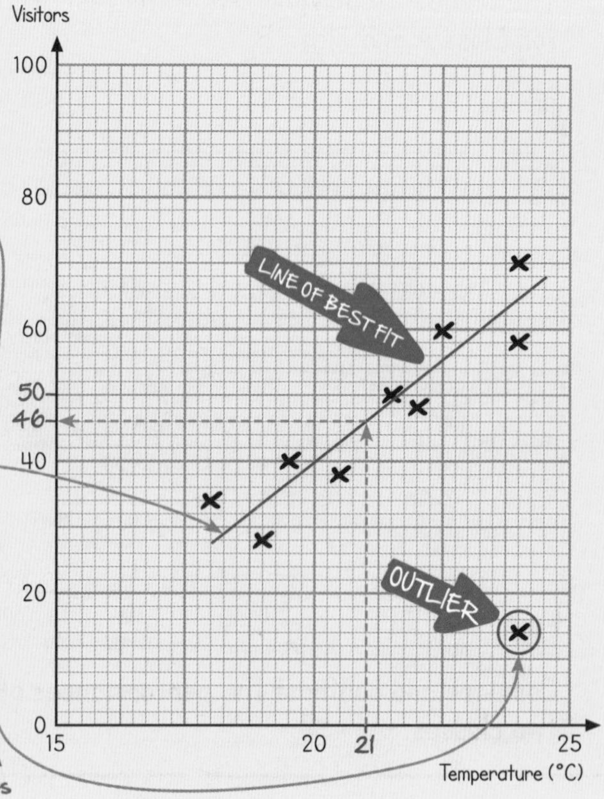

Types of Correlation

The closer the points are to the line of best fit, the stronger the correlation.

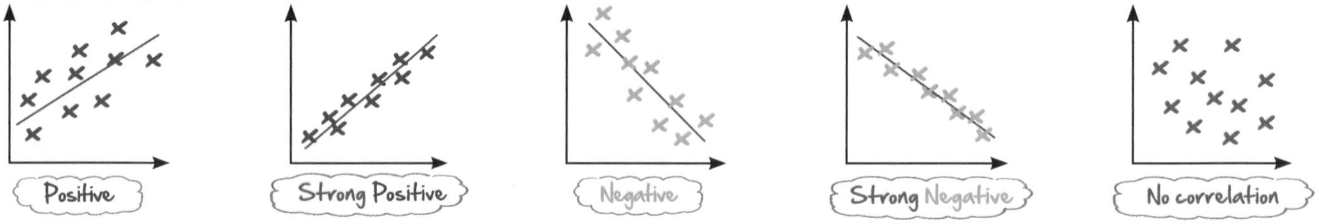

SET?

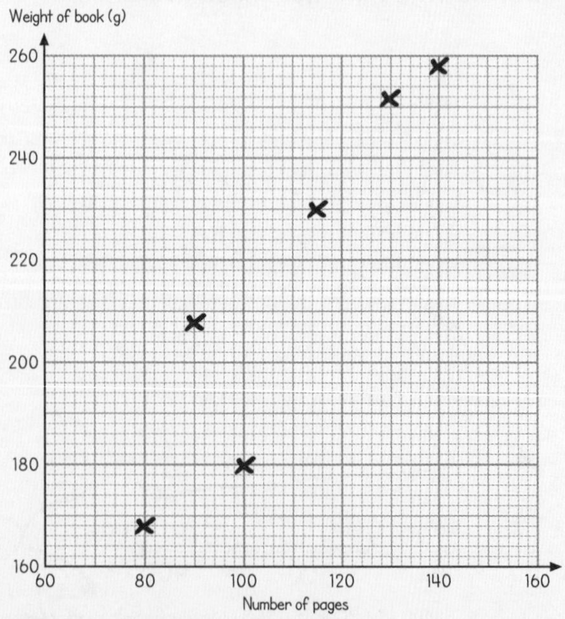

The table shows the number of pages and weights, in grams, for ten different books.

Pages	80	130	100	140	115	90	154	140	105	70
Weight (g)	168	252	180	258	230	208	256	246	210	160

a) Complete the scatter graph to show the information in the table. The first 6 points have been plotted for you.

b) For these books, describe the relationship between the number of pages and the weight of a book.

c) Draw a line of best fit.

d) Use your line of best fit to estimate:

(i) The number of pages in a book of weight 220 g.

(ii) The weight of a book with 134 pages.

SCATTER GRAPHS

Wonderful!

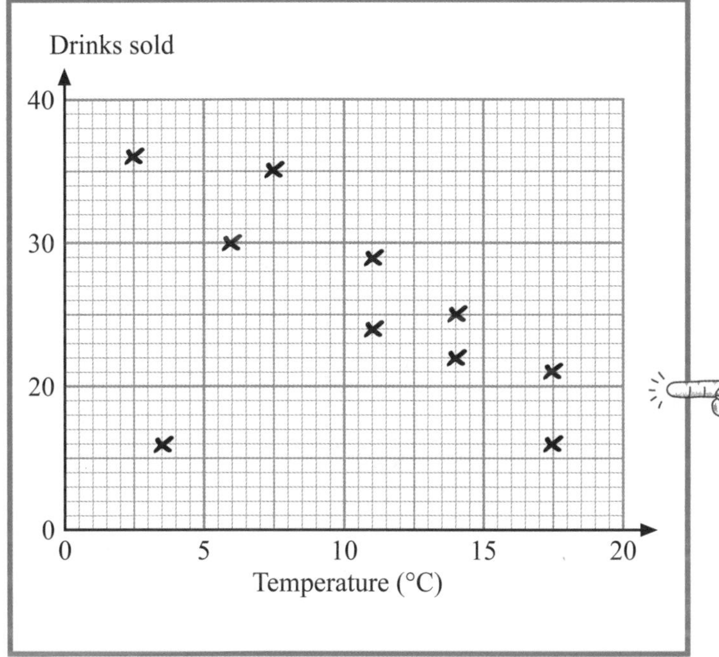

1. The graph shows information about the number of hot drinks sold from a vending machine and the outside temperature for a period of 10 days.

a) One of the points is an outlier. Circle this point.

b) What could this point represent? Give an example.

2. Rhys is constructing a scatter graph to show the results for 9 students in a science test and a maths test.

Science mark	3	5	7	8	9	13	14	17	18
Maths mark	15	23	30	29	27	31	25	34	32

His scatter graph is incorrect.
Describe two mistakes Rhys has made.

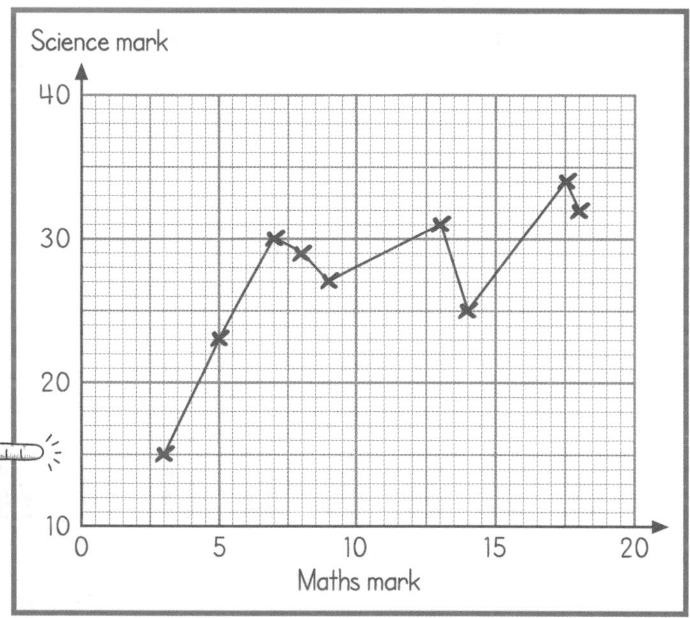

3. Match one statement from each column to create a correct relationship.

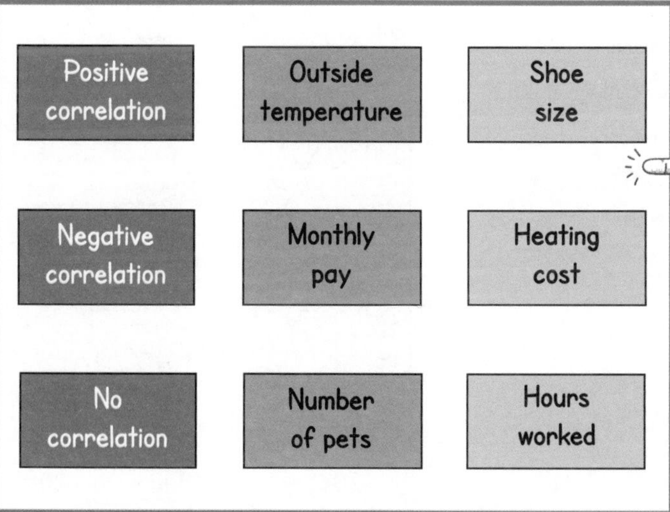

READY?

Time series graphs are used to show the trend (pattern) of data over a period of time

A time series graph plots data at regular time intervals to provide a visual representation. Measurements of time are plotted on the horizontal axis. Points are plotted to show the measurement at each point in time. The points are often joined with straight lines.

e.g. The table below gives information about the number of sales of revision guides at a school during some months of Year 11.

Month	Nov	Dec	Jan	Feb	Mar
Number of sales	14	26	34	57	68

a) Draw a time series graph. *Connect each cross with straight lines*

b) Describe the trend.

It's an increasing trend over time *It goes up*

c) Between which two months did the sales increase the most rapidly?

January and February *Look for the steepest rise*

d) Use the graph to predict the number of sales in April.

80 *This is only a prediction based on the trend of the graph (answers within a given range are acceptable)*

e) Is this prediction reliable? Explain your answer.

No, because it is outside the range of data

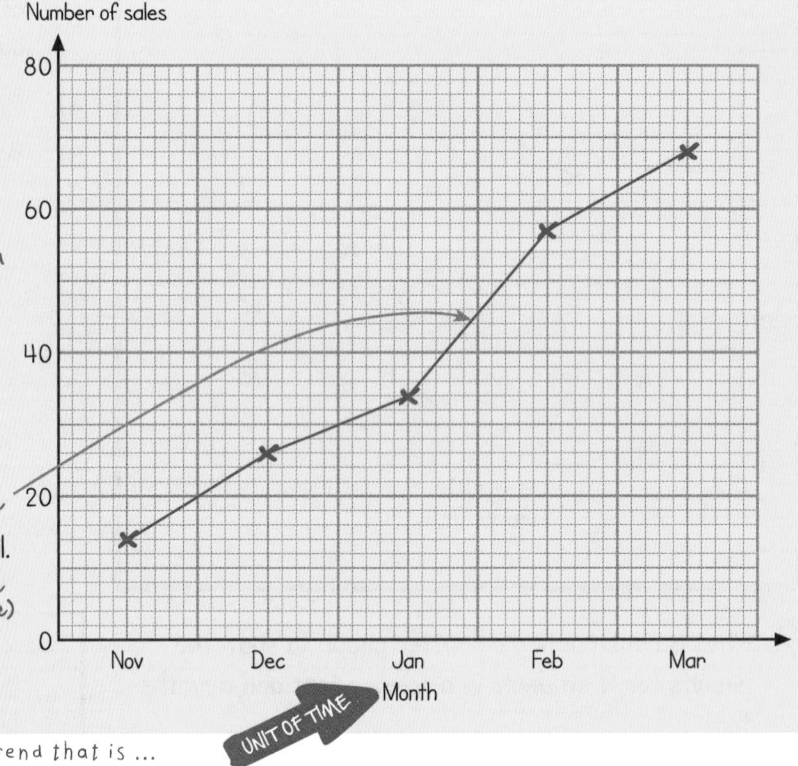

Trends

A time series graph could show a trend that is ...

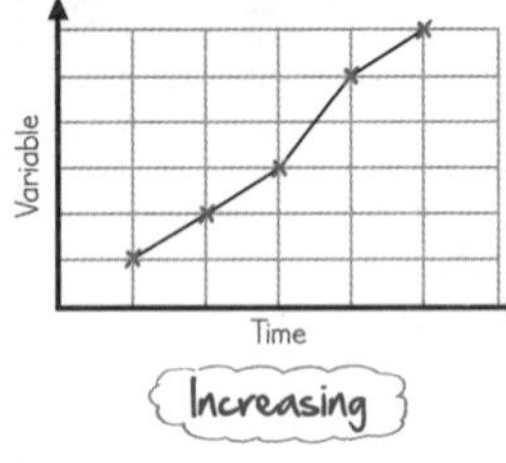

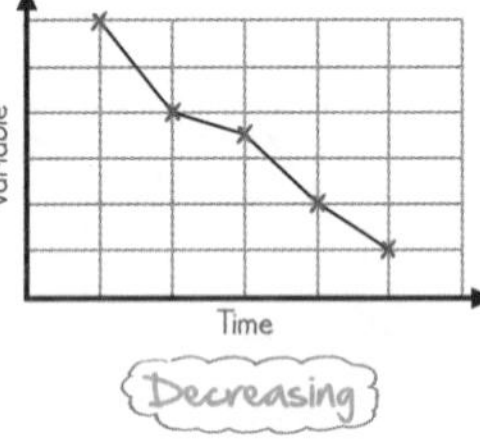

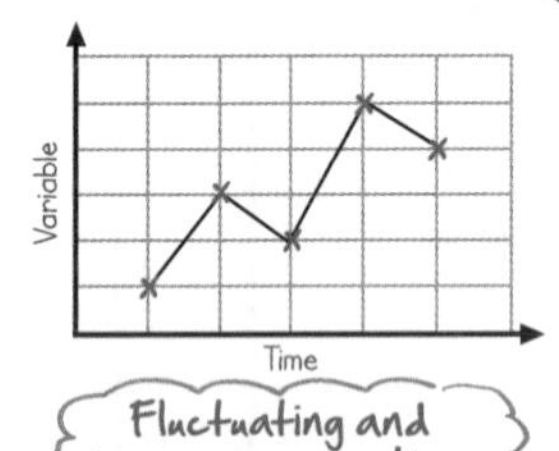

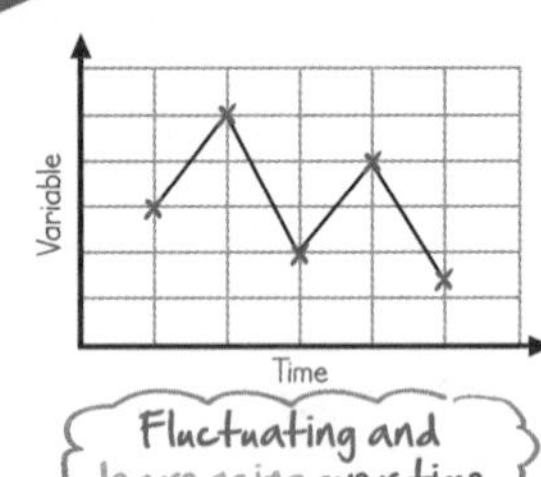

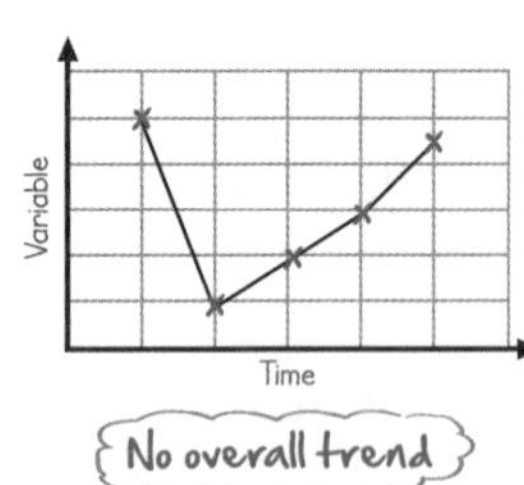

SET?

A. Draw a time series graph for the information in the table.

Day	Height (cm)
Mon	12
Tue	8
Wed	6
Thu	9
Fri	5

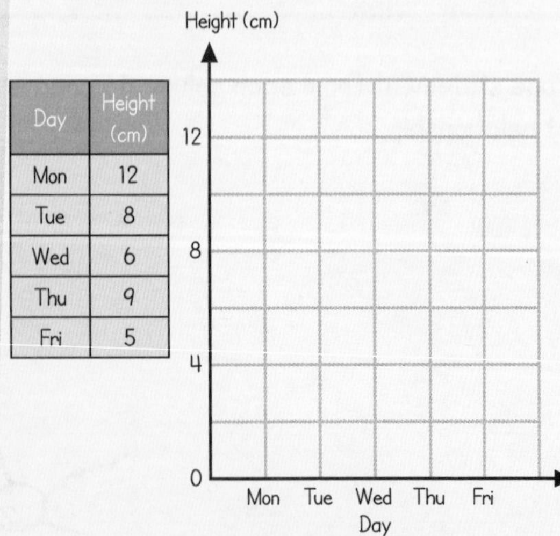

B. The time series graph shows the average percentage of pupils late to arrive at a school.

(i) Describe the trend.

(ii) What is the percentage in 2013?

(iii) What is the difference in percentage between 2014 and 2016?

(iv) When does the percentage drop most rapidly?

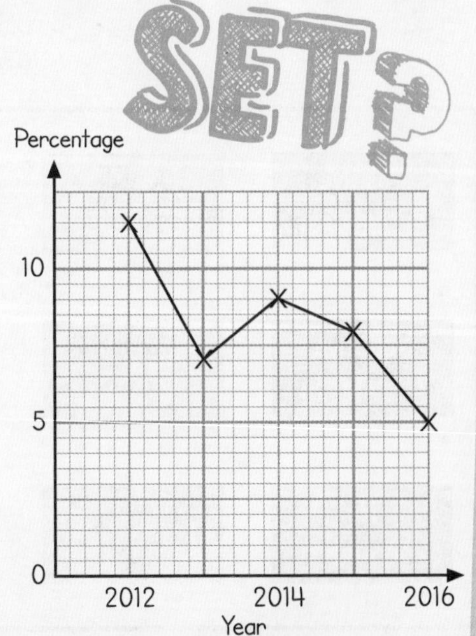

TIME SERIES

Epic!

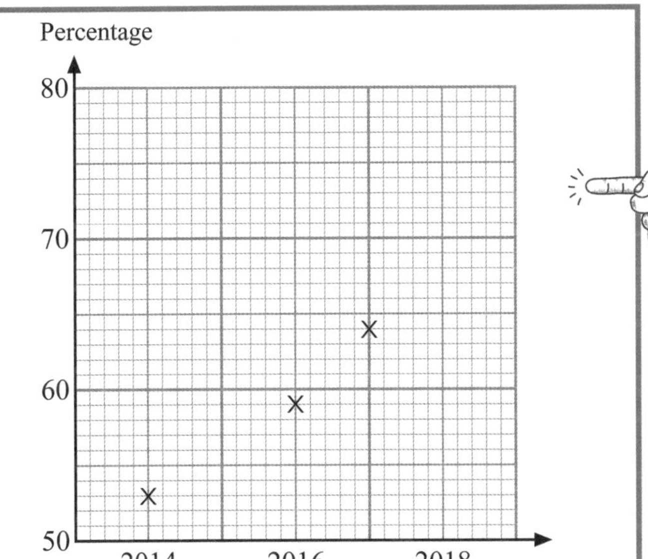

1. The table and graph gives information about the percentage of students getting a good GCSE pass at a school.

Year	2014	....	2016	2017	....
....	53	62	....	....	78

a) Complete the time series graph and table.

b) Describe the trend.

2. Rachel has drawn a time series graph for this data:

Day	Mon	Tues	Wed	Thurs	Fri	Sat	Sun
Temperature °C	8	9	4	1	5	3	1

She has made two mistakes.
Find the mistakes.

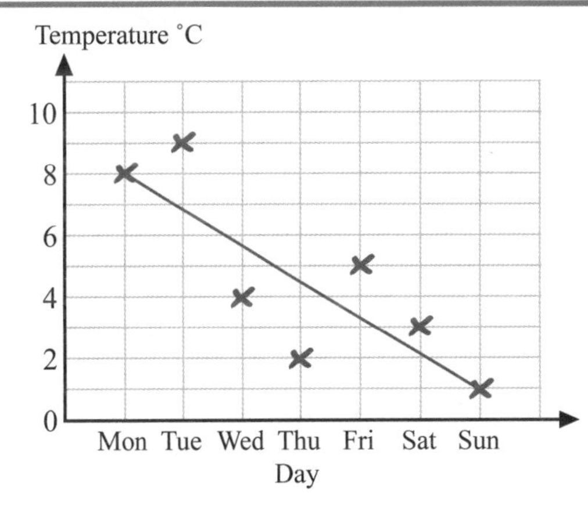

3. The times series graph shows information about the average number of car sales per week in a garage between 2007 and 2014.

a) How many more cars were sold in 2012 compared to 2008?

b) Describe the trend in car sales.

c) When do car sales decrease most rapidly?

d) The sales target in 2013 was to sell 3000 cars. Did the garage meet the sales target? Explain your answer.

e) Can you reliably use the graph to predict the number of weekly sales in 2021? Explain your answer.

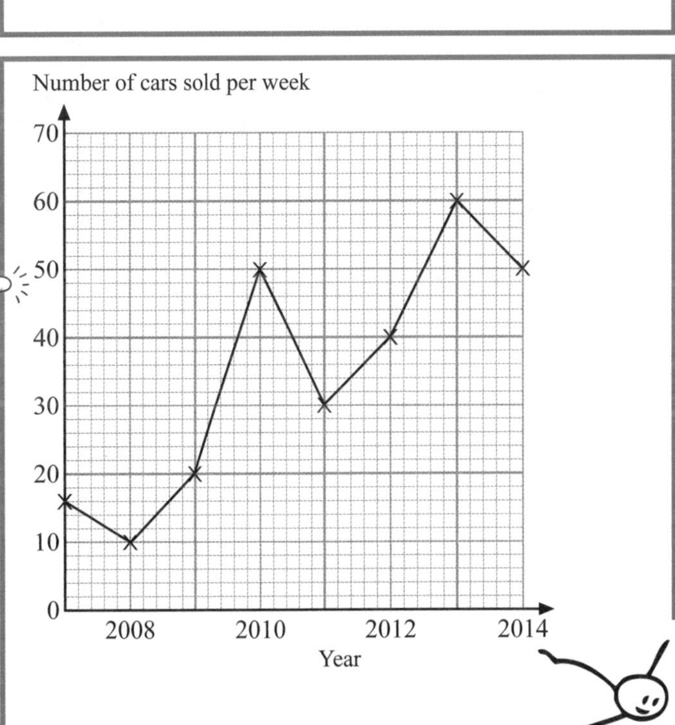

Get a protractor AND practise using it! (and remember a full circle is 360°)

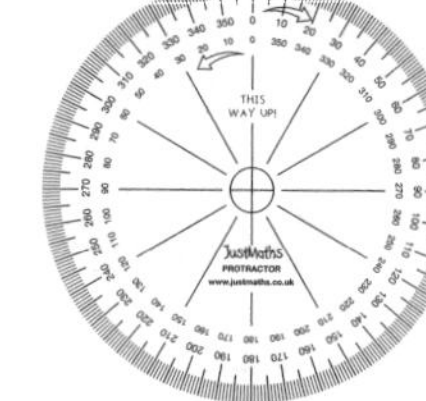

To construct a pie chart, we need to work out how many degrees represent one 'thing'.

e.g. 1 Construct a pie chart to show the information about the ages of teachers in a school.

Age	Frequency	Angle
20 to 34	11	$11 \times 6° = 66°$
35 to 44	15	$15 \times 6° = 90°$
45 to 59	27	$27 \times 6° = 162°$
60 or older	7	$7 \times 6° = 42°$
	60	

1. Work out the total frequency
2. Work out the angle for 1 teacher: $360° \div 60 = 6°$
3. Work out the angle for each category
4. Check that the angles add up to 360° → $66° + 90° + 162° + 42° = 360°$ ✓

You are usually given a circle and its radius

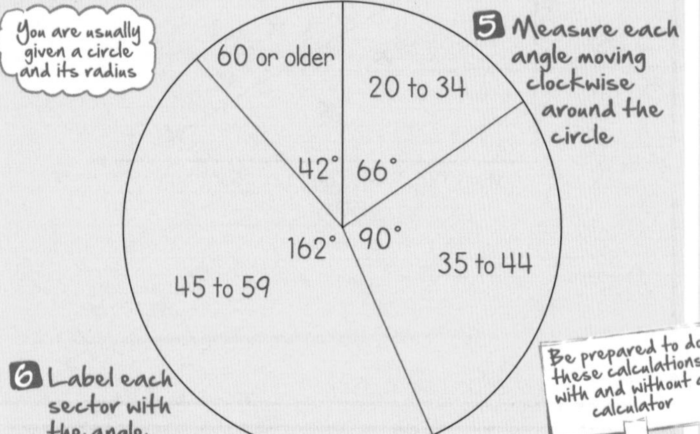

5. Measure each angle moving clockwise around the circle
6. Label each sector with the angle and title

Be prepared to do these calculations with and without a calculator

We also need to be able to interpret pie charts too.

e.g. 2 The pie chart shows information about Katrina's spending in a typical month.
Katrina spends £540 on food.
Work out how much Katrina spends on travel in a typical month.

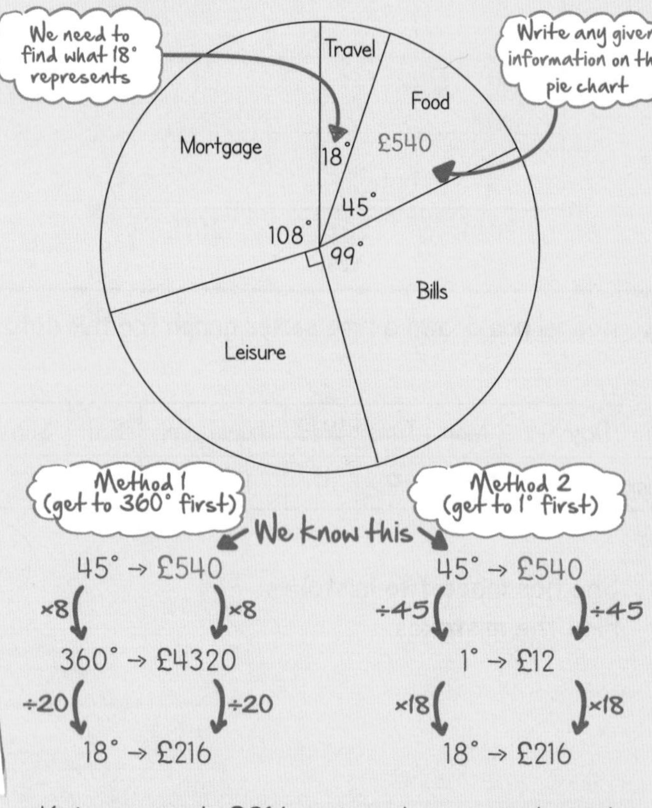

Method 1 (get to 360° first) — We know this — Method 2 (get to 1° first)

Method 1

$45° \rightarrow £540$

$\times 8$

$360° \rightarrow £4320$

$\div 20$

$18° \rightarrow £216$

Method 2

$45° \rightarrow £540$

$\div 45$

$1° \rightarrow £12$

$\times 18$

$18° \rightarrow £216$

Katrina spends £216 on travel in a typical month

A. Draw the pie chart to show this information.

Vehicles	None	1	2	3
Frequency	6	32	66	16

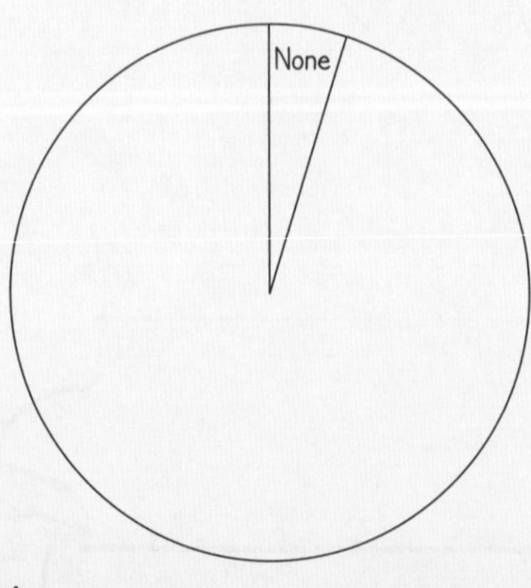

B. The pie chart shows information about the money Lydia spent on petrol, clothes, food and other items.

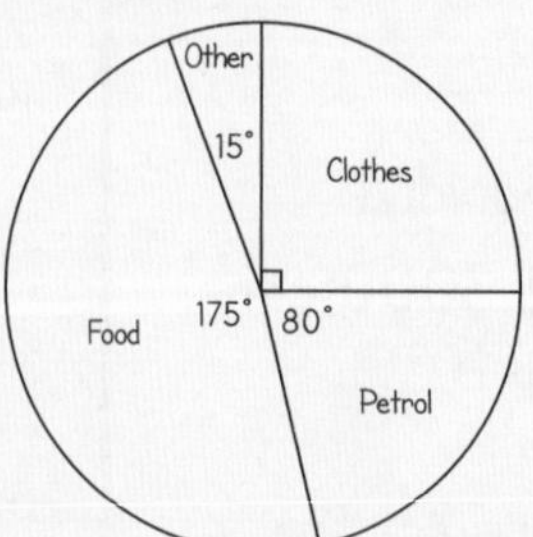

(i) What did she spend most money on?

(ii) What fraction of the money spent was on clothes?

(iii) Lydia spent £60 on petrol. In total, how much money did she spend?

C. Naimh is going to construct a pie chart for this data about a building set.
Calculate the size of the angle for each section.

Type	Frequency	Angle
Brick	348	
Plate	504	
Slope	172	
Other	416	

GO! PIE CHARTS

Solid!

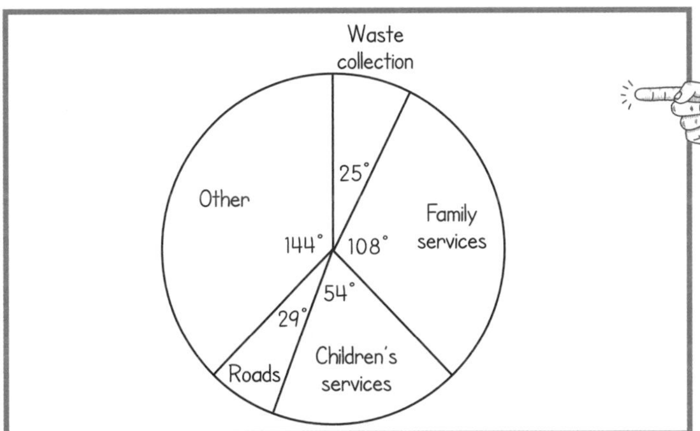

1. The pie chart shows how council tax money is spent in the UK.

   £6.6 billion is spent on children's services.

   a) How much is spent on family services?

   b) How much is spent on waste collection, to the nearest billion pounds?

2. The bar chart shows the results of a survey about the number of children living in different size houses. Construct a pie chart for the data.

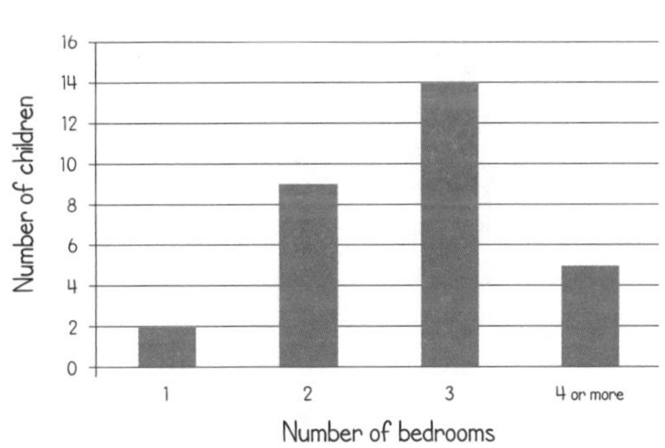

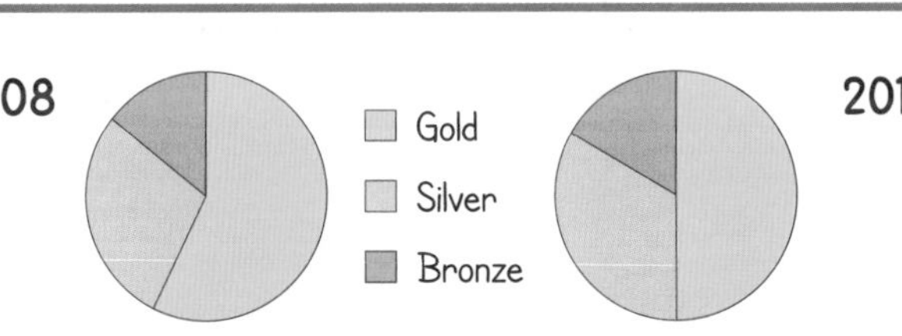

A Bronwen is correct

B Bronwen is incorrect

C There is not enough information to decide whether or not Bronwen is correct

3. The pie charts show information about medals won by Team GB cyclists at the Olympic Games in 2008 and 2016.

   The same number of bronze medals were won at both games.

   Bronwen says:

   "Team GB won more cycling medals overall in 2016"

   Choose the correct statement.
   Explain your reasoning.

4. The pie chart shows information about the sales of some theatre tickets. The diagram is not drawn accurately.

   504 adult tickets were sold.

   Three times as many concession tickets were sold than children's tickets.

   How many children's tickets were sold?

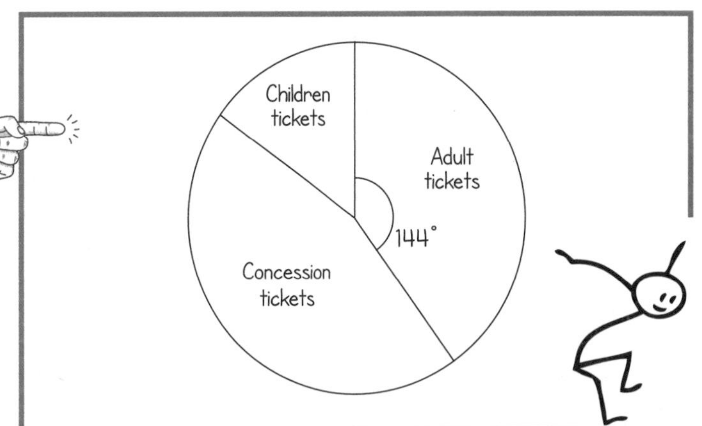

READY?

Coordinates are used to describe a position on a grid.

It is **REALLY USEFUL** to:

* know the origin is the point with coordinates (0,0)
* be able to plot coordinates (x,y)

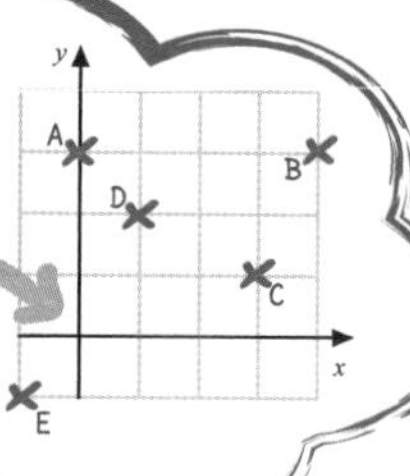

e.g. 1 The points A (-1,-1) and B (-1,3) are two corners of a square. Find the coordinates of the other corners of the square.

Sometimes there could be more than 1 solution

1 Plot the points A and B

2 Find the distance from A to B

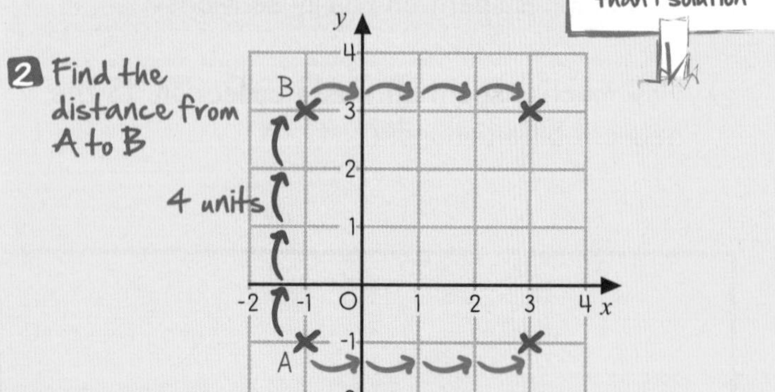

3 A square has 4 sides of equal length

The other two coordinates could be (3,3) and (3,-1)

Sometimes we are given a midpoint and one endpoint and need to work out the other endpoint.

e.g. 3 M is the midpoint of line segment PQ.
Point P is (-2,-5) and M is (-1,1)
Find the coordinates of point Q.

1 Draw a sketch

2 Find the journey from P to M
(1 right and 6 up)

3 Repeat this journey to find M to Q
(1 right and 6 up)

So the coordinates of Q = (0,7)

A line segment (just means part of a line) with a midpoint are really common questions.

e.g. 2 Point A has coordinates (3,8) and point B has coordinates (7,5)
M is the midpoint of the line segment AB.
Find the coordinates of M.

1 Make a sketch and plot the coordinates

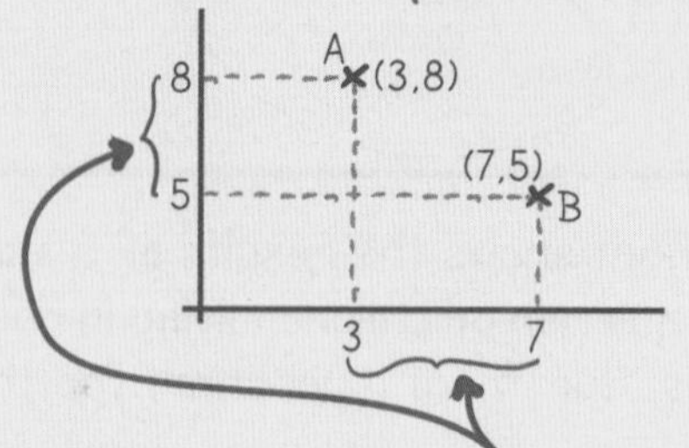

2 Find half way between these numbers

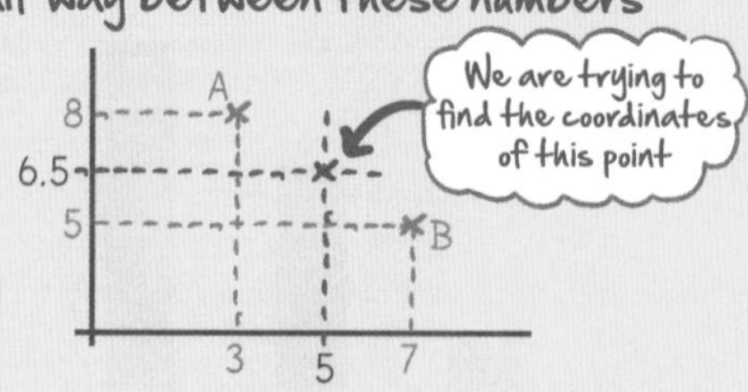

OR

We can deal directly with the coordinates instead of an image

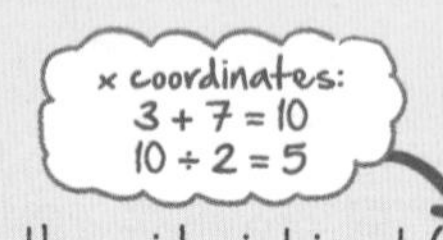

y coordinates:
8 + 5 = 13
13 ÷ 2 = 6.5

So the midpoint is at (5, 6.5)

SET?

A. The points A, B and C are three vertices of a rectangle.
Find the coordinates of the final vertex.

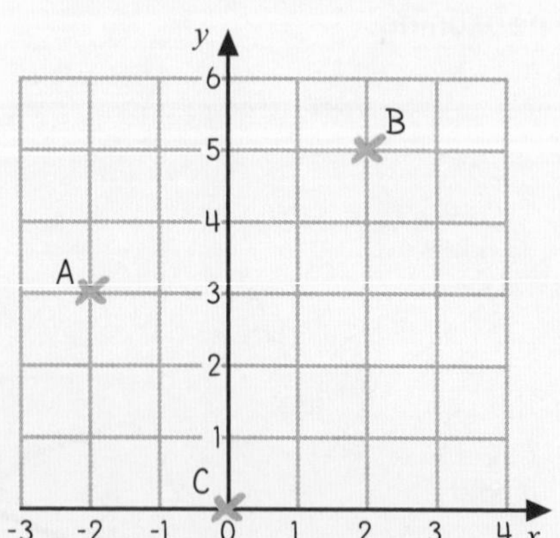

B. PQ is a line segment
Point P is (2,3) and Q is (4,1)
Find the coordinates of the midpoint of PQ.

C. ST is a line segment.
Point S has coordinates (-2,-5)
Point T has coordinates (1,7)
Find the coordinates of the midpoint of ST.

D. ST is a line segment.
U is the midpoint of line segment ST.
U has coordinates (5,7)
Point T has coordinates (7,11)
Find the co-ordinates of Point S.

COORDINATES

First-class!

1. The points A (-1,0) and B (-1,4) are two corners of a square.
   Anna thinks the only possible positions of the other two corners must be at (3,0) and (3,4)
   Do you agree with Anna?
   Explain your answer.

2. Point B has coordinates (2, -6)
   M (-1, -2) is the midpoint of line segment AB.
   Work out the coordinates of point A.

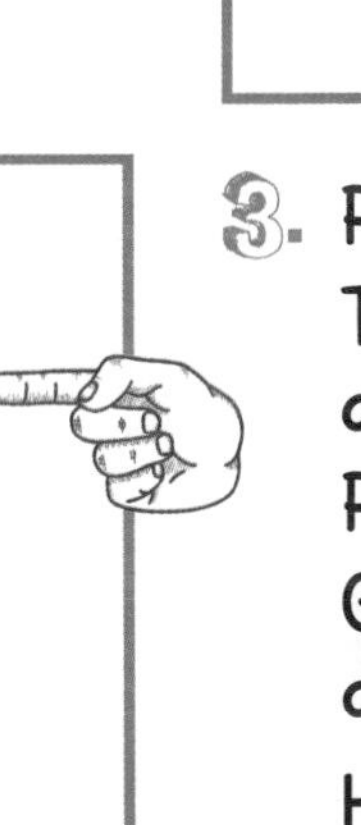

3. PQ is a line segment.
   The midpoint of the line segment has coordinates (2,4)
   Point P has coordinates (-2,6)
   Graham says the coordinates of point Q are (0,5)
   He is incorrect. Explain why.

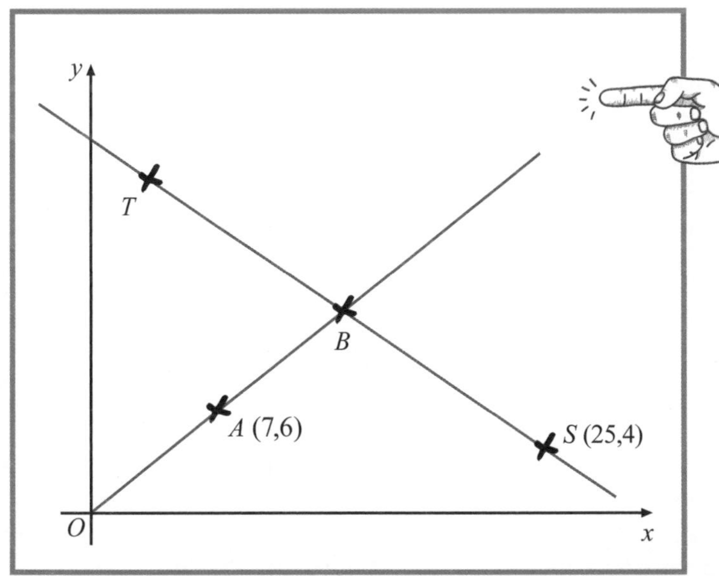

4. Two straight lines are shown.
   A is the midpoint of OB
   B is the midpoint of TS
   Work out the coordinates of T.

READY?

A table of values is often used to calculate the coordinates of a straight line graph: e.g. $y = x + 3$

x	-2	-1	0	1	2	3
y	1 (+3)	2 (+3)	3 (+3)	4 (+3)	5 (+3)	6 (+3)

So the coordinates of the points are (-2,1), (-1,2) etc.

It is **REALLY USEFUL** to know:

* the x-axis is horizontal (and also called $y = 0$)
* the y-axis is vertical (and also called $x = 0$)
* how to work with negative numbers

Sometimes we might not be given a table to complete (and sometimes the axes may not be given either). Be prepared to create them.

e.g. 1 a) Complete the table of values for $y = 2x + 3$

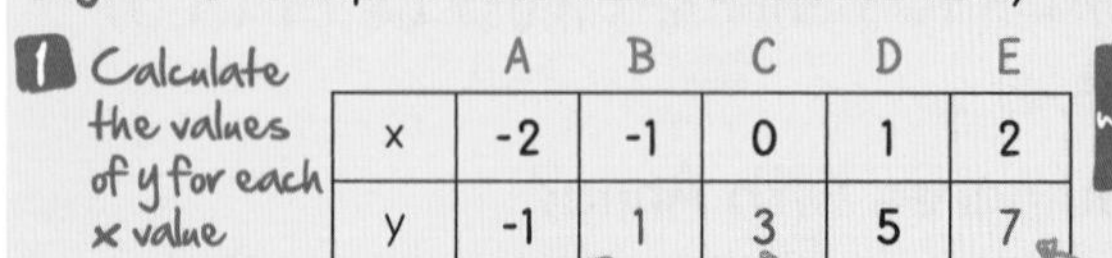

1 Calculate the values of y for each x value

	A	B	C	D	E
x	-2	-1	0	1	2
y	-1	1	3	5	7

HINT! Start with the positive x values

When $x = -1$
$y = 2 \times (-1) + 3$
So, $y = -2 + 3 = 1$

When $x = 0$
$y = 2 \times 0 + 3$
So, $y = 0 + 3 = 3$

When $x = 2$
$y = 2 \times 2 + 3$
So, $y = 4 + 3 = 7$

b) Draw the graph of $y = 2x + 3$

2 Plot the coordinates from the table

3 Join the points with a ruler

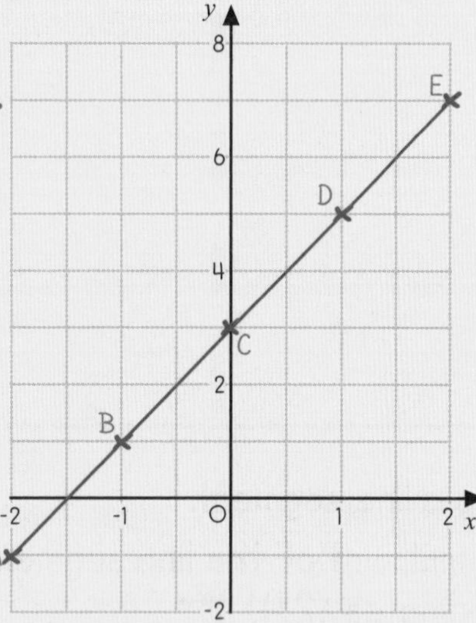

e.g. 2 Draw the graph of $y = 4 - 2x$ for values of x from -1 to 4

	A	B	C	D	E	F
x	-1	0	1	2	3	4
y	6	4	2	0	-2	-4

When $x = -1$
$y = 4 - 2 \times (-1)$
So, $y = 4 + 2 = 6$

When $x = 4$
$y = 4 - 2 \times 4$
So, $y = 4 - 8 = -4$

1 If no table given, create your own and calculate the values of y for each x value

2 Draw and label your axes

3 Plot the points and join with a straight line

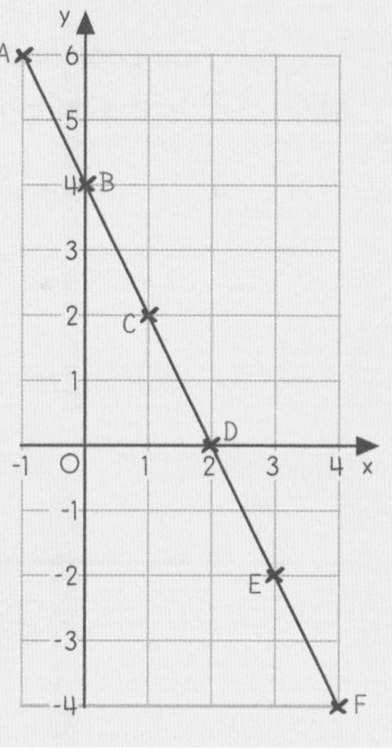

A linear equation should produce a straight line. If your coordinates do not sit on the line, check your working out

A. Complete the table of values to draw the graph of $y = 4x + 2$

x	-2	-1	0	1	2
y	-6		2		

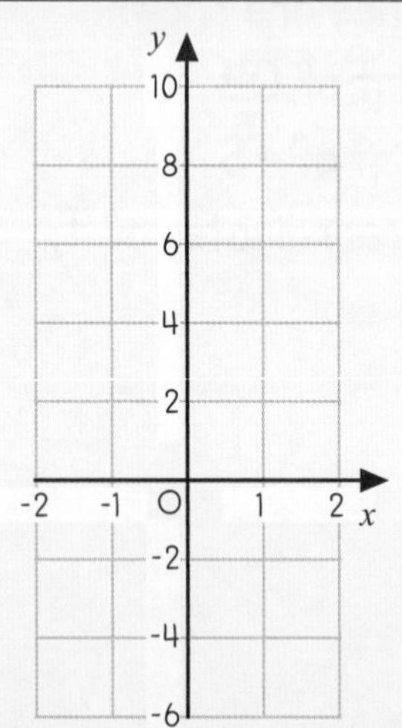

B. Draw the graph of $y = 2x - 1$ using values of x from -1 to 3

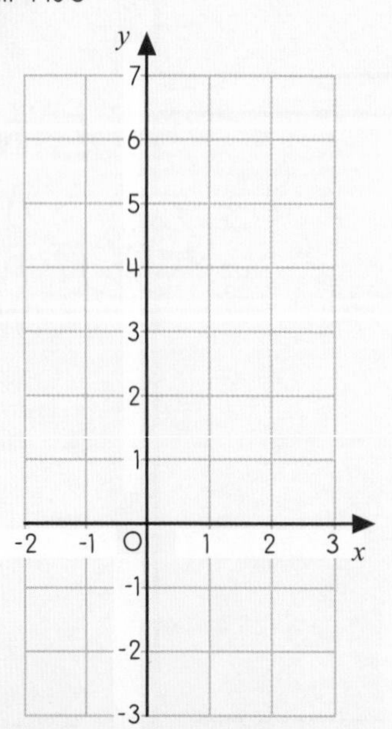

C. On the grid draw the graph of $y = 3 - 2x$ from $x = -2$ to $x = 4$

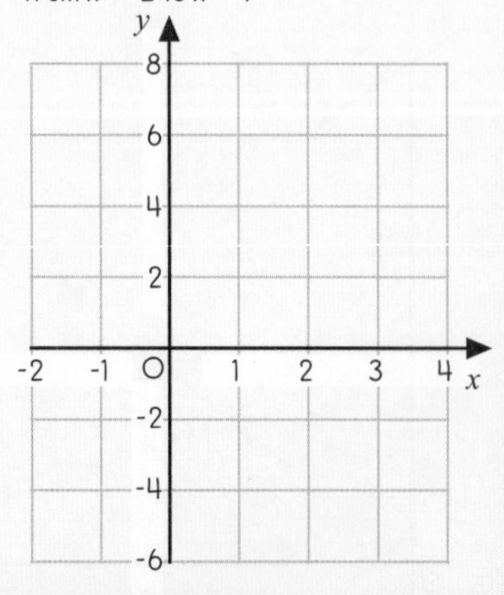

STRAIGHT LINE GRAPHS 1

(ALSO CALLED LINEAR GRAPHS)

Fab!

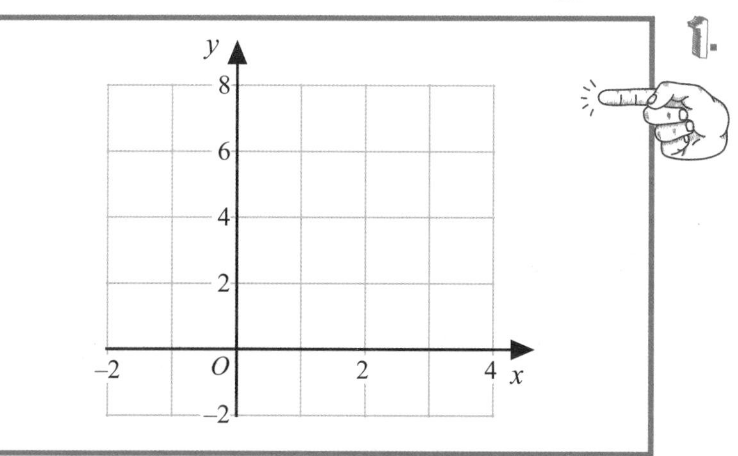

1. Draw the graph of $y = \frac{1}{2}x + 4$

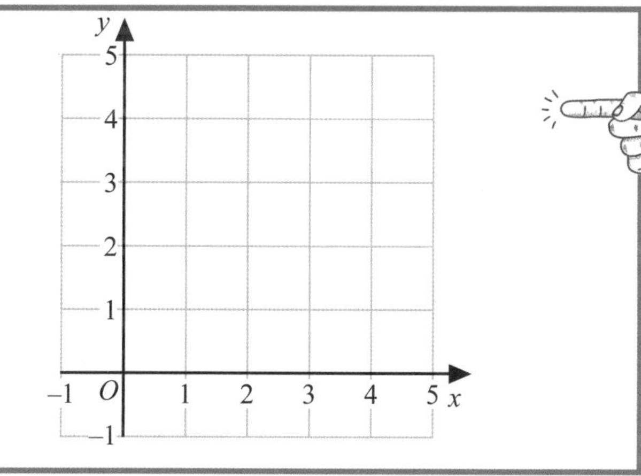

2. Draw the graph of $x + y = 4$ for values of x from -1 to 5

3. Bella the Builder charges a £40 callout fee and £25 per hour.

a) Complete the table of values that shows the total cost for up to 4 hours.

Hours worked	0	1	2	3	4
Total cost (£)					

b) Draw a graph of time worked (hours) against total cost (£).

c) Use the graph to work out how many hours Bella has worked if the total cost is £175.00

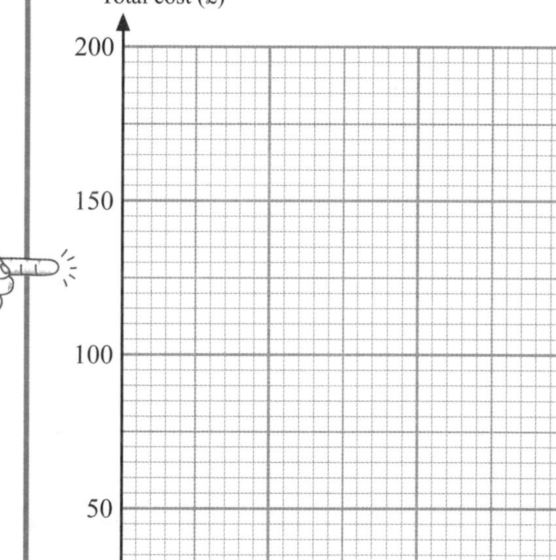

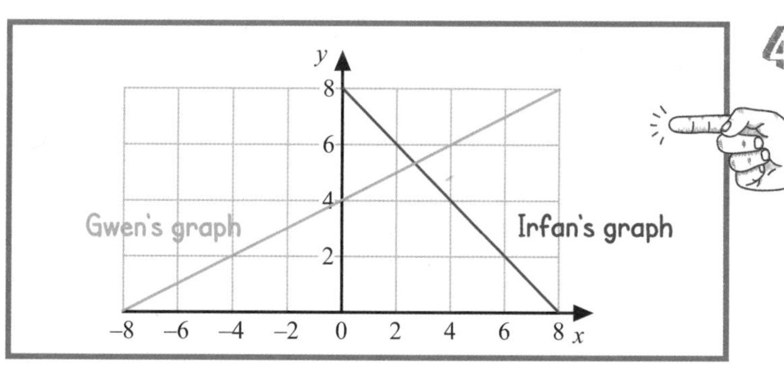

4. Irfan draws the graph of $x + y = 8$

Gwen also draws the graph of $x + y = 8$

Who is correct?

Explain your answer.

READY?

A key feature of a straight line graph is the gradient of the line. We can work out the gradient of the line passing through 2 points.

It is **REALLY USEFUL** to know that a gradient tells us how steep a line is:
A **positive** gradient goes upwards from left to right.
A **negative** gradient goes downwards from left to right.

e.g. 1 Points A and B are plotted on the grid.

What is the gradient of a line passing through A and B?

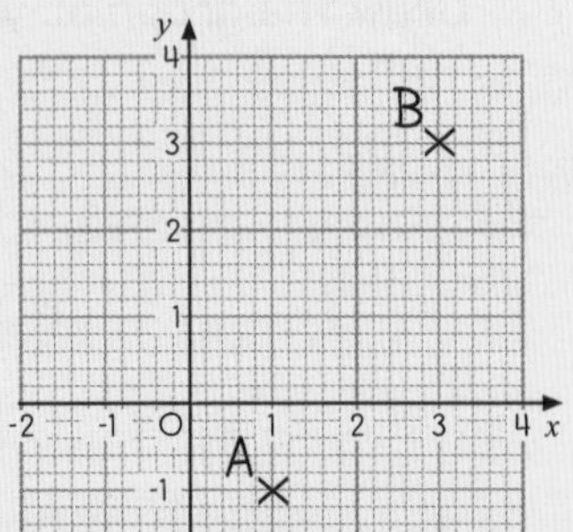

1 Join A to B with a straight line

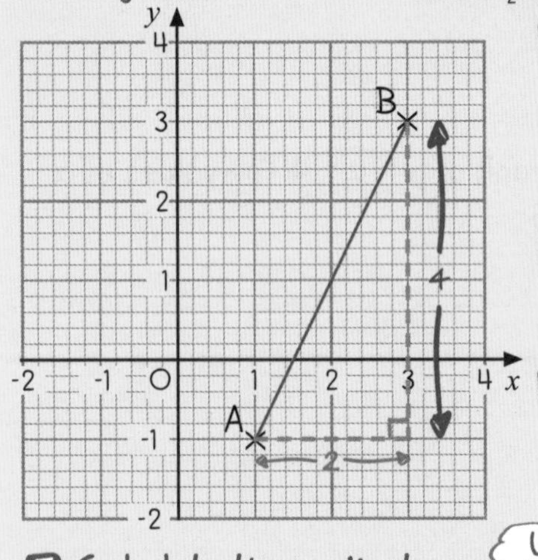

2 Make a right-angled triangle (with line AB as the hypotenuse)

3 Check the scale on the axes

4 Find the height and base of the triangle

5 Calculate the gradient

$$\text{Gradient} = \frac{\text{change in y}}{\text{change in x}}$$

Use the value of the height of the triangle

Use the value of the base of the triangle

$$= \frac{4}{2} = 4 \div 2 = 2$$

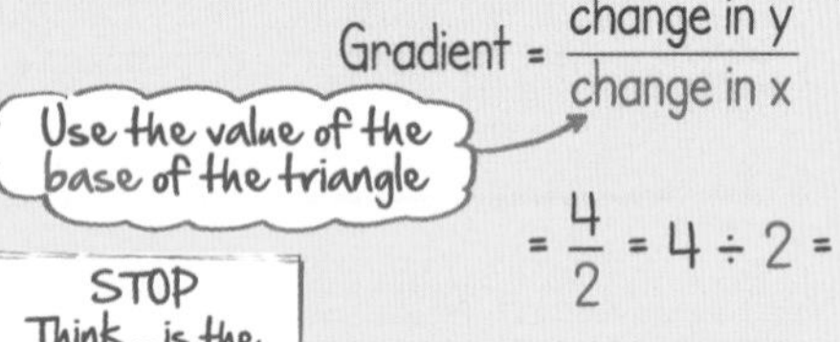

STOP Think ... is the gradient + or − ?

Gradient = 2

Gradient = vertical ÷ horizontal
NOT horizontal ÷ vertical

Sometimes we are given the coordinates of the points and no grid.

e.g. 2 Point A has coordinates (-2,11) and point B has coordinates (1,-1)

Find the gradient of line AB.

1 Draw a sketch

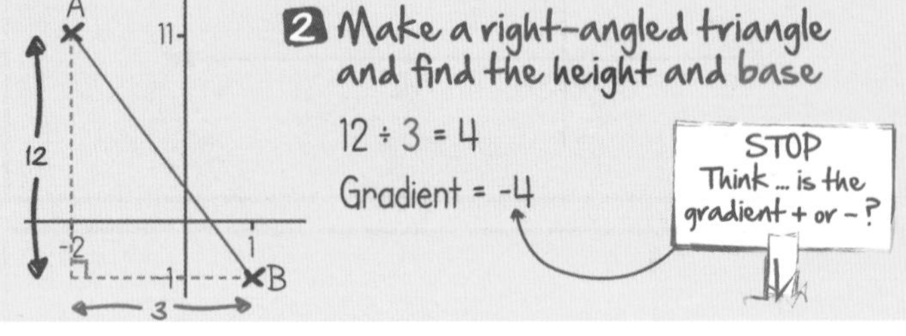

2 Make a right-angled triangle and find the height and base

$12 \div 3 = 4$

Gradient = -4

STOP Think ... is the gradient + or − ?

Sometimes no points are given.

e.g. 3 Here is a graph of a straight line.
What is the gradient of the line?

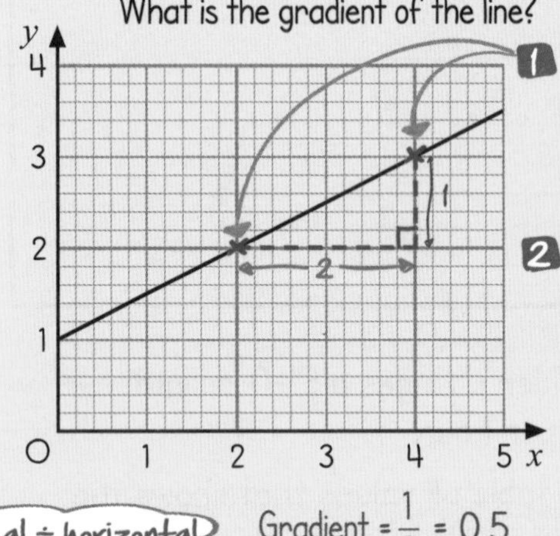

1 Choose two points on the line with obvious coordinates

2 Make a right-angled triangle and find the height and base

STOP Think ... is the gradient + or − ?

$$\text{Gradient} = \frac{1}{2} = 0.5$$

SET?

A. Calculate the gradient of the line passing through the points:

(i) A and B

(ii) B and C

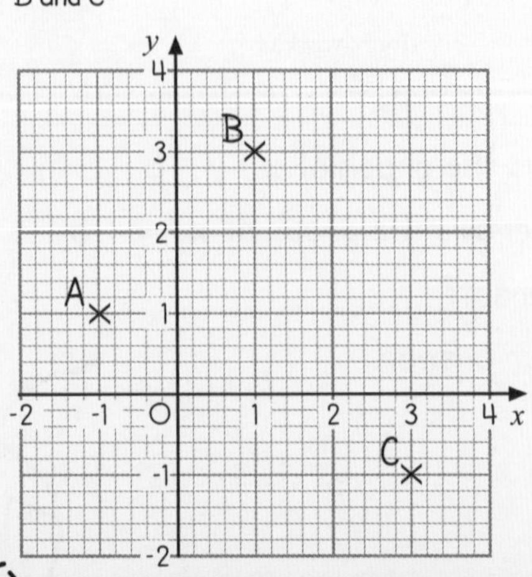

B. What is the gradient of the straight line that passes through (3,2) and (5,8)?

C. A is the point (2,-5)
B is the point (4,-9)
Work out the gradient of the straight line passing through A and B.

D. Calculate the gradient of the line segment.

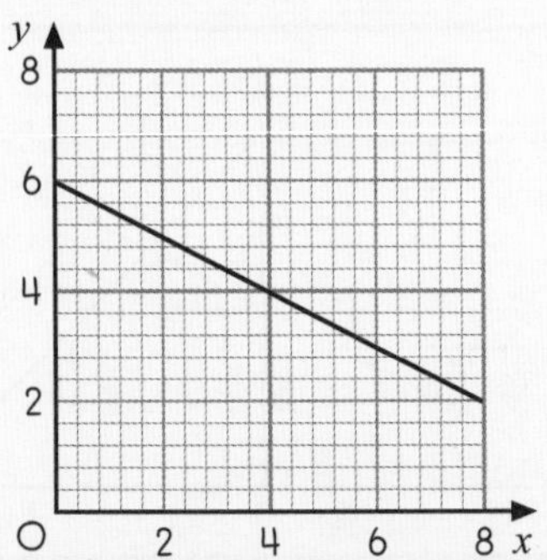

Grand!

GO! STRAIGHT LINE GRAPHS 2

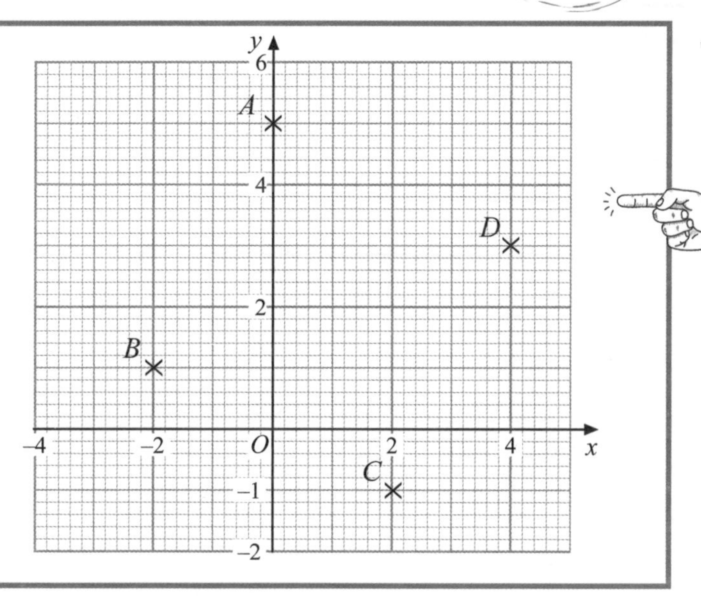

1. a) Calculate the gradient of the straight line passing through points A and B.

   b) Calculate the gradient of the straight line passing through points C and D.

   c) What can you say about the line AB and the line CD?

2. Tim works out the gradient between the points (6,2) and (9,4)

   Here is his working:

   $$\text{Gradient} = \frac{9 - 6}{4 - 2} = \frac{3}{2} = 1.5$$

   So, the gradient = 1.5

a) Tim is wrong. Explain why.

b) Work out the correct gradient.

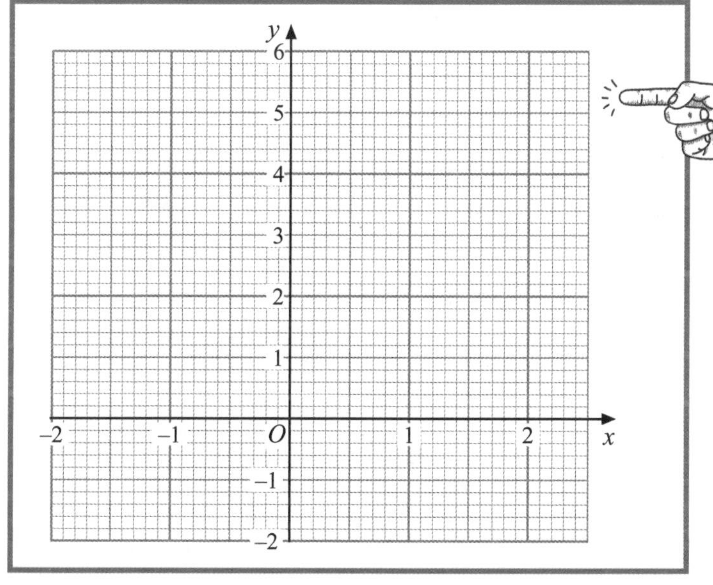

3. Point X has coordinates (-2,5) and point Y has coordinates (1.5, -2)

   What is the gradient of the line segment between points X and Y?

4. A is the point with coordinates (2,10)

   B is the point with coordinates (5,d)

   The gradient of the line AB is 4

   Work out the value of d.

READY?

REMEMBER:

* Parallel lines are lines that never meet
* The **gradient** measures the steepness of a line

Every straight line (linear graph) can be written using the equation $y = mx + c$ where "m" is the **gradient** and "c" is the point where the line crosses the y-axis (the posh name is the **y-intercept**).

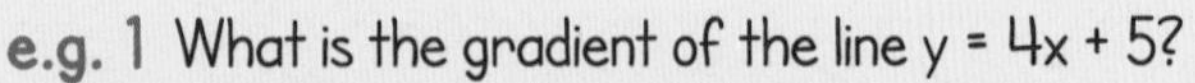

e.g. 1 What is the gradient of the line $y = 4x + 5$?

Compare $y = 4x + 5$ with
$y = mx + c$ (gradient)

The gradient is 4

e.g. 2 What is the y-intercept of the line $y = 4x + 5$?

Compare $y = 4x + 5$ with
$y = mx + c$ (y-intercept)

The y-intercept is +5

Lines with the same **gradient** are parallel to each other.

e.g. 3 Show that the lines $y = 2 + 3x$ and $2y - 6x = 8$ are parallel to each other.

1 Get both equations in the form $y = mx + c$

$y = 2 + 3x$ and $2y - 6x = 8$

$y = 3x + 2$

$+6x \quad +6x$

$2y = 6x + 8$

$\div 2 \quad \div 2$

$y = 3x + 4$

2 Compare the gradients

Both lines have a gradient of 3 so are parallel to each other

We need to be able to find the equation of a line when given information about the **gradient** and a point the line passes through.

e.g. 4 Find the equation of a straight line with gradient 3 and passing through the point (-1,2)

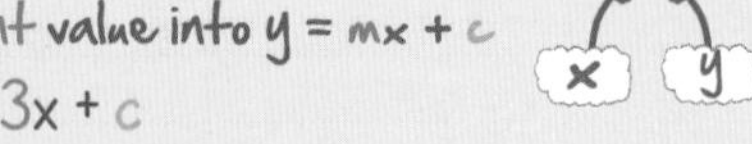

1 Substitute the gradient value into $y = mx + c$

$y = 3x + c$

2 Substitute the x and y values of the point into $y = 3x + c$ to find c

$2 = (3 \times -1) + c$

$2 = -3 + c$

$5 = c$

3 Substitute the value of c into $y = 3x + c$

Equation of the line is $y = 3x + 5$

e.g. 5 A pool is filled up with water. The graph shows the depth (d cm) after t minutes.

a) Find the y-intercept and explain what this represents.

The y-intercept is 20 cm and it represents the depth of water when the time is zero (the water already in the pool).

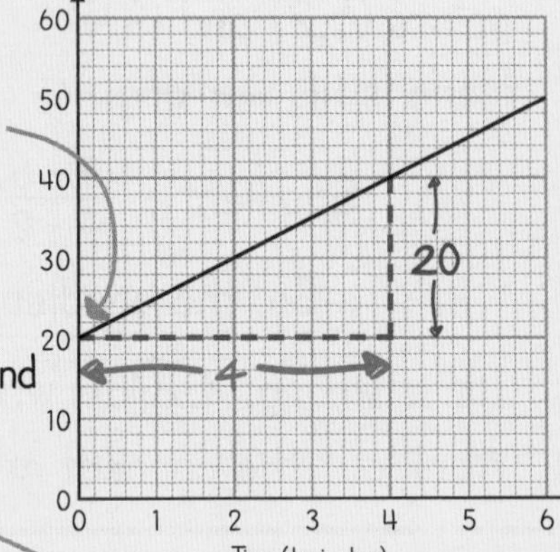

b) Find the gradient and explain what this represents.

The gradient is 5 and it represents the rate the pool fills with water (5 cm per minute).

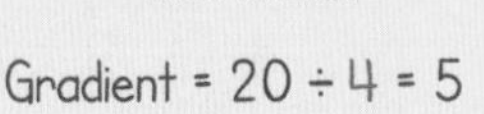
Gradient = 20 ÷ 4 = 5

A. Find the gradient and the y-intercept of the line $y = 2x + 1$

B. Find the gradient and the y-intercept of the line $y = 2 - 4x$

C. Find the gradient and the y-intercept of the line $y = 5x - 2$

HINT: The y-intercept can be negative too

D. The graph shows the depth (d cm) of a pool after t minutes.

(i) Work out the gradient of the line.

(ii) What does the gradient represent?

(iii) State the y-intercept and explain what it represents.

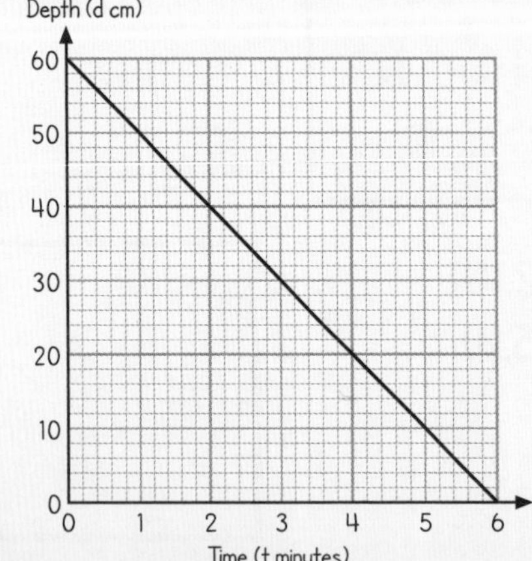

E. A straight line passes through (2,3) and (4,7)

(i) Find the gradient of the line.

(ii) Find the equation of the straight line.

HINT: Make a sketch

GO! STRAIGHT LINE GRAPHS 3

Skills!

1. Here are the equations of five straight lines:

A $y = 3x - 2$
B $2y - 4x = 6$
C $2x - 3y = 6$
D $y - 8 - 2x = 0$
E $2y = 4 + 6x$

Which lines are parallel with each other?

2. An electrician charges a £60 callout fee and £30 per hour.

Hours worked (h)	0	1	2	3	4	5
Total cost (£C)	60					210

a) Complete the table of values.
b) Draw a graph of hours worked against cost.
c) Write down a practical interpretation of the value of the gradient.
d) What does the y-intercept represent?
e) Work out the equation of the line.

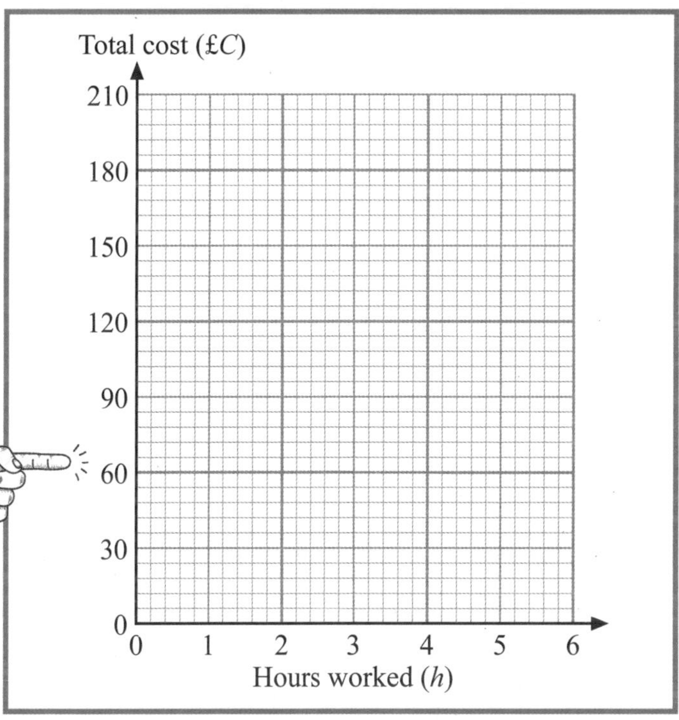

3. a) Chen says:

"The graphs of $y = 3x + 2$ and $2y = 6x - 2$ are not parallel because one has a gradient of 2 and the other has a gradient of -2"

Explain why Chen is incorrect.

b) Draw the graphs of $y = 3x + 2$ and $2y = 6x - 2$ to show they are parallel.

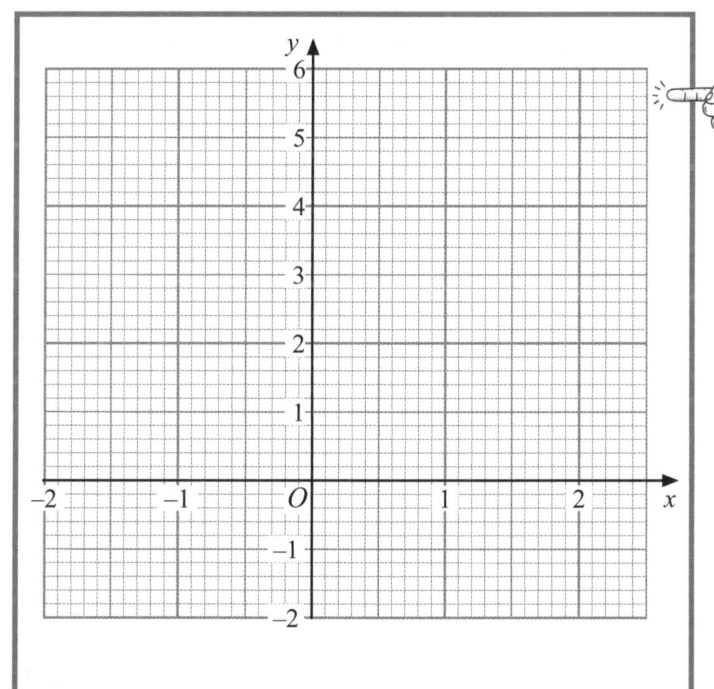

READY?

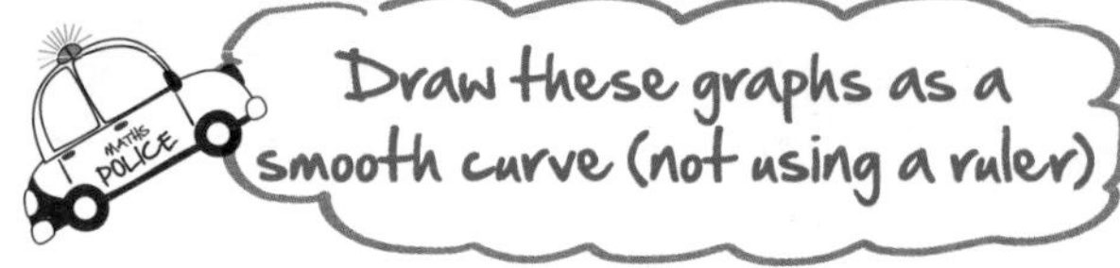

Quadratic graphs (when x^2 is the highest power) have the general shape:

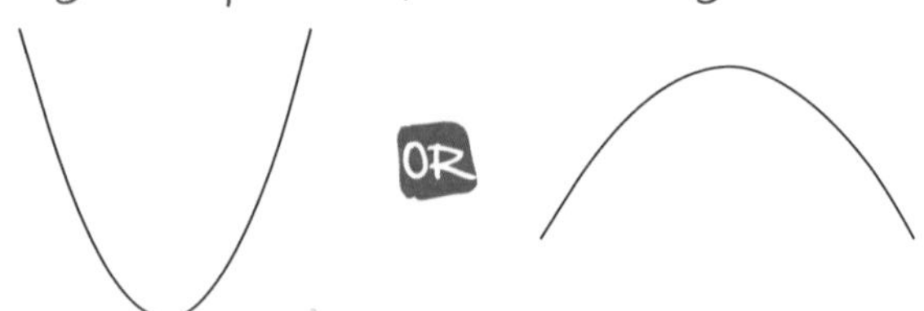

Cubic graphs (when x^3 is the highest power) could look like any of these:

OR OR

e.g. 1 a) By completing the table of values, draw the graph of $y = x^2 - 2x - 3$ for values of x from -2 to 4

When $x = -1$
$y = (-1)^2 - 2 \times (-1) - 3$
So, $y = 1 + 2 - 3 = 0$

	A	B	C	D	E	F	G
x	-2	-1	0	1	2	3	4
y	5	0	-3	-4	-3	0	5

When $x = 4$
$y = 4^2 - 2 \times 4 - 3$
So, $y = 16 - 8 - 3 = 5$

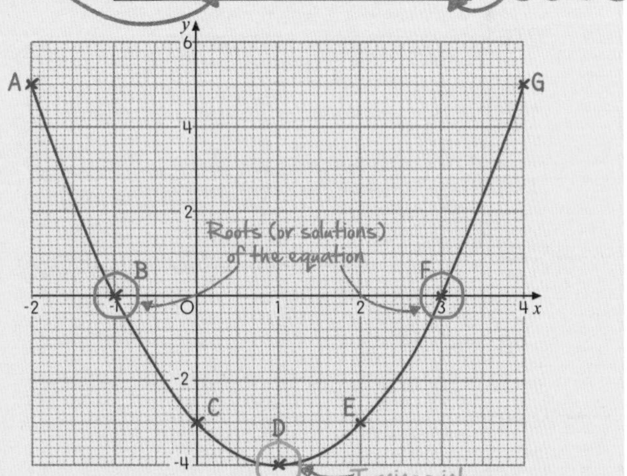

b) Write down the coordinates of the turning point. (1,-4)

c) Use the graph to find the roots of $x^2 - 2x - 3 = 0$

(-1,0) and (3,0)

e.g. 2 Draw the graph of $y = x^3 + 2$ for values of x from -2 to 2

If you're not given a table of values ... draw one

When $x = -2$
$y = (-2)^3 + 2$
So, $y = -8 + 2 = -6$

	A	B	C	D	E
x	-2	-1	0	1	2
y	-6	1	2	3	10

When $x = 2$
$y = 2^3 + 2$
So, $y = 8 + 2 = 10$

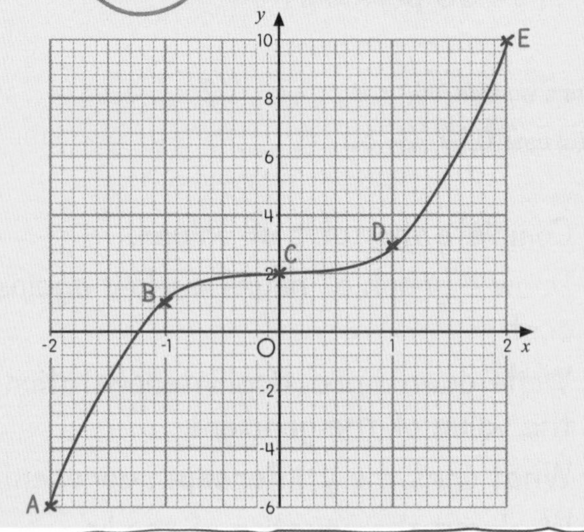

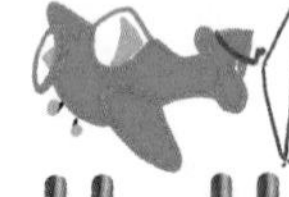

The turning point is the point where the graph changes direction, also called the maximum or minimum point

A. By completing the table of values, draw the graph of $y = x^2 + 2x$ for values of x from -3 to 3

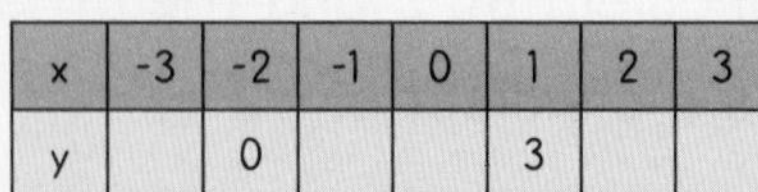

x	-3	-2	-1	0	1	2	3
y		0			3		

B. By completing the table of values, draw the graph of $y = x^3 + 3$ for values of x from -3 to 3

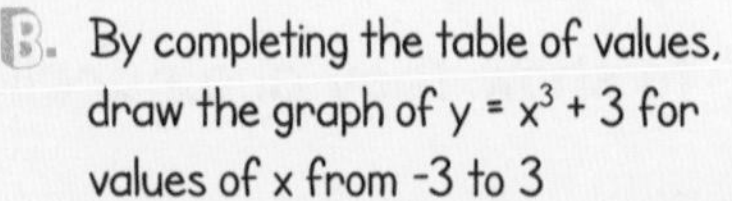

x	-3	-2	-1	0	1	2	3
y		-5			4		

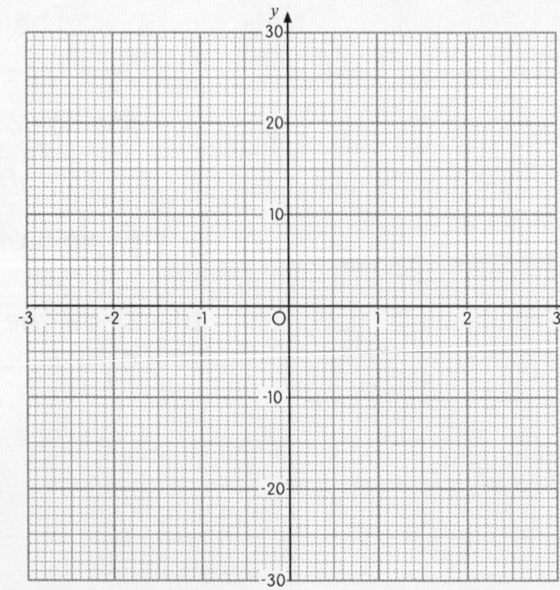

C. On the grid, draw and label the graph of $y = 3x - x^2 - 5$ for values of x from -3 to 3

D. On the grid, draw and label the graph of $y = 3 - x^3$ for values of x from -3 to 3

Use the same grid for the questions here (you may want to use different colours)

NON-LINEAR GRAPHS

Sterling!

1. Nisha has completed the table of values for $y = x^2 + 5$

She has made three mistakes.

Correct the table.

x	-2	-1	0	1	2
y	1	4	0	6	9

2. a) Draw the graph of $y = 2x^2 - 4x + 1$

b) Write down the coordinates of the turning point of the graph of $y = 2x^2 - 4x + 1$

c) Use the graph to estimate the roots of $2x^2 - 4x + 1 = 0$

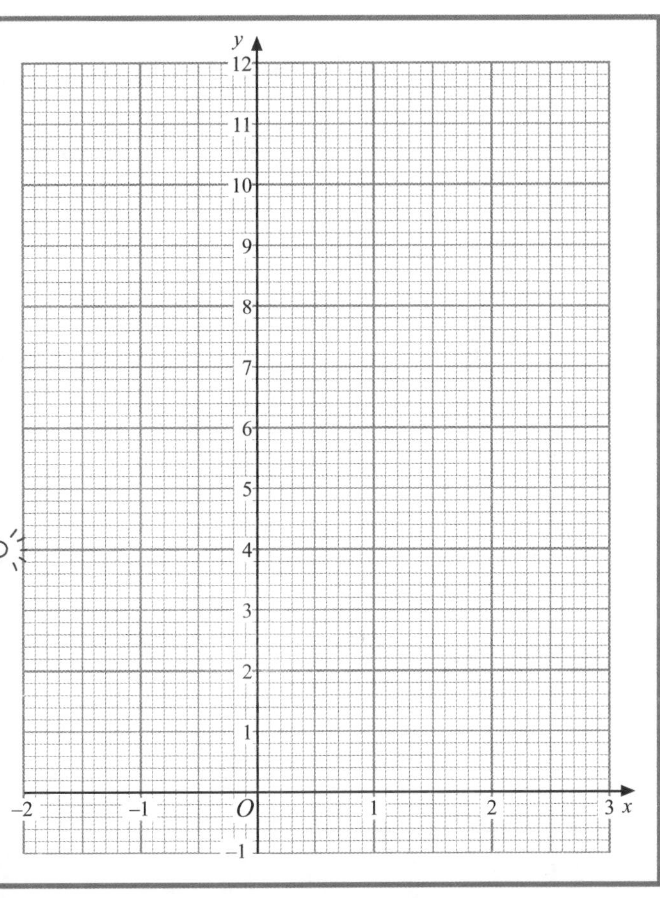

3. Use the table of values to draw the graph of $y = \frac{6}{x}$ for $0.5 \le x \le 6$

x	0.5	1	2	3	4	5	6
y							

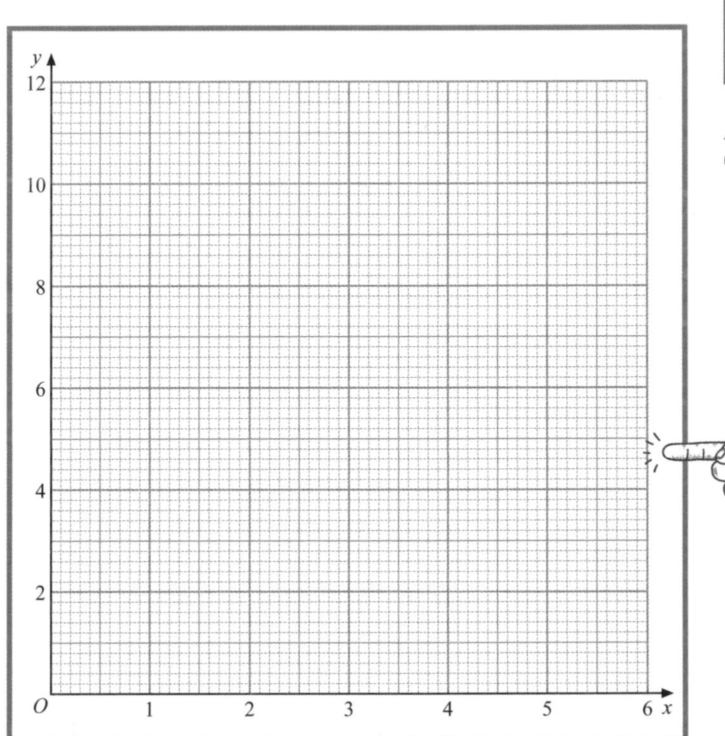

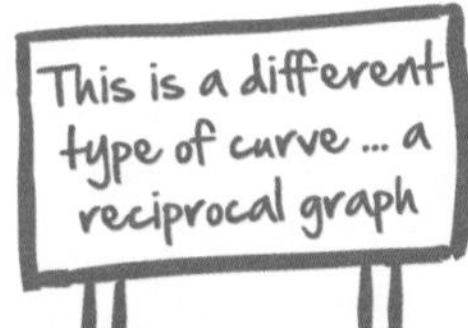

READY?

It is **REALLY USEFUL** to remember:

* 60 seconds = 1 minute and 60 minutes = 1 hour
* 30 minutes = $\frac{1}{2}$ hour and 15 minutes = $\frac{1}{4}$ hour
* 1000 m = 1 km and 5 miles = 8 km

To solve problems involving speed, distance or time you can use a formula triangle but it is sometimes easier to use a bit of logic (common sense!).

$\text{speed} = \frac{\text{distance}}{\text{time}}$

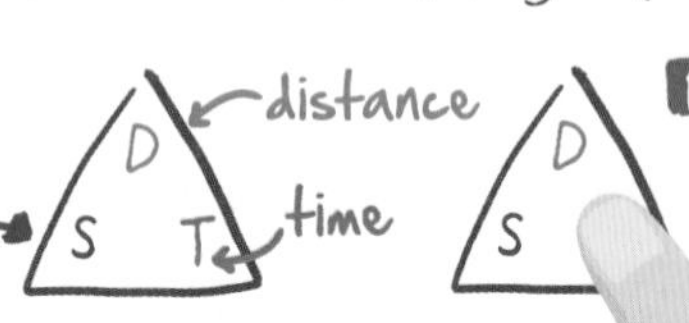

1 Cover the one you want to find with your finger.

2 What is left visible will help you work out what to do ...

$T = \frac{D}{S}$ or $S = \frac{D}{T}$ or $D = S \times T$

e.g. 1 Jim ran 20 km in $2\frac{1}{2}$ hours. Work out his average speed.

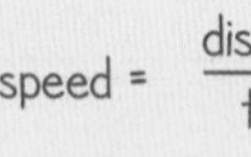

$\text{speed} = \frac{\text{distance}}{\text{time}} = \frac{20}{2.5} = 8$ km/h

kilometres per hour

÷5 20 km → 2.5 hours ÷5

4 km → 30 mins

×2 8 km → 1 hour ×2

speed = 8 km/h

Need to get to 1 hour as it's km per hour

e.g. 2 A train leaves Cheltenham at 14:40 and arrives in Manchester at 17:00

The train travels at an average speed of 90 km/h to Manchester.

Work out the total distance travelled.

Total time = 2 hours 20 minutes = $2\frac{1}{3}$ hours

S × T

distance = speed × time = $90 \times 2\frac{1}{3}$ = 210 kilometres

OR

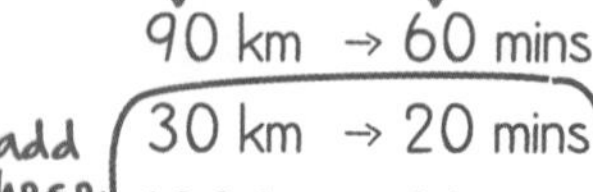

90 km → 60 mins

add these: 30 km → 20 mins ÷3 ; 180 km → 2 hours ×2

210 km → 2 hours 20 mins

distance = 210 km

2 hrs 20 mins is not 2.20 hrs it's $2\frac{1}{3}$ hrs

e.g. 3 Bethia travelled 100 miles at an average speed of 40 mph. How long was her journey?

$\text{time} = \frac{\text{distance}}{\text{speed}} = \frac{100}{40} = 2.5$ hours

40 mph means 40 miles in 1 hour

40 miles → 1 hour

add these: 20 miles → 30 mins ÷2 ; 80 miles → 2 hours ×2

100 miles → 2.5 hours

time = 2 hours 30 mins

A. (i) Tim cycled 24 miles in 4 hours. Work out his average speed.

(ii) Aamir ran 12 km in $1\frac{1}{2}$ hours. Work out his average speed.

(iii) Julia drove 63 miles at an average speed of 21 mph. How long did the journey take?

(iv) Mary travelled at an average speed of 45 km/h for 3 hours. How far did Mary travel?

B. Ed leaves Malvern at 10:54 and travels to London.

He arrives in London at 13:09

The distance travelled from Malvern to London is 144 miles.

Work out his average speed.

HINT: 15 mins = 0.25 hrs

C. Lisa walks at an average speed of 6 km/h for $1\frac{1}{4}$ hours.

Dan completes the same distance in $\frac{3}{4}$ of an hour.

Calculate Dan's average speed.

SPEED, DISTANCE, TIME

Sound!

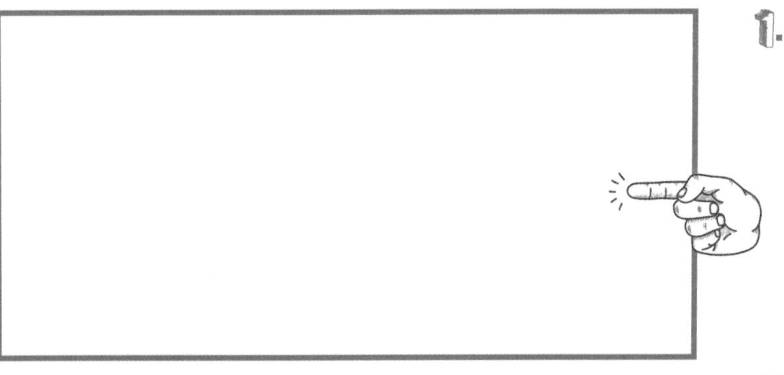

1. Vic travels 3 miles at an average speed of 12 mph.
   She calculates the time taken by dividing the distance by the speed.

   $3 \div 12 = 0.25$ hours

   Vic says: The journey took 25 minutes'.

   Explain why Vic is incorrect.

2. David travelled from Bath to London.

   David's train left Bath at 09:27 and it arrived in London at 10:57

   The train travelled at an average speed of 95 km/h.

   On his return, he left London at 16:25 but the train was diverted and had to travel an extra 29 km. The train arrived in Bath at 18:10

   Work out the difference between the average speeds of the two journeys.

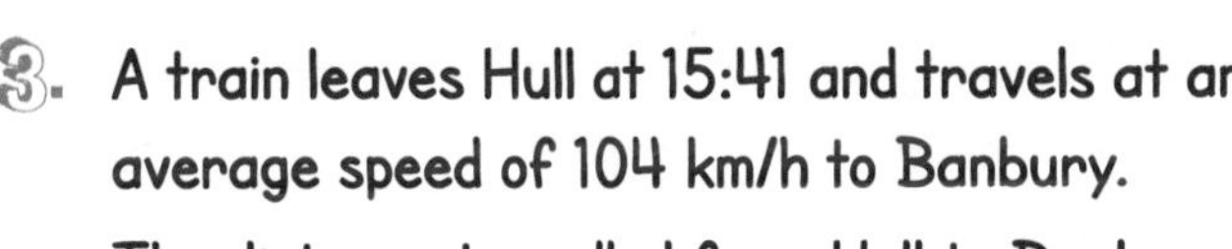

3. A train leaves Hull at 15:41 and travels at an average speed of 104 km/h to Banbury.

   The distance travelled from Hull to Banbury is 260 km.

   Work out the arrival time in Banbury.

4. Maria travels from Town X to Town Y on Road A at an average speed of 40 mph.

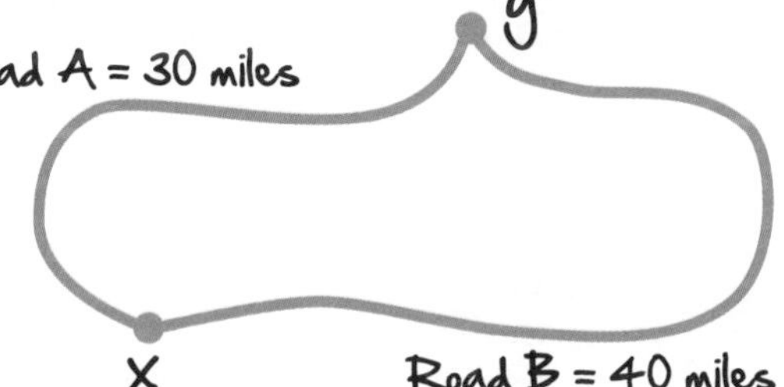

Karl travels from Town X to Town Y on Road B and arrives before Maria. They left Town X at the same time.

Find Karl's minimum average speed. Give your answer as a whole number.

Compound meaures are made up of two different measurements such as:

It is **REALLY USEFUL** to remember how to use the formula triangles for compound measures such as speed:

Cover up the one you are working out

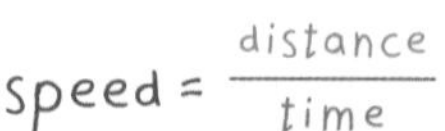

speed = $\frac{\text{distance}}{\text{time}}$ pressure = $\frac{\text{force}}{\text{area}}$ density = $\frac{\text{mass}}{\text{volume}}$ population density = $\frac{\text{number of people}}{\text{area}}$

e.g. 1 A gold ring weighs 7 grams and has a volume of 0.362 cm^3. Calculate the density of gold to one decimal place.

$D = \frac{M}{V}$ density = $\frac{7}{0.362}$ = 19.3 g/cm^3 (1 d.p.)

grams per cm^3

OR

÷0.362 7 g → 0.362 cm^3
19.3370165... g → 1 cm^3 ÷0.362

density = 19.3 g/cm^3

e.g. 2 The density of zinc is 7 g/cm^3. Calculate the mass of a cube of zinc with side length 0.5 m. (0.5 m = 50 cm)

M = D × V

1. volume = 50 × 50 × 50 = 125,000 cm^3
2. mass = density × volume = 7 × 125,000 = 875,000 g = 875 kg

OR

7g/cm^3 means 7 g per 1 cm^3

Volume = 50×50×50 = 125,000 cm^3

×125,000 7 g → 1 cm^3 ×125,000
875,000 g → 125,000 cm^3

mass = 875,000 g = 875 kg

e.g. 3 Silver has a density of 10.5 grams per cm^3. A silver chain has a mass of 52.5 grams. Work out the volume of silver in the chain.

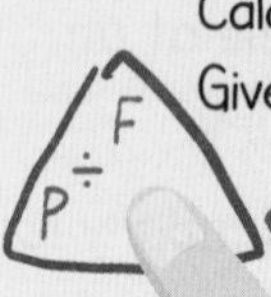

$V = \frac{M}{D}$ volume = $\frac{52.5}{10.5}$ = 5 cm^3

OR

52.5 ÷ 10.5 = 5

×5 10.5 grams → 1 cm^3 ×5
52.5 grams → 5 cm^3

volume = 5 cm^3

e.g. 4 A book of weight 15 N rests on a table. The total pressure exerted on the table is 150 N/m^2. Calculate the total area of the book touching the table. Give units with your answer.

$A = \frac{F}{P}$ area = $\frac{15}{150}$ = 0.1 m^2

Pressure is N/m^2 so area must be m^2

OR

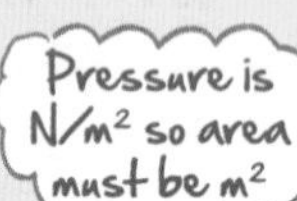

15 ÷ 150 = 0.1

×0.1 150 Newtons → 1 m^2 ×0.1
15 Newtons → 0.1 m^2

area = 0.1 m^2

A. Silver has a density of 10.5 g/cm^3. A silver box has a volume of 94.5 cm^3. Work out the mass of the box to one decimal place.

B. Platinum has a density of 21.4 g/cm^3. A platinum ring has a mass of 5 g. Calculate the volume of the ring to two significant figures.

C. A cube of gold has side 6 cm. The density of gold is 19,300 kg/m^3. Calculate the mass of the cube in kilograms. Give your answer correct to one decimal place.

HINT: 6 cm = 0.06 m

D. Complete the table.

	UK	Hong Kong
Number of people (nearest million)	62	
Area (nearest km^2)	243,610	1,104
Population Density (number of people per km^2)		6,349

Use: population density = $\frac{\text{number of people}}{\text{area}}$

E. A man has a weight of 800 N and his feet cover a total area of 320 cm^2. Calculate the pressure his feet put on the ground.

COMPOUND MEASURES

Spot on!

1. Gold has a density of 19.3 g/cm^3.
A gold ring has a mass of 8 g.
Louis works out the volume as follows:

$$19.3 \div 8 = 2.4125 \text{ cm}^3$$

Louis is wrong, explain why.

2. Sandi knows: $\text{pressure} = \dfrac{\text{force}}{\text{area}}$

She thinks that if you want to halve the pressure, you need to halve the area.

Do you agree with Sandi?
Explain your answer.

3. Dawn is on safari in Africa.

National Park A has 1200 elephants and an area of 392 square kilometres. National Park B has an area of 1500 square kilometres and a population density of 1.6 elephants per square kilometre.

Which National Park should Dawn visit to maximise her chances of seeing elephants? Justify your decision.

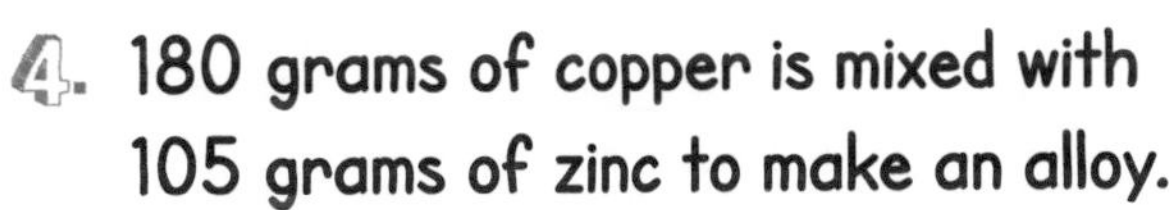

4. 180 grams of copper is mixed with 105 grams of zinc to make an alloy.

The density of copper is 9 g/cm^3
The density of zinc is 7 g/cm^3

What is the density of the alloy?
Give your answer correct to two decimal places.

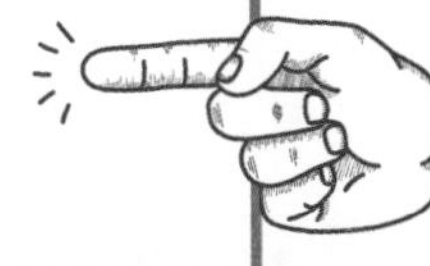

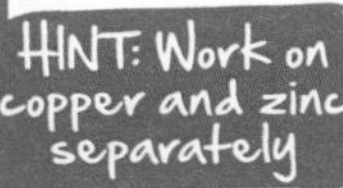

READY?

REMEMBER:
- The gradient of a distance-time graph is the speed
- Average speed = $\frac{\text{total distance}}{\text{total time}}$

Graphs can be used to model real life situations: distance-time graphs are really common ones.

e.g. 1 Bob travels from his home to a meeting but is stuck in traffic on the way to his destination. The distance time graph shows this information.

a) How long was Bob stuck in traffic? 1 hour (11:00 to 12:00)

b) What was Bob's speed before he got stuck in traffic?

Speed = distance ÷ time
= 100 ÷ 2 = 50 km/h

(From 9 to 11 he travels 100 km)

c) What time did Bob arrive at the meeting? 12:30 (The start of the 2nd horizontal section)

d) How long was the meeting?

1 hour 30 minutes (12:30 to 14:00)

e) Calculate Bob's average speed for the journey to the meeting (give your answer to 1 d.p.)

Speed = 125 ÷ 3.5 = 35.714... = 35.7 km/h (1 d.p.)

f) Bob returned home at a steady speed of 50 km/h with no stops.

Complete the distance time graph.

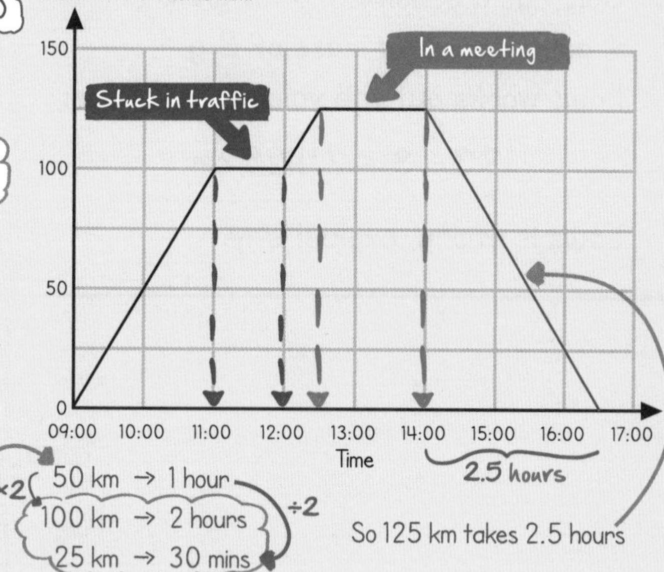

×2 50 km → 1 hour
100 km → 2 hours ÷2
25 km → 30 mins
125 km → 2 hours 30 mins

So 125 km takes 2.5 hours

e.g. 2 Water drips steadily from a tap into this container. Sketch a graph of the depth of water against time.

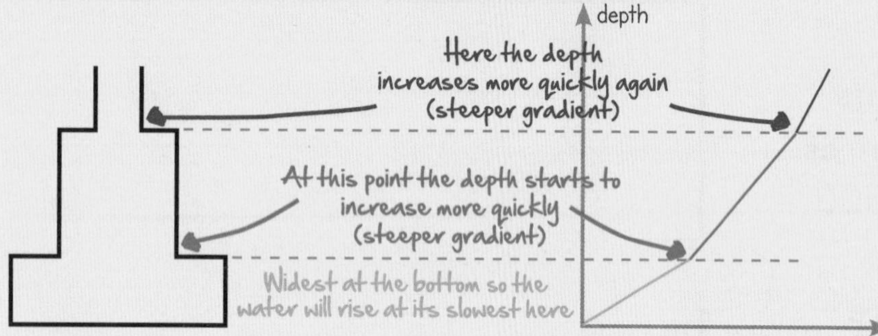

You need to be able to convert between units used in measures.

e.g. 3 Convert 15 metres per second to kilometres per hour.

1. Change to metres per minute (60s in 1 min)
   15 × 60 = 900 metres per minute
2. Change to metres per hour (60 min in 1 hr)
   900 × 60 = 54,000 metres per hour
3. Change to kilometres per hour (1000 m in 1 km)
   54,000 ÷ 1000 = 54 kilometres per hour

SET?

A. The graph shows information about Polly's trip to the park. She stopped at a friend's house for 10 minutes on the way to the park.

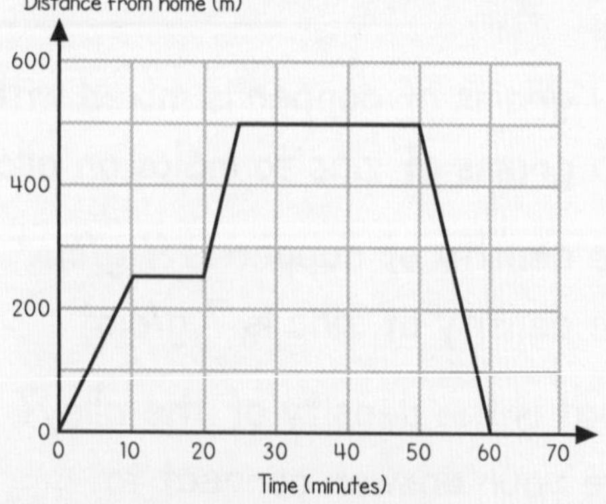

(i) How far is it to her friend's house?
(ii) How long do they stay at the park?
(iii) Calculate Polly's speed when she travelled from the park back to her home in metres per minute.
(iv) Calculate Polly's average speed to the park in km/h.

B. Some containers are filled with water at a steady rate. The graphs show the depth of water against time. Match the container with the correct graph.

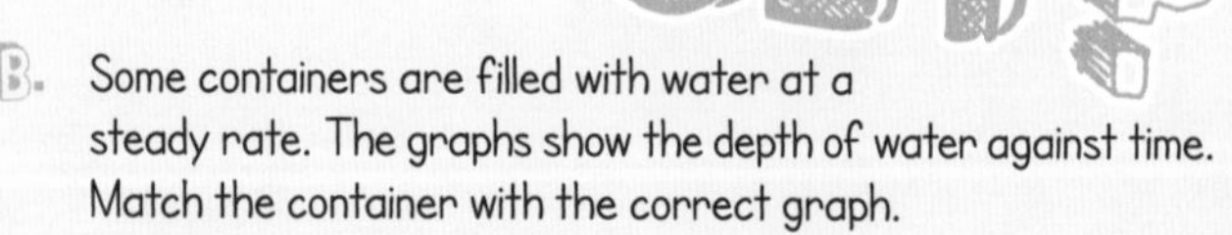

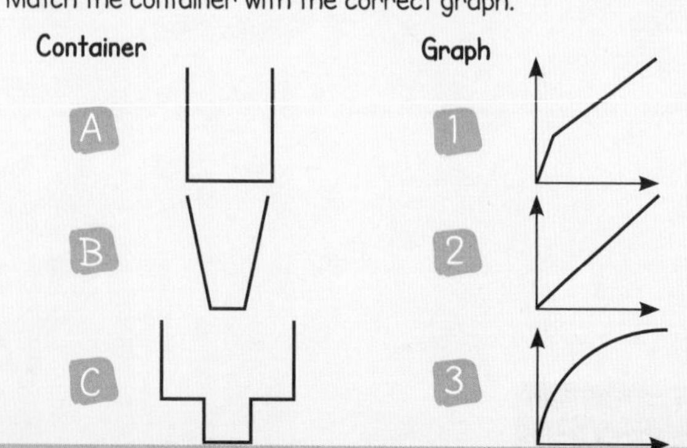

GO! REAL LIFE GRAPHS

Extra!

1. Callum rides his bike from his house to a festival. The distance is 25 miles.
He leaves at 0900 as shown by the travel graph.
At 10:00 he gets a puncture and he stops for 30 minutes to fix it.
He arrives at the festival at 12:00
The festival lasts 2.5 hours.
He then travels home at a steady speed of 20 miles per hour with no stops.
Complete the travel graph to show this information.

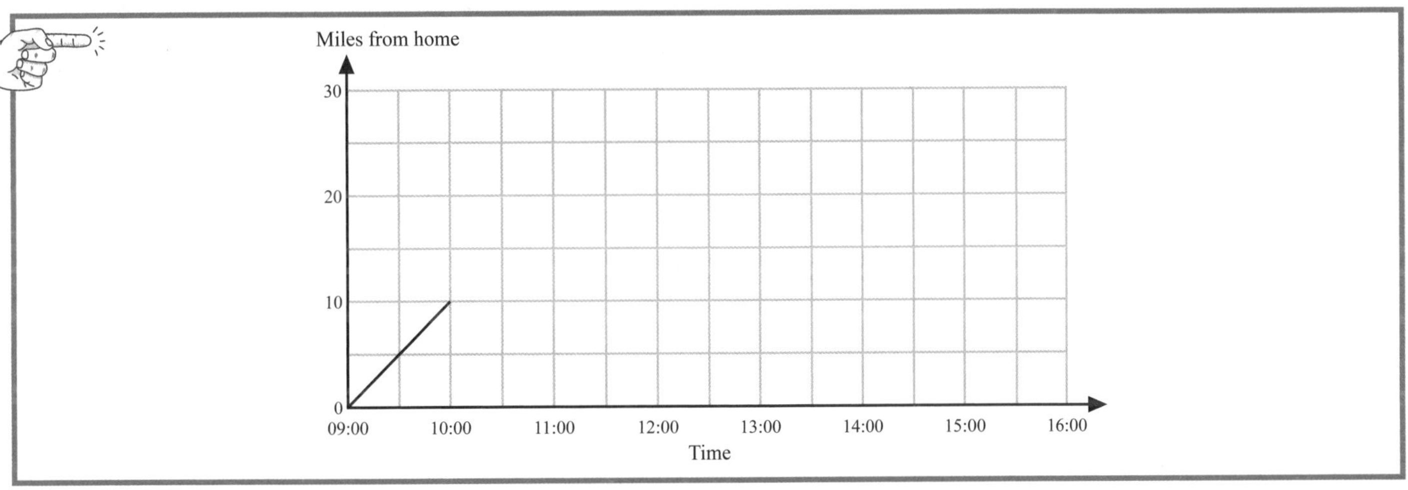

2. Sketch a graph of the depth of water against time when water flows at a constant rate into this bottle:

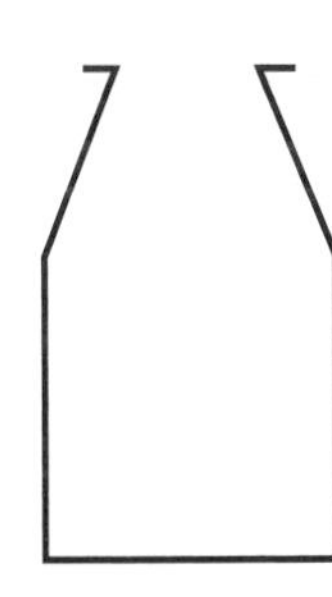

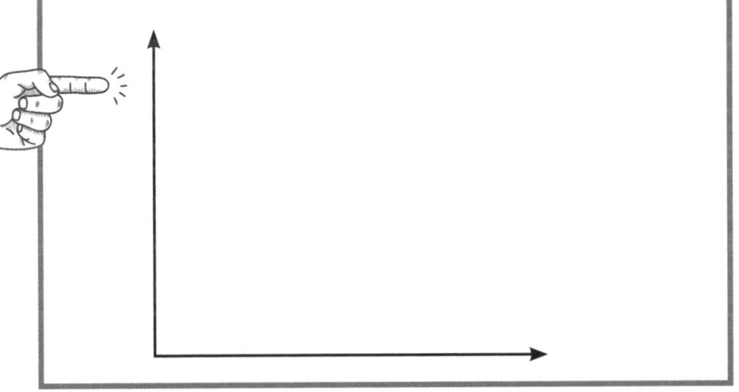

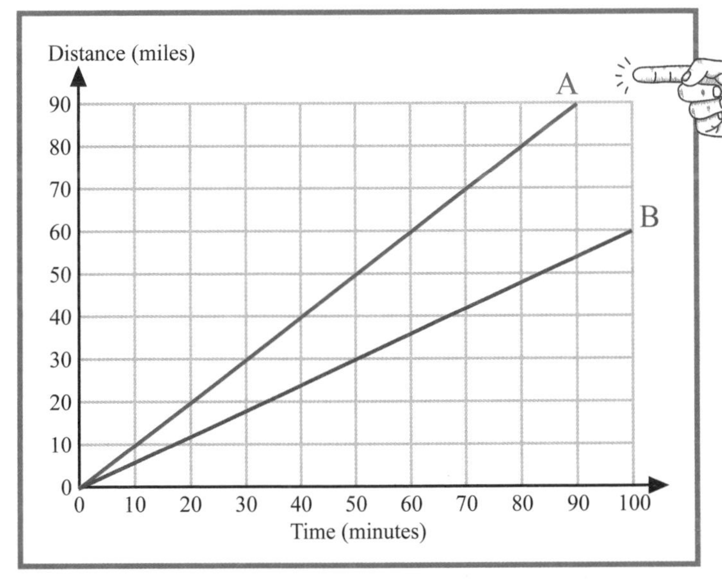

3. Car A and Car B both complete a journey of 150 miles. The graph shows the first part of their journeys.

a) Which car is travelling at the greater speed? Explain your answer.

b) Owen thinks the speed of Car B is 60 mph. Do you agree? Explain your answer.

c) How much longer, in minutes, is the 150 mile journey for Car B? State any assumptions that you make.

READY?

Congruent shapes are identical ... the side lengths and angles in shapes that are congruent are the same. Congruent shapes are still congruent even if they have been rotated or reflected. We sometimes have to prove congruence. Two triangles are congruent if:

It is **REALLY USEFUL** to remember:

* The sum of the angles in a triangle is 180°
* The hypotenuse is the longest side of a right-angled triangle, which is always opposite the right angle

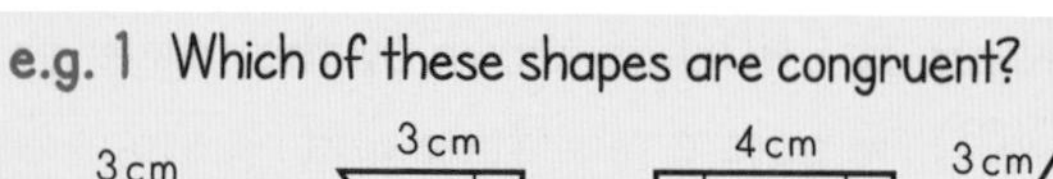

- The three sides are equal. (Side, Side, Side = SSS)

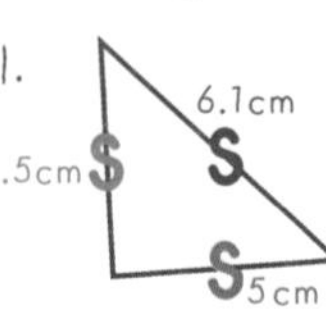

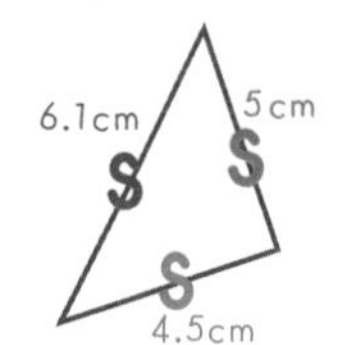

- Two angles **AND** a corresponding side are equal. (Angle, Angle, Side = AAS)

"Corresponding side" means the equivalent side on each triangle

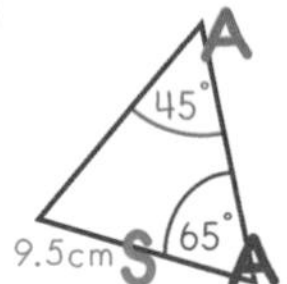

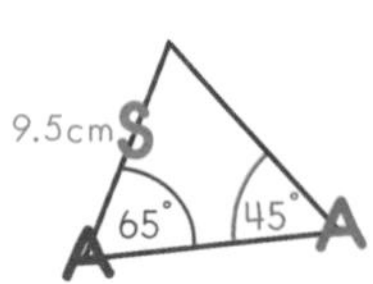

- Two sides are equal **AND** the angle between those sides is also equal. (Side, Angle, Side = SAS)

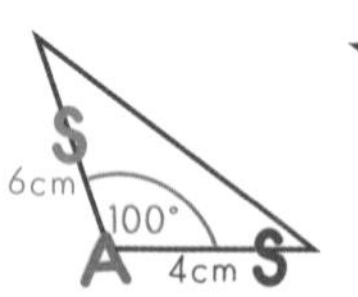

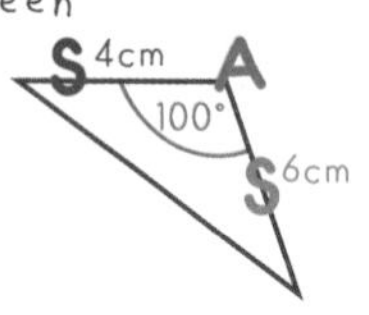

- They both have a right angle, each hypotenuse is the same length and another side is also the same length. (Right angle, Hypotenuse, Side = RHS)

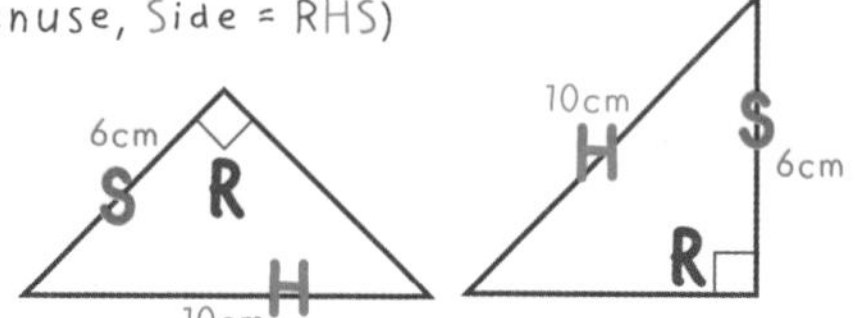

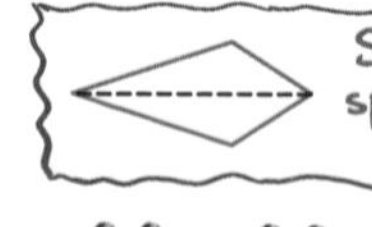

e.g. 1 Which of these shapes are congruent?

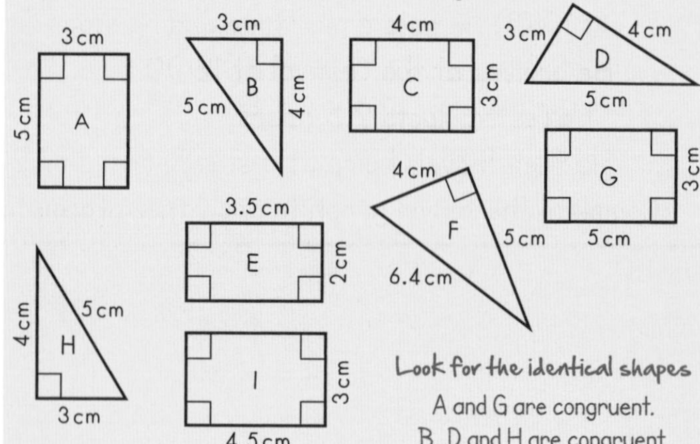

A and G are congruent.
B, D and H are congruent.

e.g. 2 Explain why triangle ABC and triangle DEF are congruent.

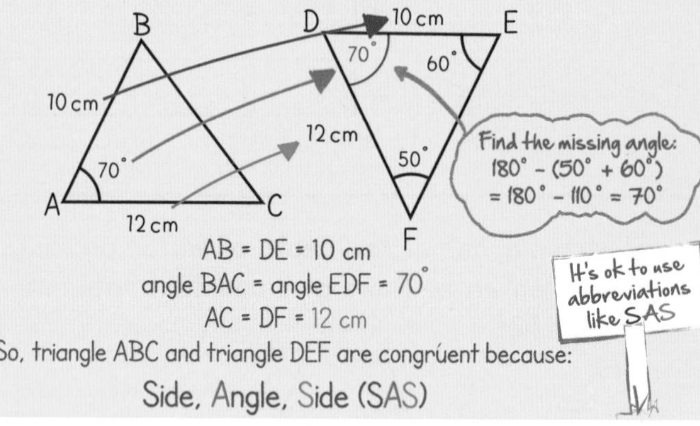

AB = DE = 10 cm
angle BAC = angle EDF = 70°
AC = DF = 12 cm

So, triangle ABC and triangle DEF are congruent because:

Side, Angle, Side (SAS)

It's ok to use abbreviations like SAS

SET?

A. Circle the shapes below that are congruent to shape A.

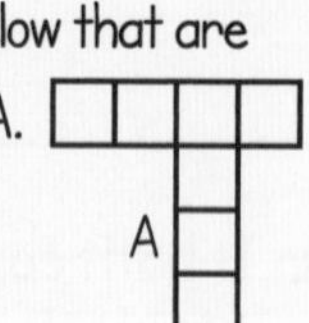

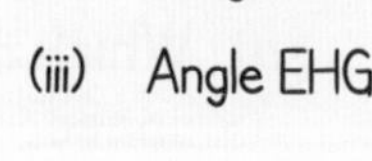

B. Parallelogram ABCD is congruent to parallelogram EFGH.

Find:

(i) Angle FEH

(ii) Length GH

(iii) Angle EHG

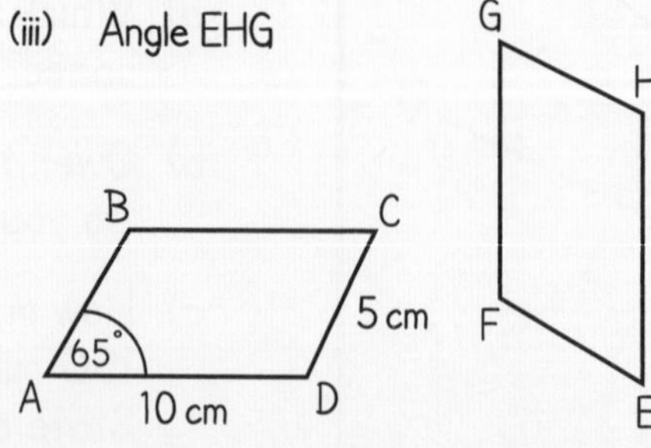

C. KLMN is a kite.

Show that triangle LKN is congruent to triangle LMN.

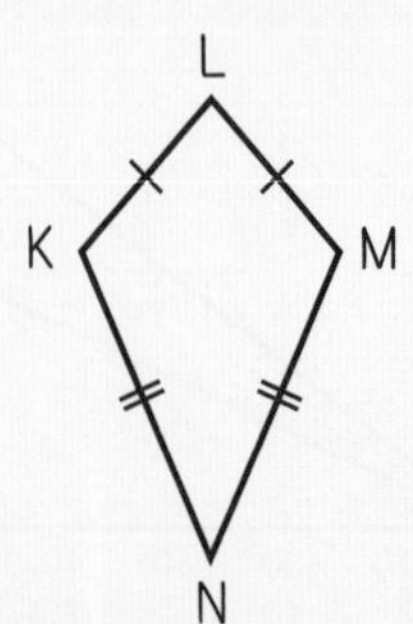

CONGRUENCE

Tidy!

1. Neave thinks three of these shapes are congruent.

Do you agree with Neave?
Give reasons for your answer.

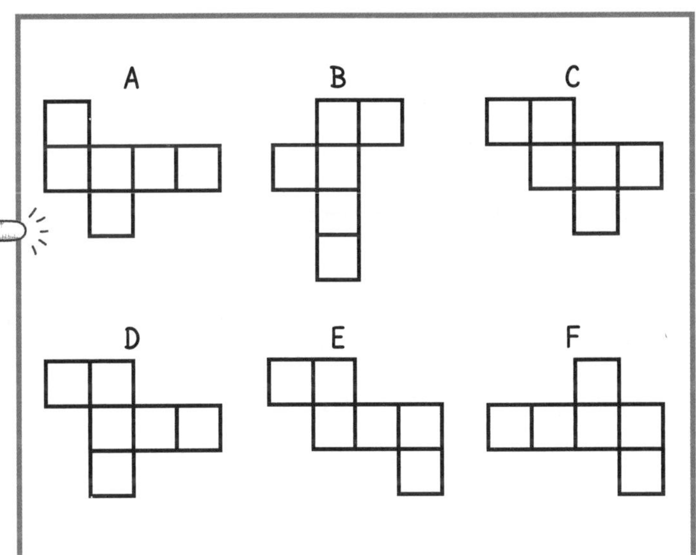

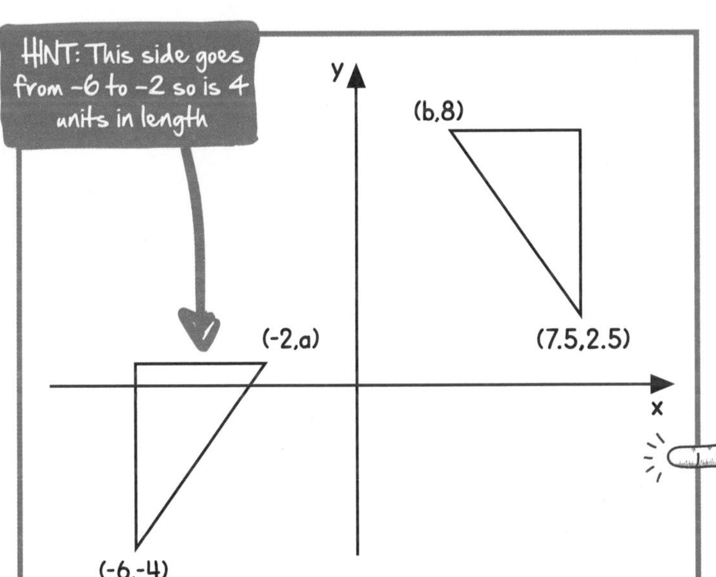

2. Two right-angled triangles are shown on a coordinate grid.

The triangles are congruent.

Work out the values of a and b.

3.

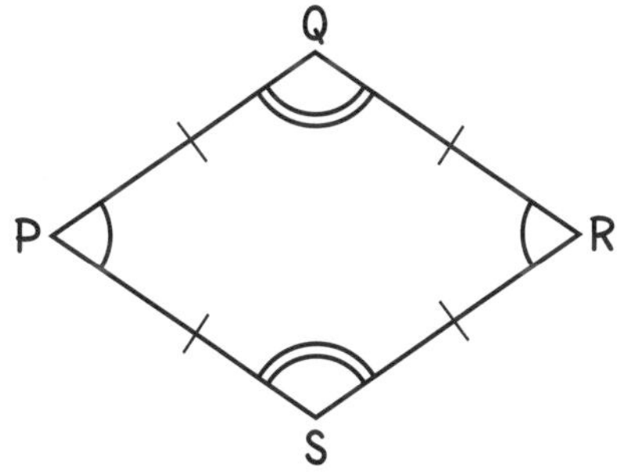

Use two different ways to show that triangle PQR is congruent to triangle PSR.

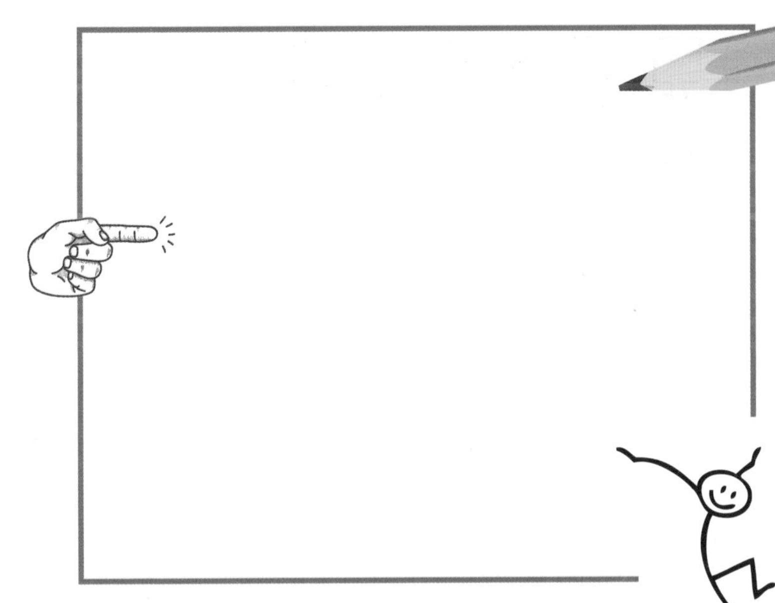

READY?

Similar shapes are the same type of shape but are a different size. The side lengths are different but are always in the same proportion... this ensures the angles in similar shapes are the same values.

REMEMBER:
When two or more shapes are identical in shape and size they are called congruent shapes

Congruent

Similar

e.g. 1 Which shapes are similar?

All the side lengths of shape A are doubled to get shape D ...
A and D are similar

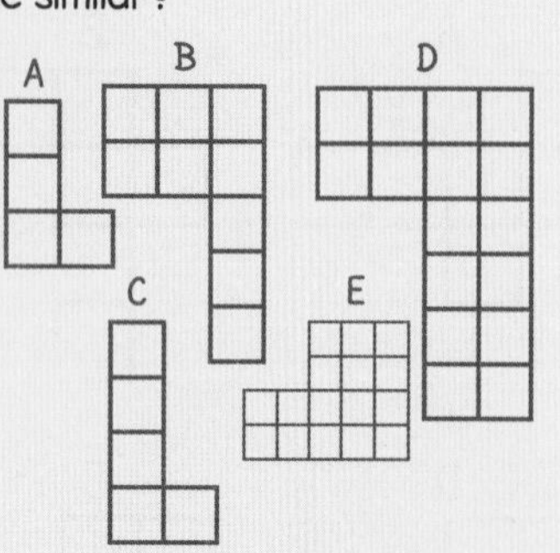

Finding the scale factor between similar shapes is key to finding any missing lengths.

S.F. means Scale Factor

e.g. 2 Quadrilaterals ABCD and LMNP are mathematically similar.

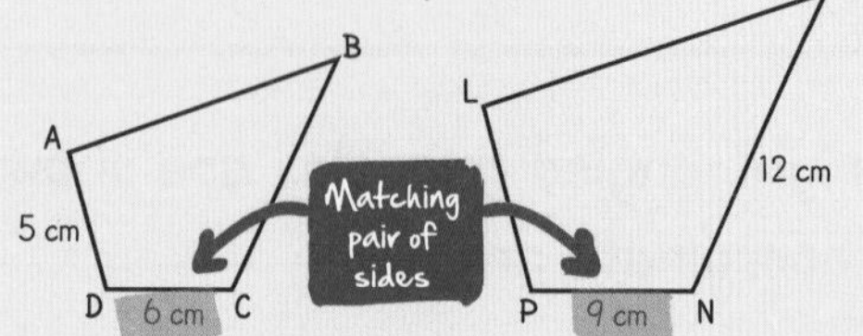

First, find the scale factor from a matching pair of sides:
$9 \div 6 = 1.5$
(This means LMNP is 1.5 times larger than ABCD)

a) Work out the length of LP.
AD is a pair with LP ➔ $5 \times S.F. = 5 \times 1.5 = 7.5$ cm

b) Work out the length of BC.
BC is a pair with MN ➔ $12 \div S.F. = 12 \div 1.5 = 8$ cm
(BC must be smaller than MN)

Sometimes it's not so easy to spot the two similar shapes.

e.g. 3 In the triangle ADE, BC is parallel to DE.

AB = 8 cm
AC = 5 cm
BD = 6 cm
BC = 9 cm

Note that these are not on the diagram

A, 8 cm, B, C, 6 cm, D, E

a) Work out the length of DE.

1 Split the diagram into 2 similar shapes

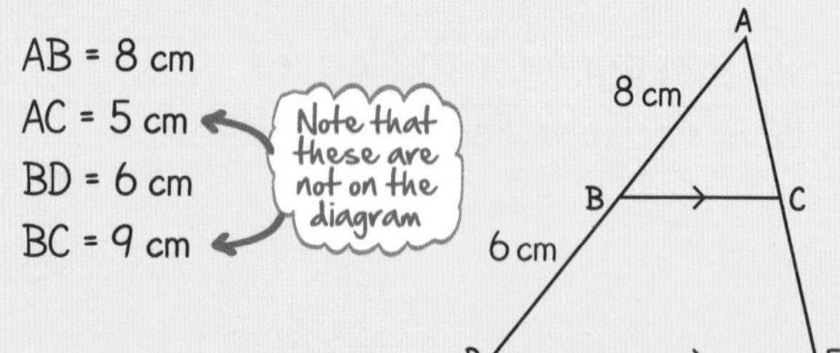

2 Find the scale factor from the matching pair
$14 \div 8 = 1.75$

3 DE is a pair with BC
$9 \times S.F. = 9 \times 1.75 = 15.75$ cm

b) Work out the length of CE.

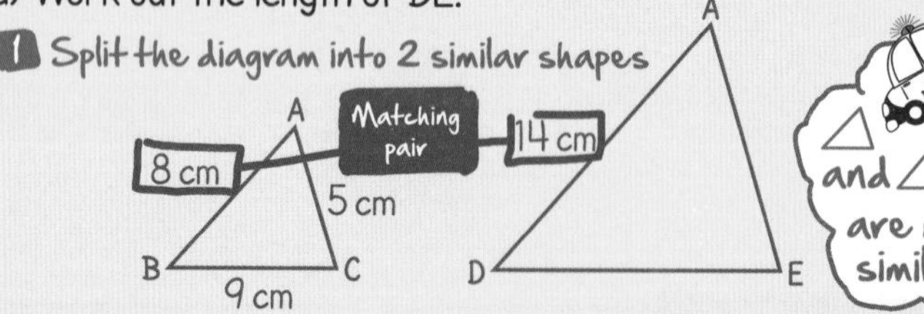

CE = AE − 5 cm
AE is a pair with AC
$AE = AC \times S.F. = 5 \times 1.75 = 8.75$ cm
$CE = 8.75 - 5 = 3.75$ cm

SET?

A. Which shapes are similar?

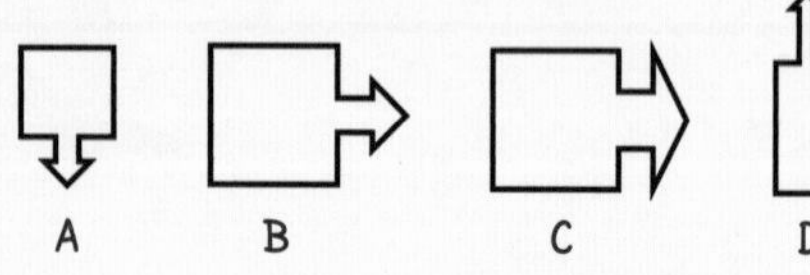

B. These triangles are similar:

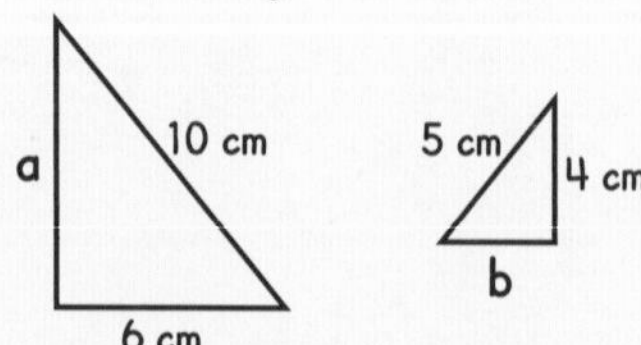

(i) Work out the value of a.

(ii) Work out the value of b.

C. Parallelograms A and B are similar.

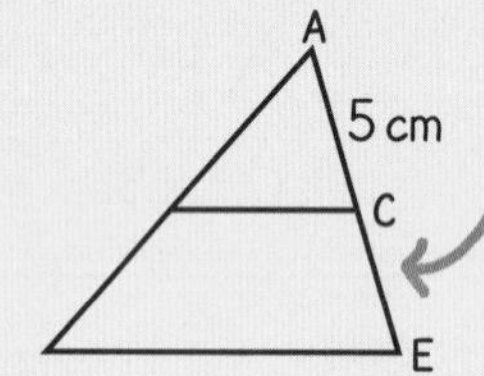

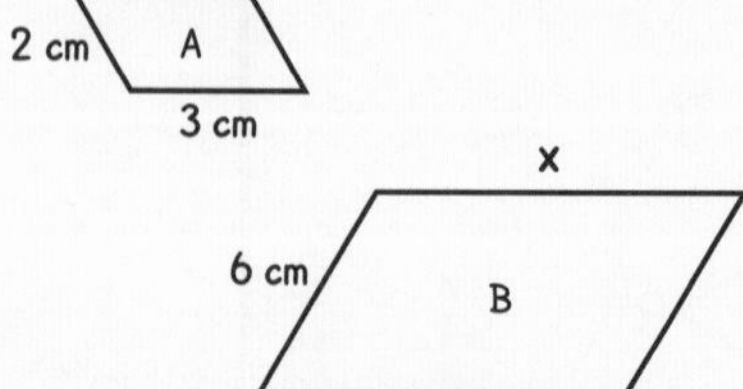

Work out the value of x.

D. Hexagons ABCDEF and PQRSTU are similar.

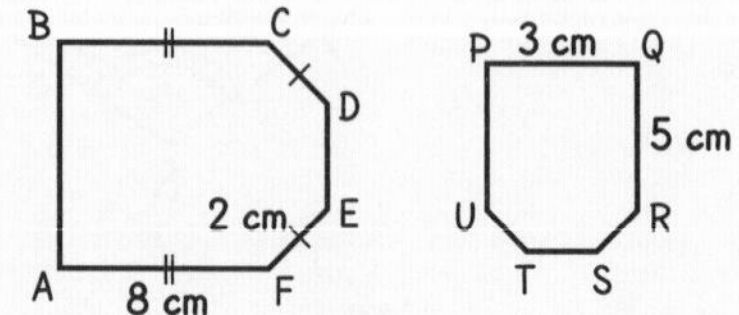

(i) Work out the length of AB.

(ii) Work out the length of TU.

SIMILAR SHAPES

Corker!

1. John thinks these two triangles are similar because the sides have a difference of 3 cm.

   Do you agree with John? Explain your answer.

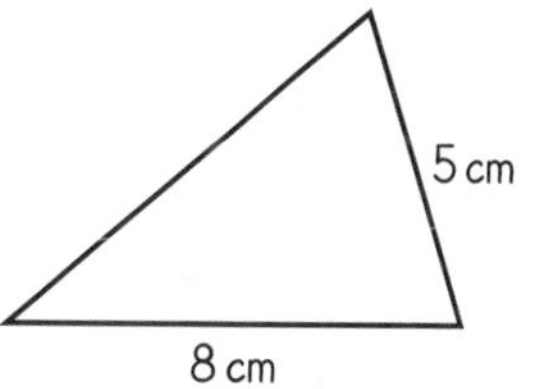

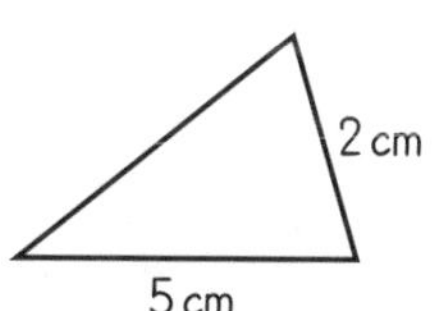

2. Trapezium PQRS is mathematically similar to trapezium WTUV.

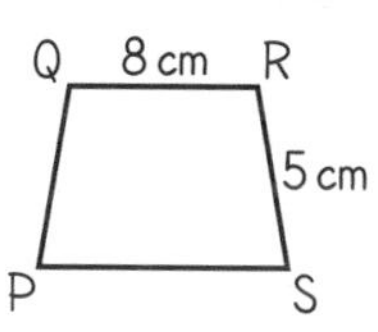

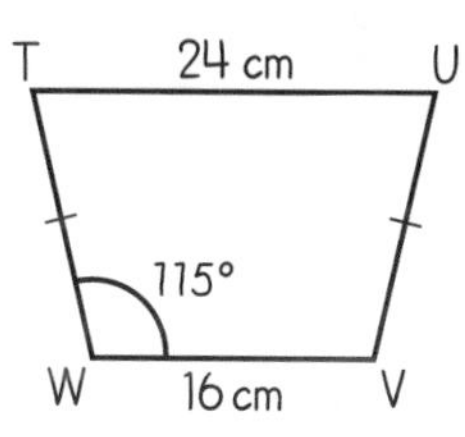

a) Work out the length of PS.

b) Work out the length of TW.

c) Find the value of angle PQR.

3. In the diagram, BC and DE are parallel.

   Work out the length of CE.

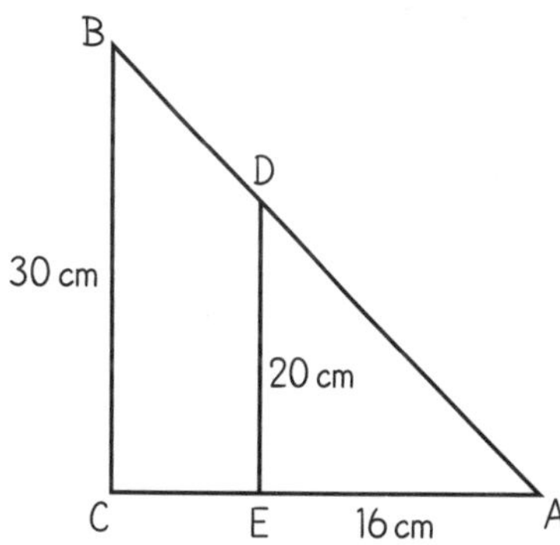

4. A swimming pool is in the shape of the two similar rectangles ABCD and DEFG.

BC = 5 m
AG = 11 m
FG = 2 m

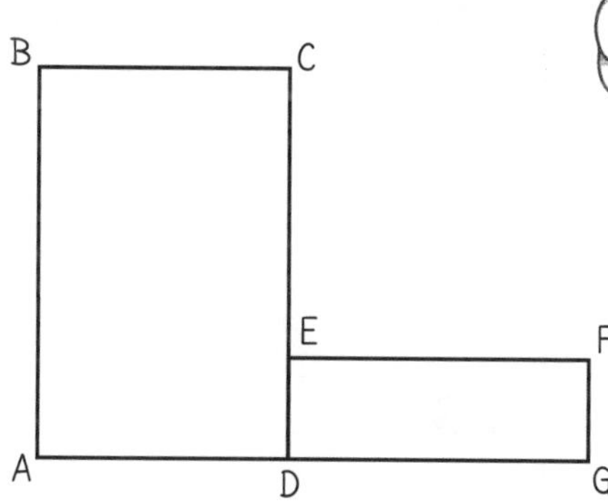

Find the perimeter of the swimming pool.

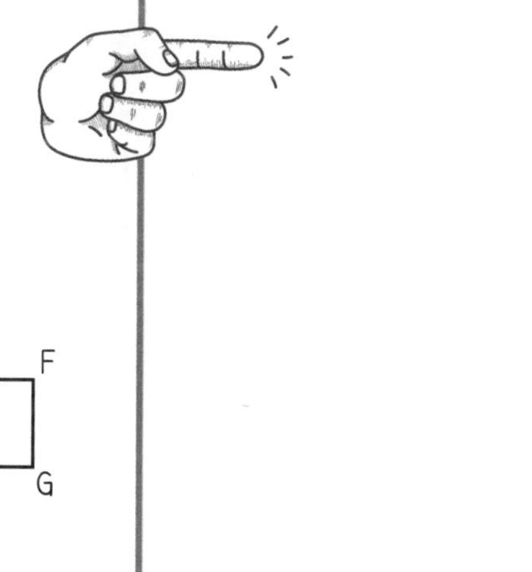

READY?

Reflections are one of the four transformations (reflect, rotate, translate, enlarge). We reflect shapes on a coordinate grid using a **mirror line**.

It is **REALLY USEFUL** to remember equations of straight lines such as:

* y = 3, which goes through all points with a y coordinate of 3
* y = x, which goes through all points where the x and y coordinates are the same

e.g. 1 Reflect the triangle in the line x = 3

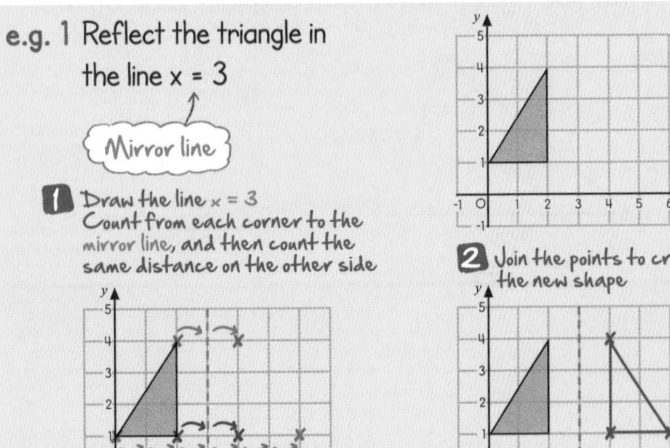

The reflection can sometimes overlap the original shape. Also, the **mirror line** can be diagonal.

e.g. 2 Reflect the rectangle in the line y = x

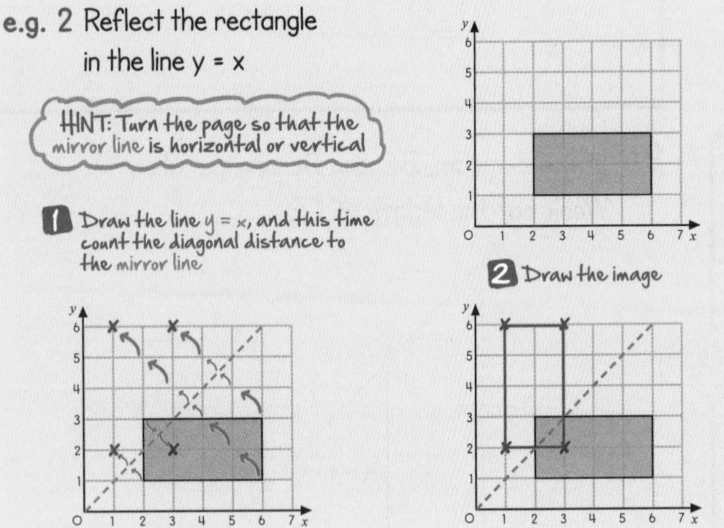

Sometimes you need to describe a reflection.

e.g. 3 Shape P is reflected and the image is labelled Q.
Describe the single transformation that maps shape P onto shape Q.

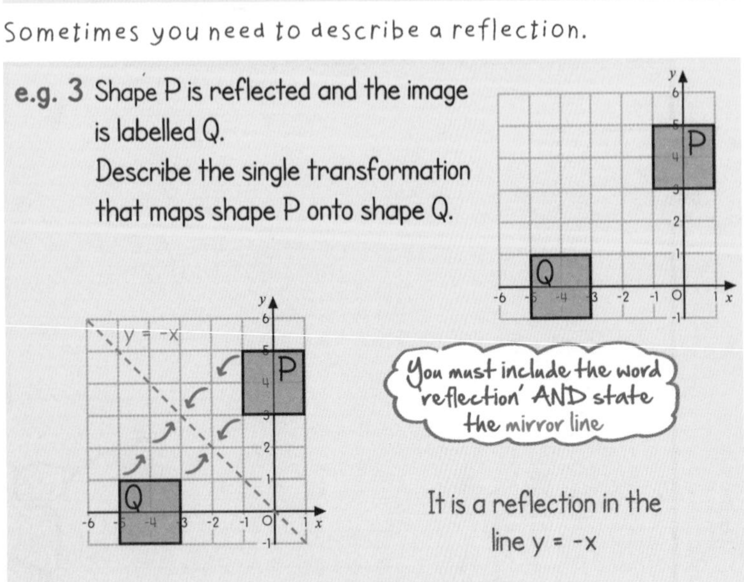

It is a reflection in the line y = -x

SET?

A. Reflect the rectangle in the line y = 4

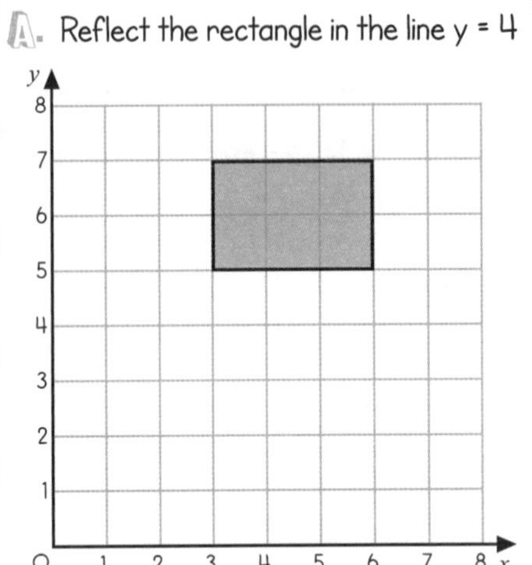

B. Reflect the kite in the line x = -1

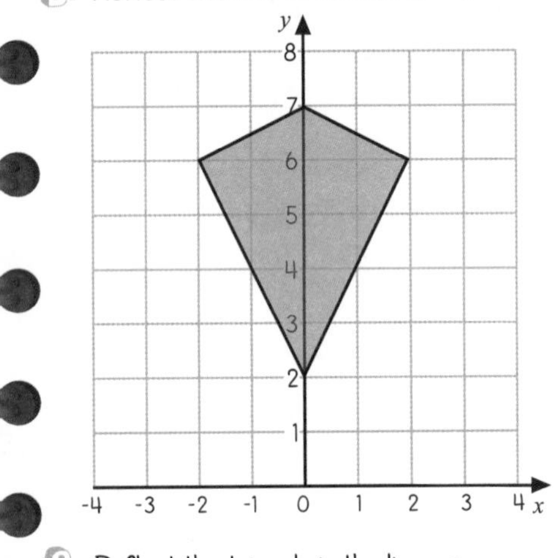

C. Reflect the triangle in the line y = x

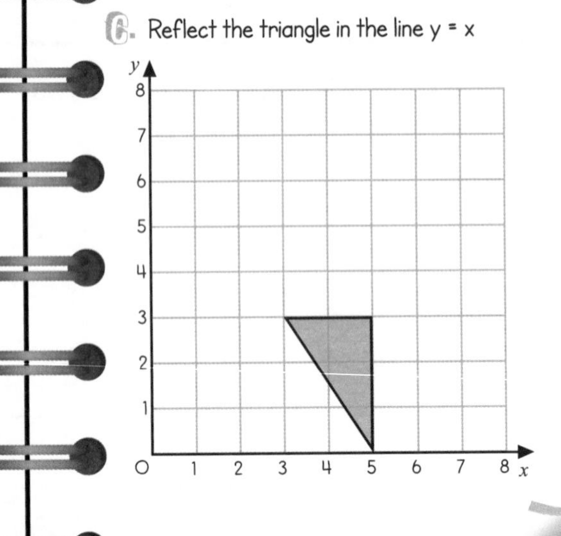

GO! REFLECTIONS

Astounding!

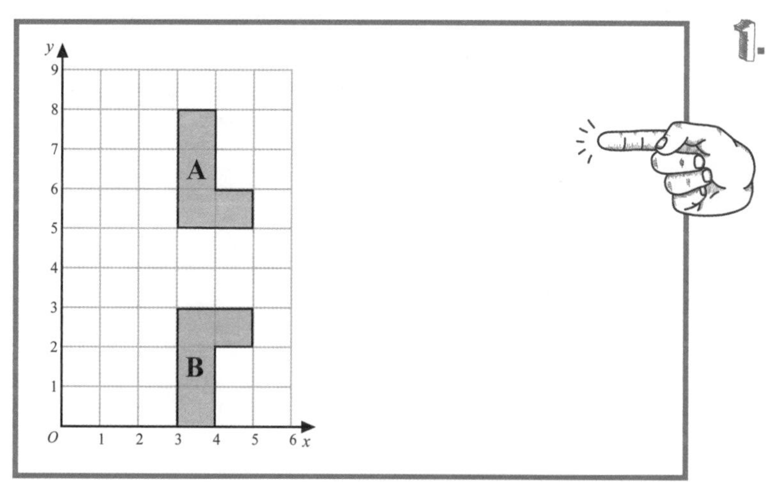

1. Shape A is reflected and the result is labelled B.

Emma thinks that shape A has been reflected in the line x = 4

Is she correct? Explain your answer.

2. Describe the reflection that maps square A onto square B.

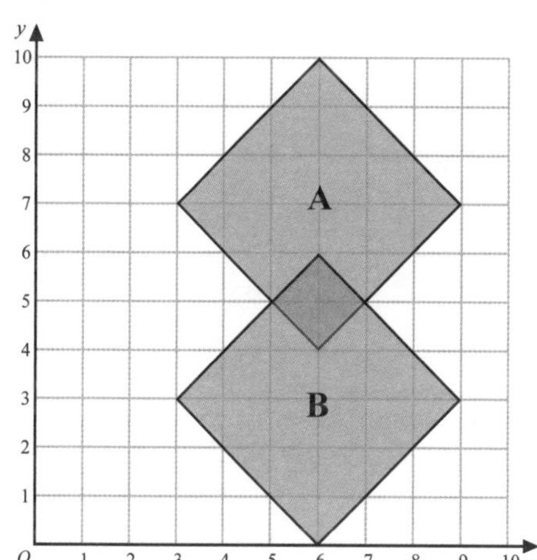

The word 'map' means 'transform'

3. Is the following statement always true, sometimes true or never true?

Every corner is moved when a shape is reflected

Explain your answer.

4. The diagram shows the coordinates of the three vertices of triangle ABC.

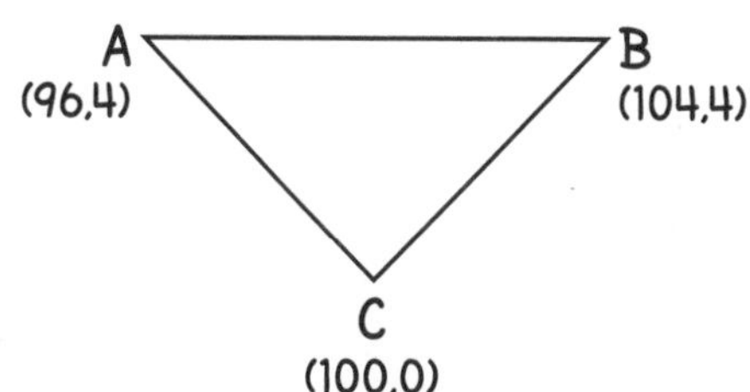

Triangle ABC is reflected in the line x = 102

What are the coordinates of the new position of C?

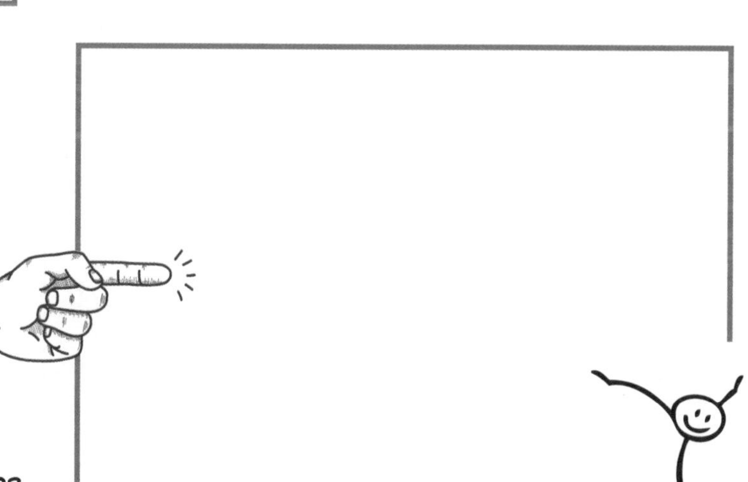

READY?

Rotations are one of the four transformations (rotate, reflect, translate, enlarge). Along with your pencil and ruler, tracing paper is really helpful when carrying out rotations.

You **REALLY NEED** to know the language of rotations:

* The **centre of rotation** is the point about which the shape turns ... usually given as a pair of coordinates
* The **angle** of rotation tells you the amount the shape turns ... it probably will be 90°, 180° or 270°
* The **direction** ... clockwise or anti-clockwise

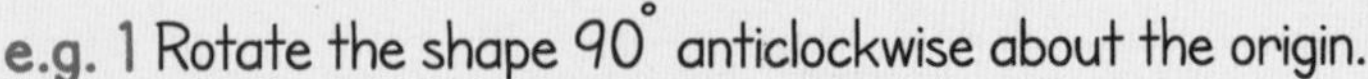

e.g. 1 Rotate the shape 90° anticlockwise about the origin.

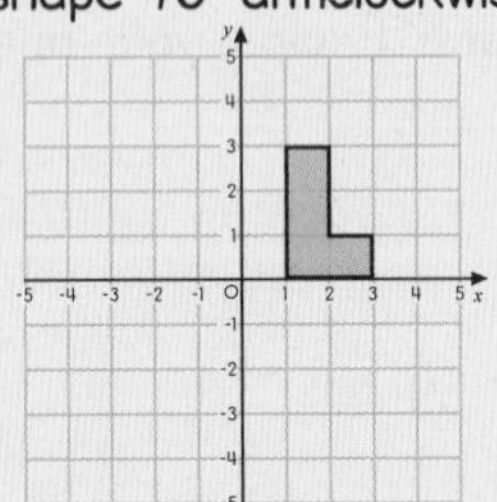

1. Plot the centre of rotation
2. Draw the shape onto tracing paper. Also, draw an arrow ↑ pointing upwards ... this will be pointing left when rotated 90° anticlockwise

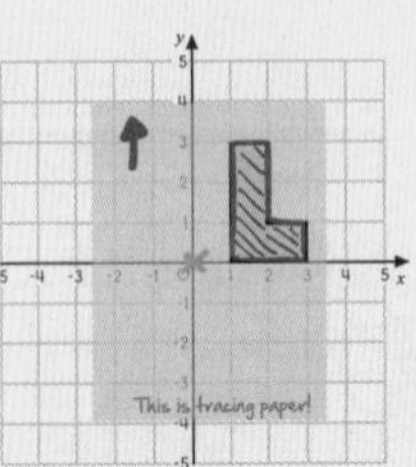

3. Hold your pencil at the centre of rotation and turn the tracing paper until your shape has turned 90° anticlockwise

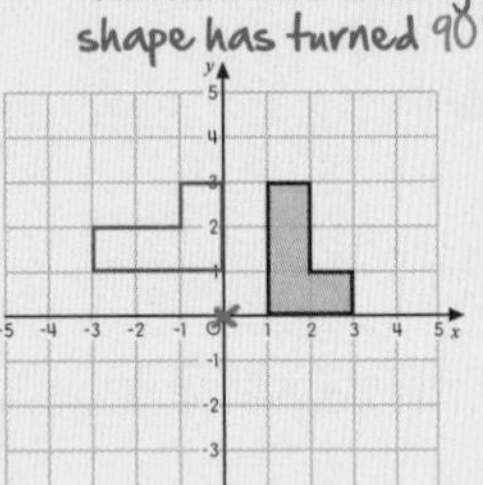

4. Being careful, remove the tracing paper and draw in the new shape

e.g. 2 Describe the transformation that maps rectangle A onto rectangle B.

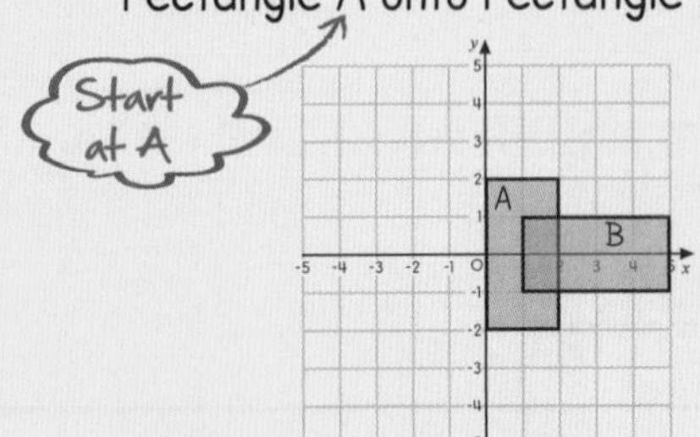

1. On tracing paper, draw rectangle A and ↑

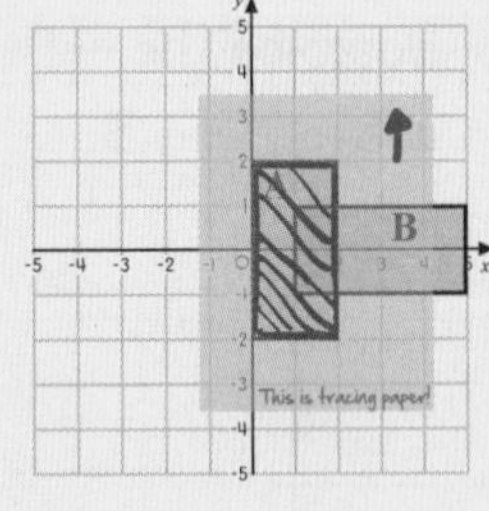

2. Experiment ... place your pencil at various points to try and find the centre of rotation

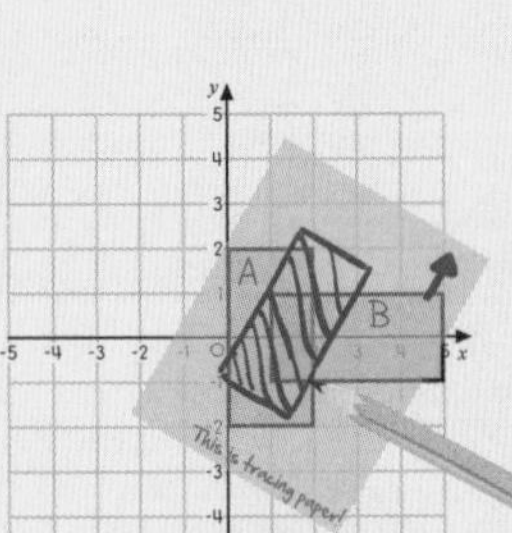

You must include the word 'rotation' AND state the angle, direction and centre of rotation

It's a rotation of 90° clockwise with a centre of rotation (2,-1)

SET?

A. Rotate triangle P 90° clockwise about the origin.

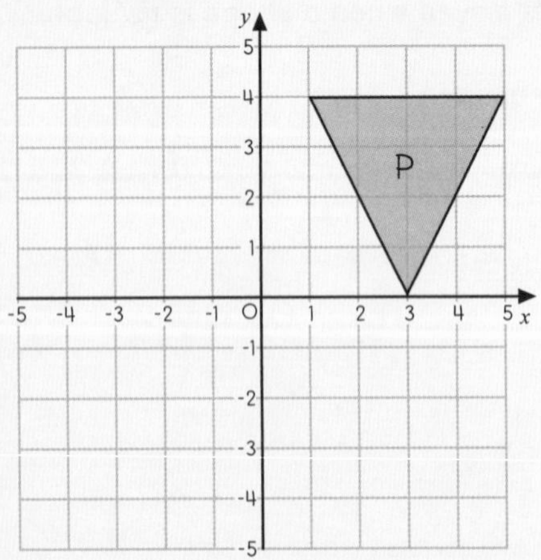

B. Rotate the rectangle 90° anticlockwise, centre (-1,0)

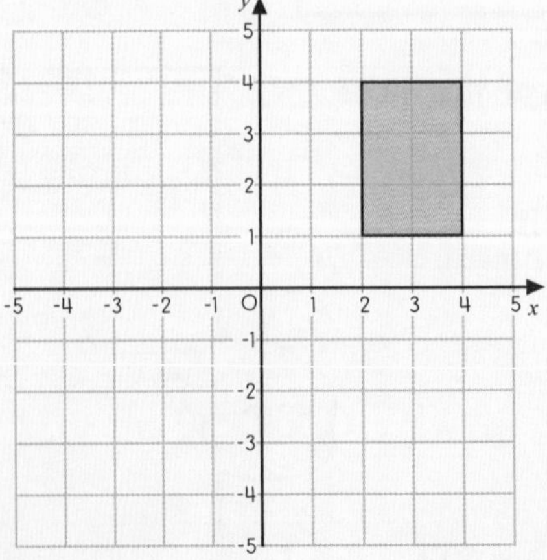

C. Rotate the kite 180° about the point (-2,-1)

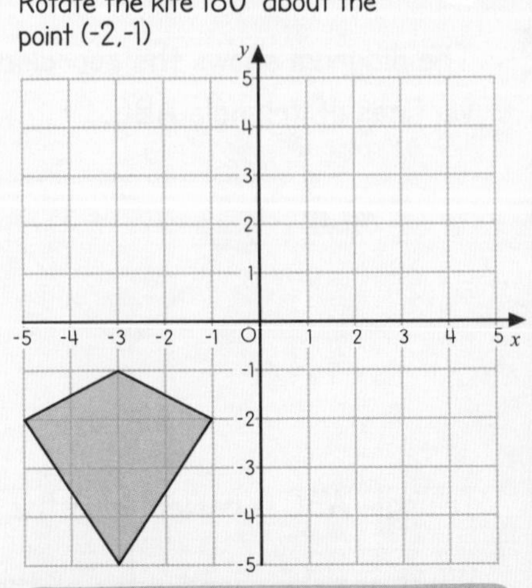

HINT: 180° clockwise is the same as 180° anticlockwise

GO! ROTATIONS

Skilful!

1. Describe the single transformation that maps shape A onto shape B.

2. Gary thinks shape P has been rotated anticlockwise 270° about the point (1,1) to give shape Q.

   Do you agree with Gary?

   Explain your answer.

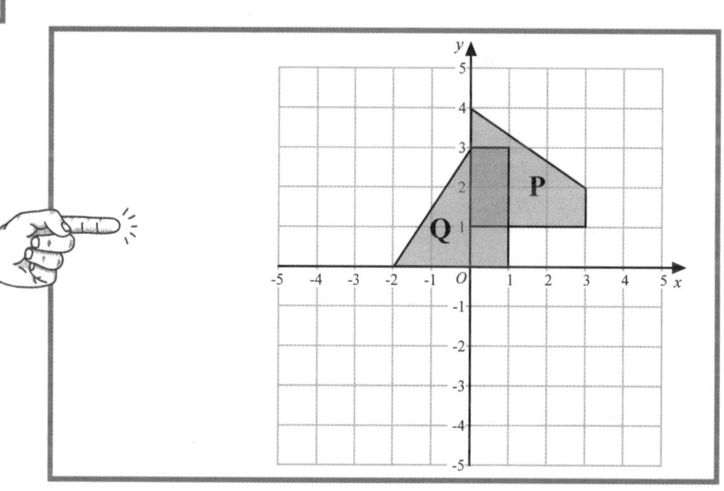

3. Rotate rectangle A 90° anticlockwise about the point (-1,0). Label the image B.

   Rotate rectangle B 90° clockwise about the point (0,-3). Label the image C.

   Describe the single rotation that maps rectangle A onto rectangle C.

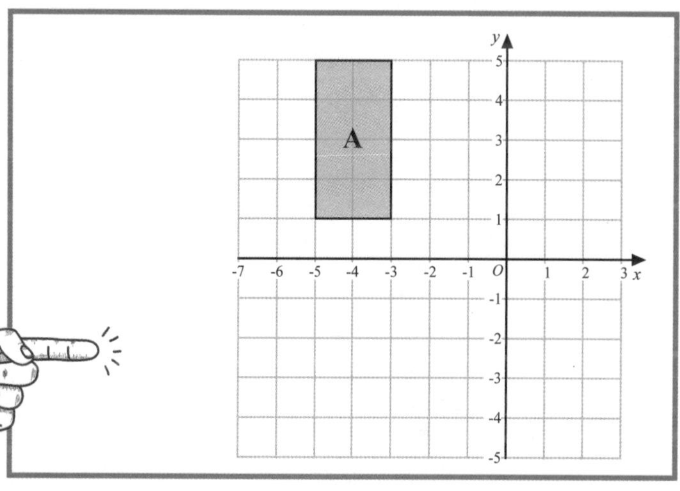

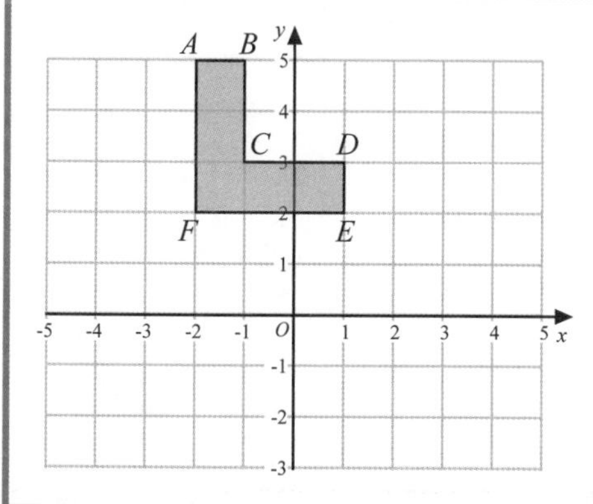

4. The diagram shows a hexagon ABCDEF.

   The hexagon is rotated.
   The rotation maps point A to (-4,-1)
   The rotation also maps point F to (-1,-1)

   Describe the rotation in full.

READY?

Translations are the one of the four transformations (reflect, rotate, translate, enlarge).

A translation slides a shape to a new position - no twisting, no flipping! A column vector is often used to describe the movement.

It's not a fraction!

$\begin{pmatrix}4\\1\end{pmatrix}$ this number tells you the horizontal movement (+ right, – left)

and this is the vertical movement (+ up, – down)

e.g. 1 Translate shape A using the vector $\begin{pmatrix}4\\1\end{pmatrix}$

Label the image B.

1 Choose a corner, move it 4 units to the right and then 1 up

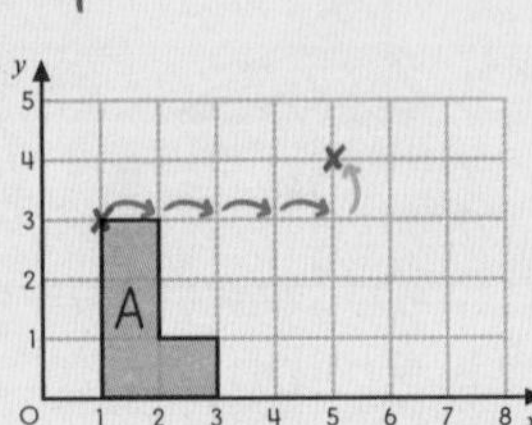

2 Repeat for all the other corners and join them up

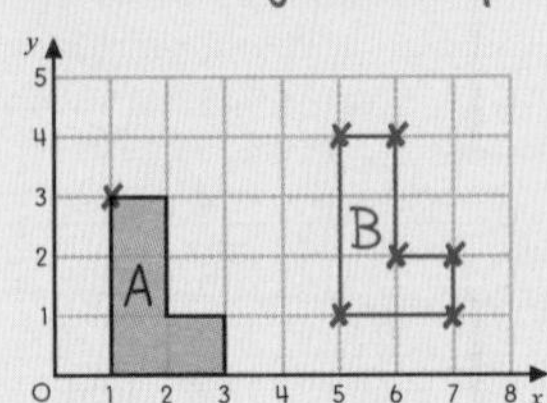

e.g. 2 Translate shape M using the column vector $\begin{pmatrix}-3\\2\end{pmatrix}$

Label the image N.

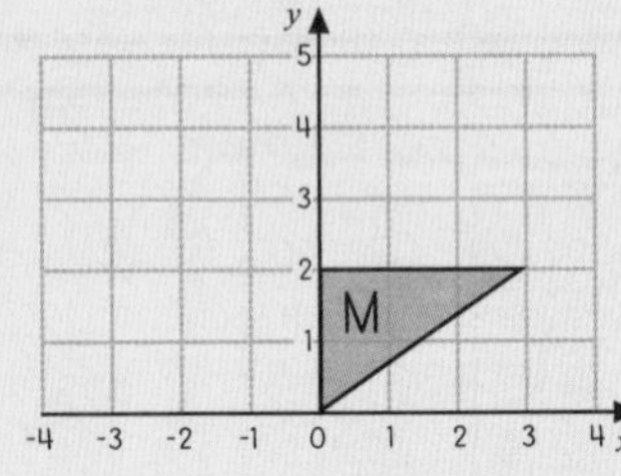

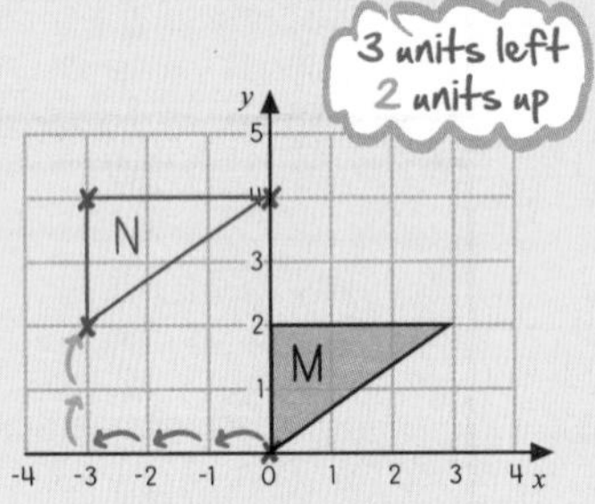

You also need to be able to identify and describe a translation.

e.g. 3 Describe fully the single transformation that maps shape Q onto shape P.

Start at Q

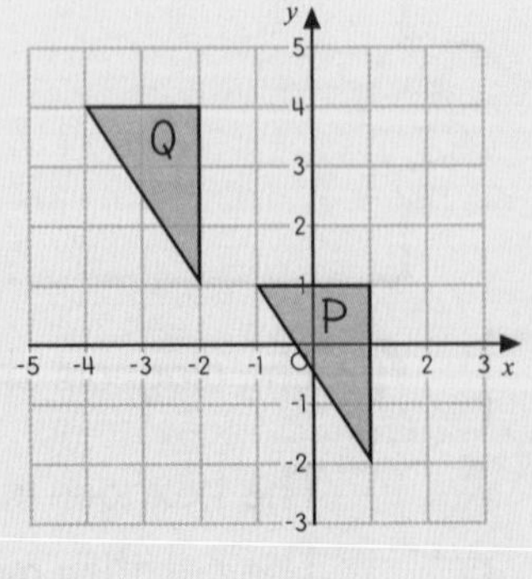

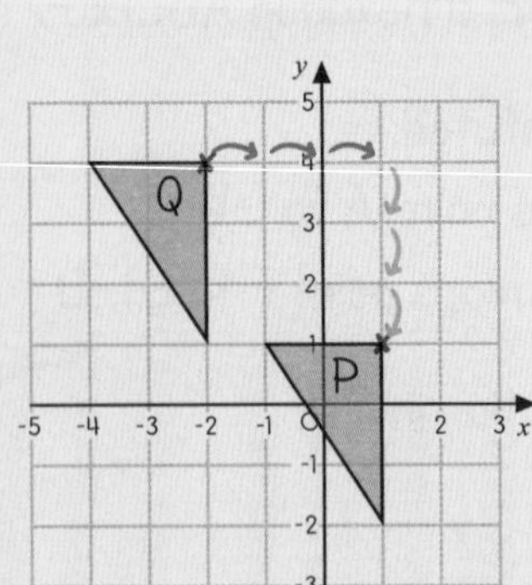

You must include the word 'translation' AND state the vector

Shape P is a translation using the vector $\begin{pmatrix}3\\-3\end{pmatrix}$

A. Translate the rectangle using the vector $\begin{pmatrix}4\\3\end{pmatrix}$

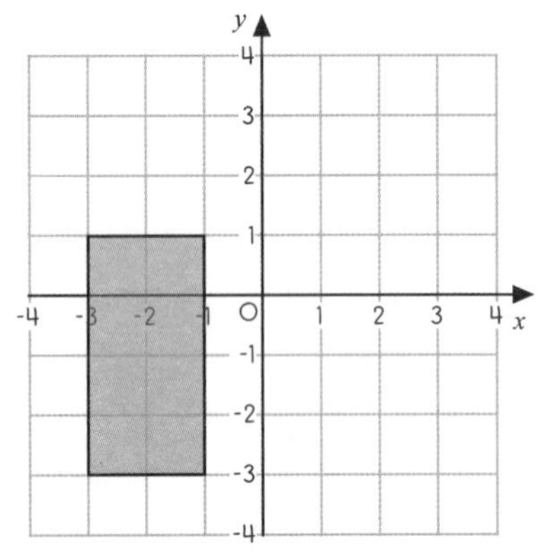

B. Translate shape A using the vector $\begin{pmatrix}-4\\4\end{pmatrix}$

Label the image B.

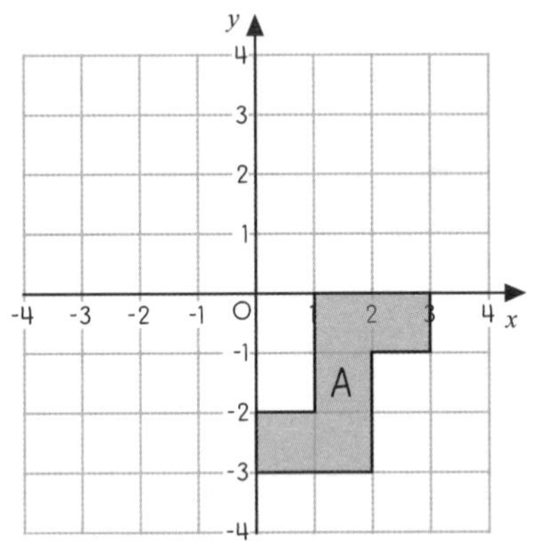

C. Translate shape P using the vector $\begin{pmatrix}0\\-3\end{pmatrix}$

Label the image Q.

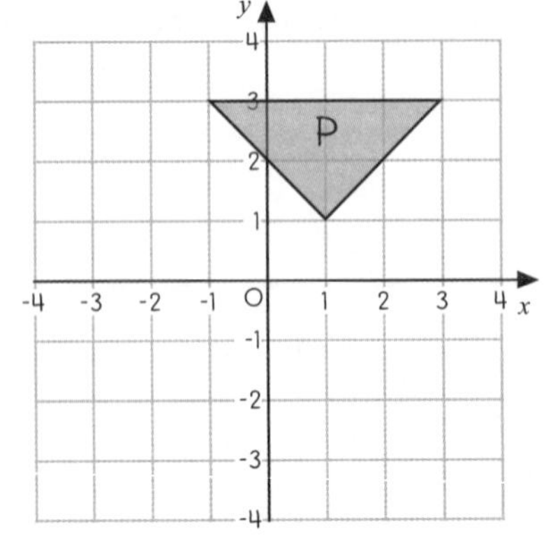

GO! TRANSLATIONS

Glorious!

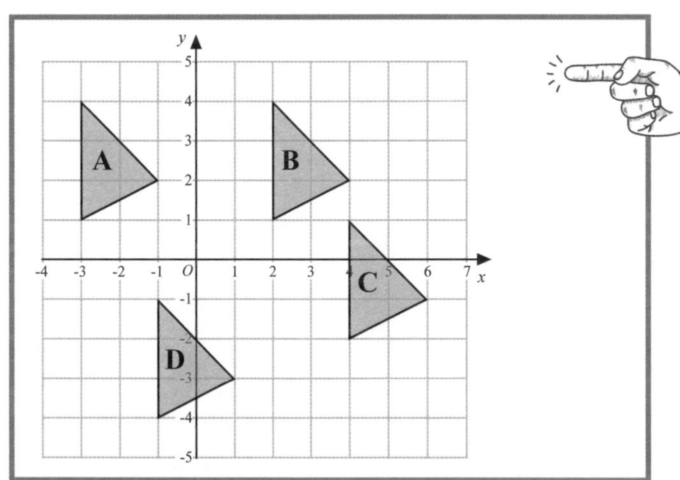

1. Find the vector that translates:

a) A onto B
b) C onto B
c) B onto D
d) D onto A

2. Translate shape P using the vector $\begin{pmatrix} 2 \\ -1 \end{pmatrix}$
Label the image Q.

Translate shape Q using the vector $\begin{pmatrix} -4 \\ -1 \end{pmatrix}$
Label the image R.

Describe fully the single transformation that maps shape P onto shape R.

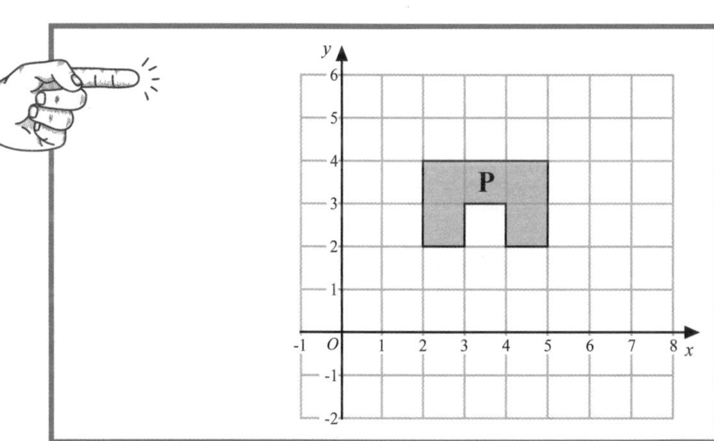

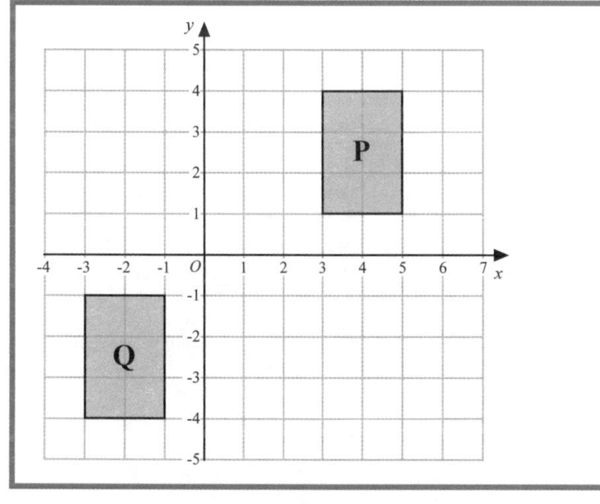

3. Saad is asked to describe the single transformation that maps shape P onto shape Q.

He gives the answer:

Translate P using the vector $\begin{pmatrix} 4 \\ 2 \end{pmatrix}$

Do you agree with Saad?

Explain your answer.

4. A rectangle ABCD is drawn on a grid.
Each corner has coordinates:

A at (30,10)
B at (34,10)
C at (34,4)
D at (30,4)

The rectangle is translated using the vector $\begin{pmatrix} 10 \\ 4 \end{pmatrix}$

Work out the new coordinates of C.

READY?

You **REALLY NEED** to know the language of enlargements:

* The **scale factor** tells you how much larger (or smaller) the new shape will be
* The **centre of enlargement** tells you where the rays meet

Enlargements are one of the 4 transformations:

reflect, rotate, translate, enlarge

We enlarge a shape using a **centre of enlargement** and a **scale factor**.

e.g. 1 Enlarge the rectangle by a scale factor of 2 using (0,2) as the centre of enlargement.

1 Plot the centre of enlargement, and draw rays from it through the corners of the shape

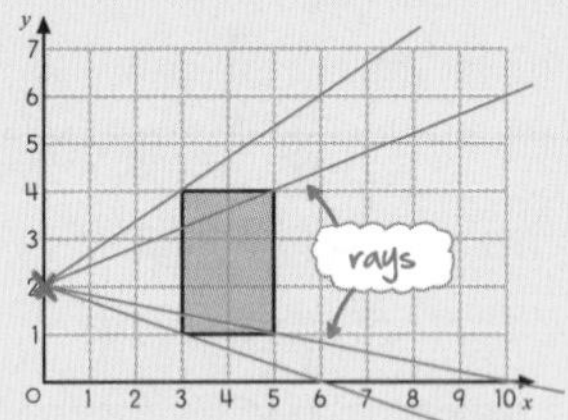

2 Choose a corner of the shape, and count ↔ and ↕ from the centre to that corner

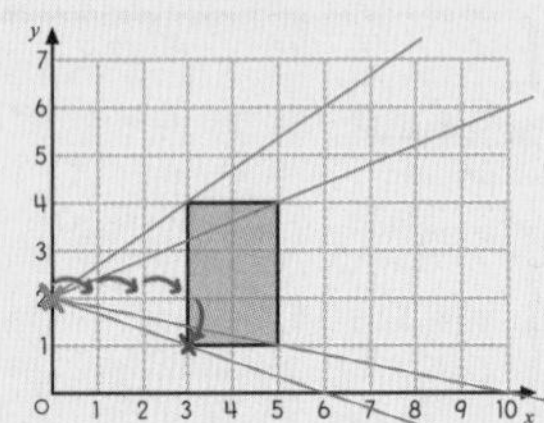

3 Multiply the movement by the scale factor and plot the new corner (3 right, 1 down becomes 6 right, 2 down)

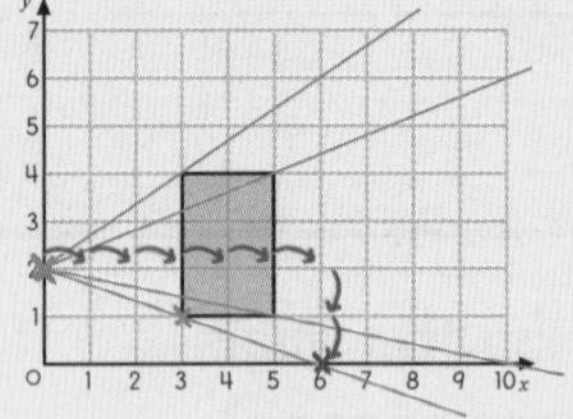

4 Repeat for the other corners and join them up to create the new shape

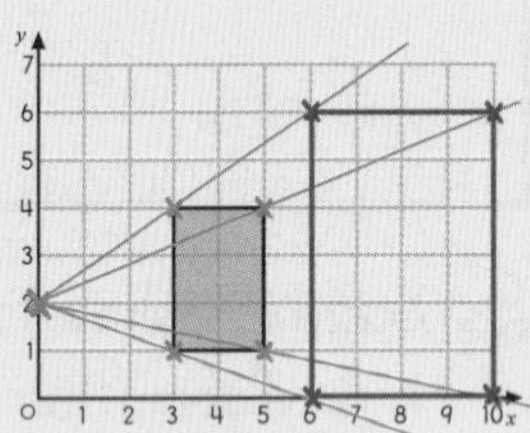

e.g. 2 Enlarge the triangle by a scale factor of $\frac{1}{3}$, centre (1,3).

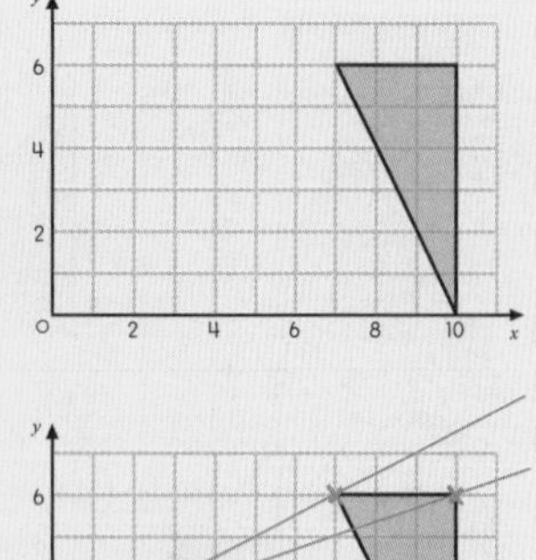

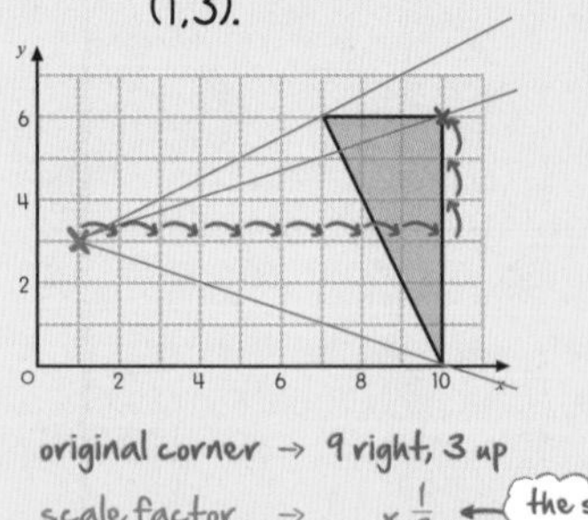

original corner → 9 right, 3 up

scale factor → $\times \frac{1}{3}$ ← the same as ÷ 3

new corner → 3 right, 1 up

e.g. 3 Describe fully the single transformation that maps shape A onto shape B.

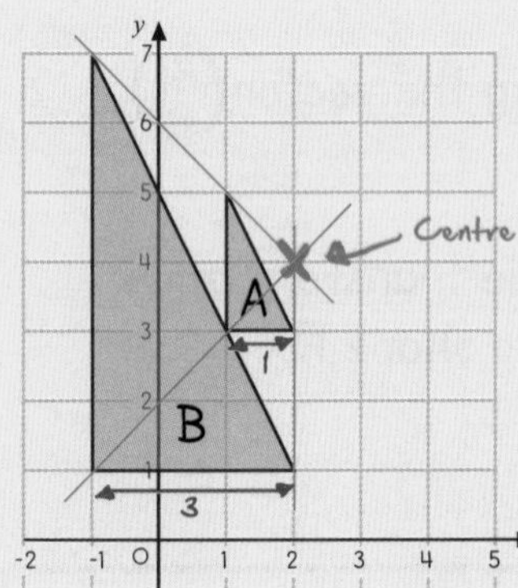

1 Draw rays through the matching corners

2 Find the coordinates where they meet (this is the centre of enlargement)

3 Work out the scale factor using matching sides:
SF = 3 ÷ 1 = 3

It's an enlargement, with a scale factor of 3 and a centre of enlargement of (2,4)

You must include the word 'enlargement' AND state the centre and scale factor

SET?

A. Enlarge the triangle by a scale factor of 2 using (0,0) as the centre of enlargement.

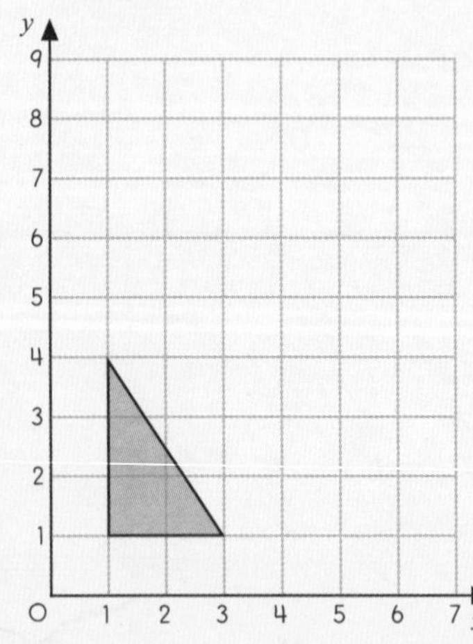

B. Enlarge the triangle using a scale factor of 3, centre (2,3).

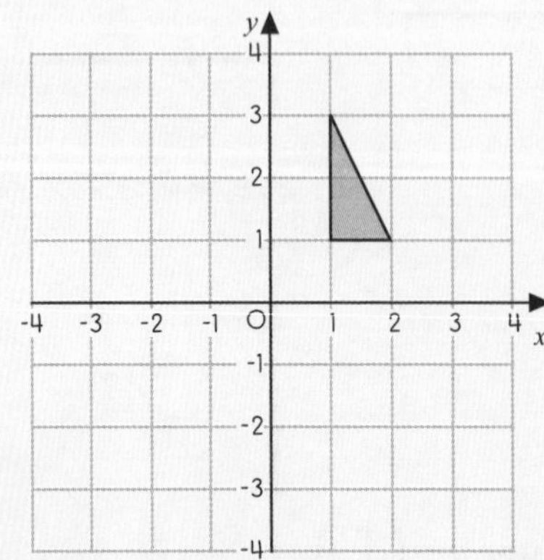

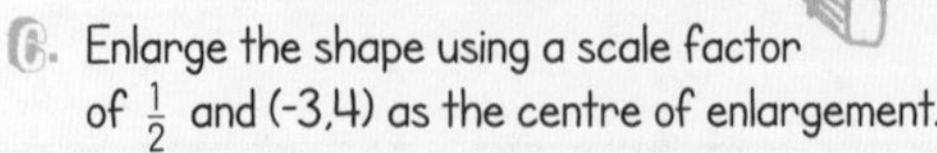

C. Enlarge the shape using a scale factor of $\frac{1}{2}$ and (-3,4) as the centre of enlargement.

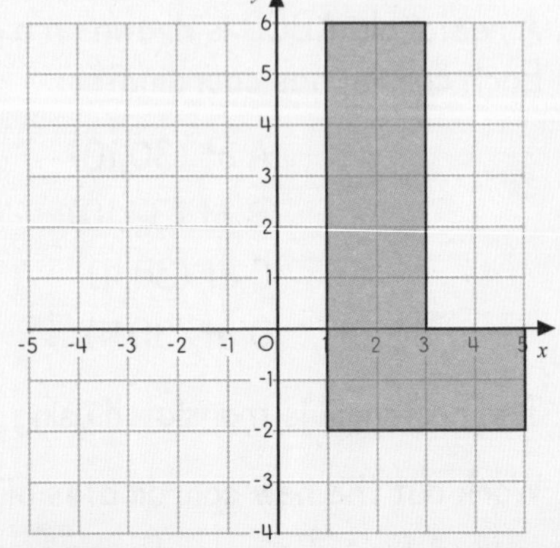

GO! ENLARGEMENTS

Lush!

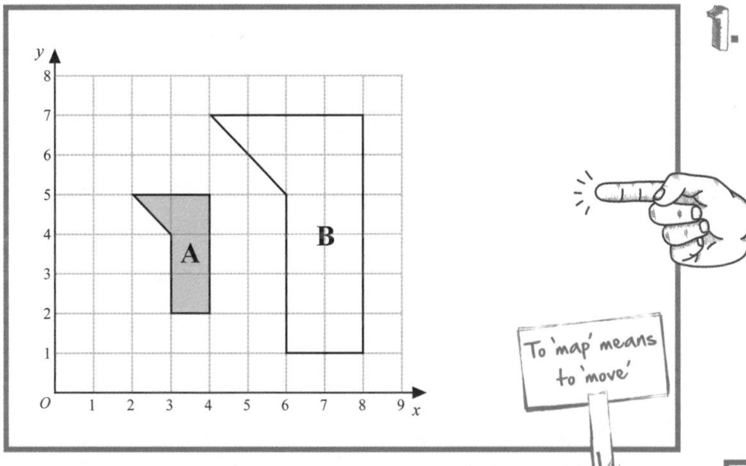

1. Describe the single transformation that maps shape B onto shape A.

2. Enlarge shape Q by a scale factor of 2.5 using (0,5) as the centre of enlargement. Label the image R.

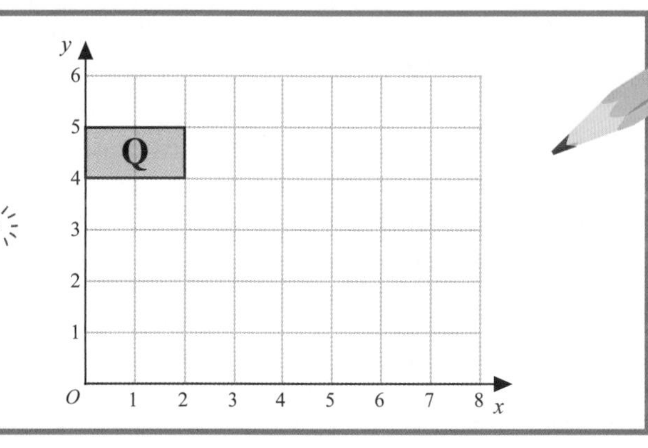

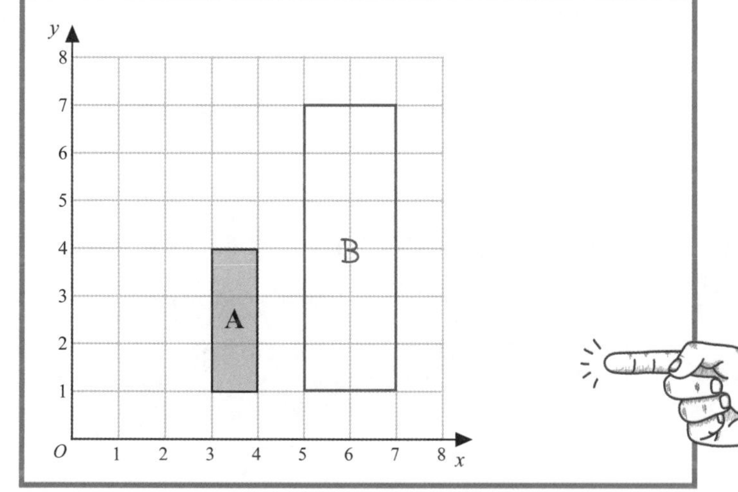

3. Martha is asked to enlarge rectangle A using a scale factor of 2 and centre (5,1).

   She has labelled her enlargement B.

   Do you agree with Martha?
   Explain your answer.

4. The diagram shows an enlargement of triangle ABC.

   The centre of enlargement is at P.
   The enlargement is labelled LMN.

   PA = 10 cm
   AL = 15 cm

   What is the scale factor of the enlargement?

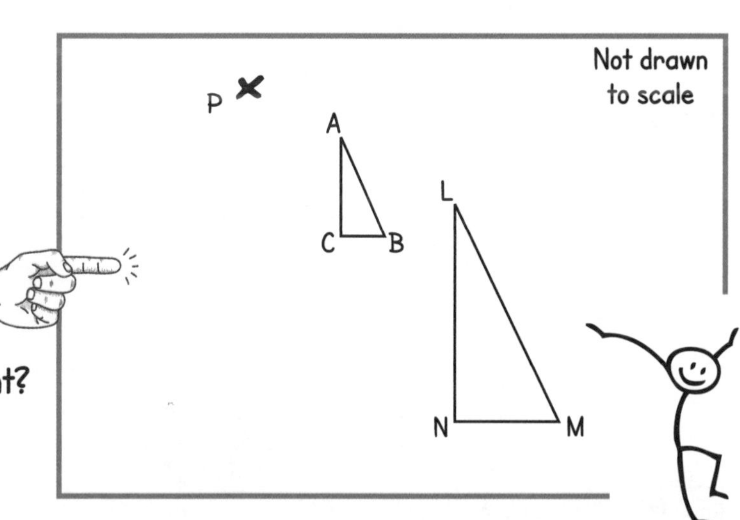

You have already seen how to carry out single transformations (reflect, rotate, translate, enlarge) but sometimes transformations are combined

Often, a combination of two or more transformations results in the same position as a SINGLE transformation.

e.g. 1 a) Reflect triangle A in the x-axis. Label the image B.

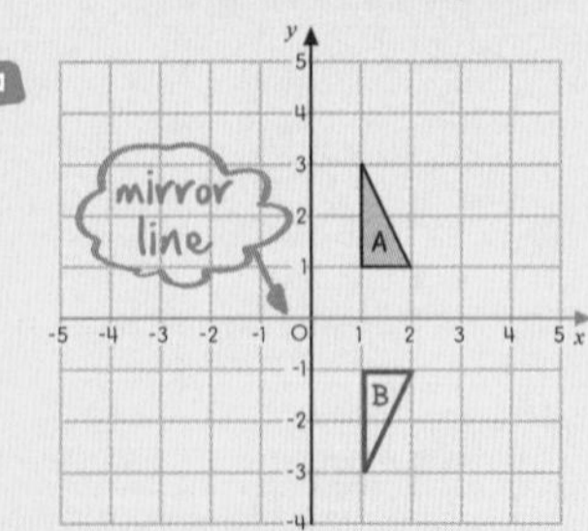

b) Rotate triangle B 90° clockwise about the origin. Label the image C.

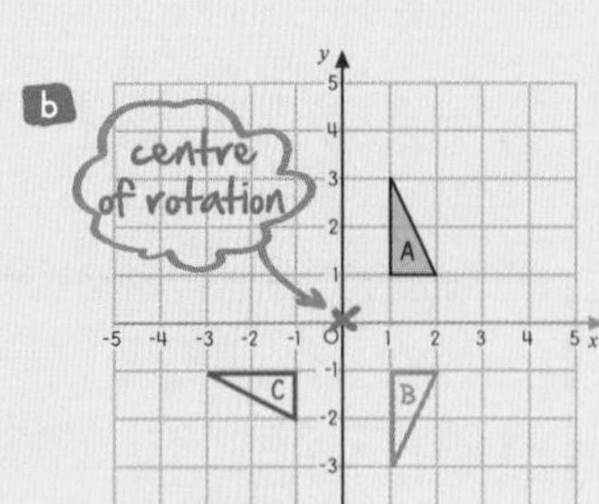

c) Describe fully the single transformation that maps triangle A onto triangle C.

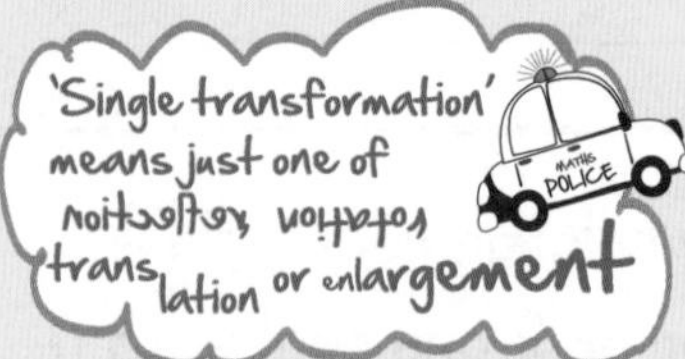

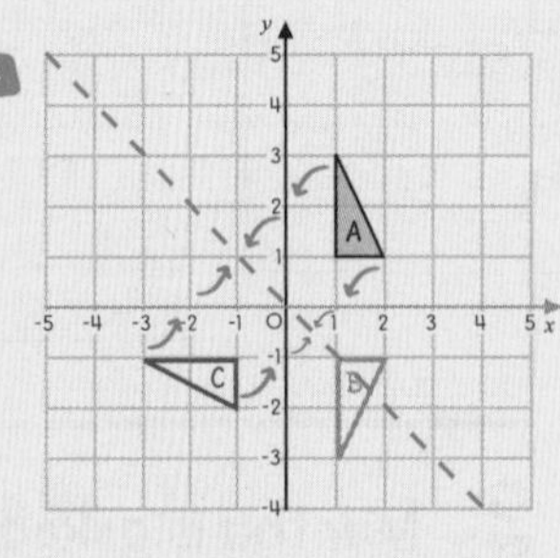

A is mapped onto C by a reflection in the line y = -x

e.g. 2 a) Reflect shape A in the line x = 1. Label the image B.

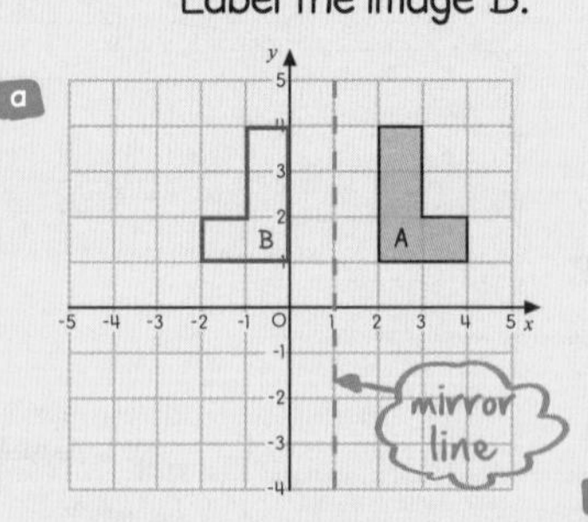

b) Reflect shape B in the line y = 0. Label the image C.

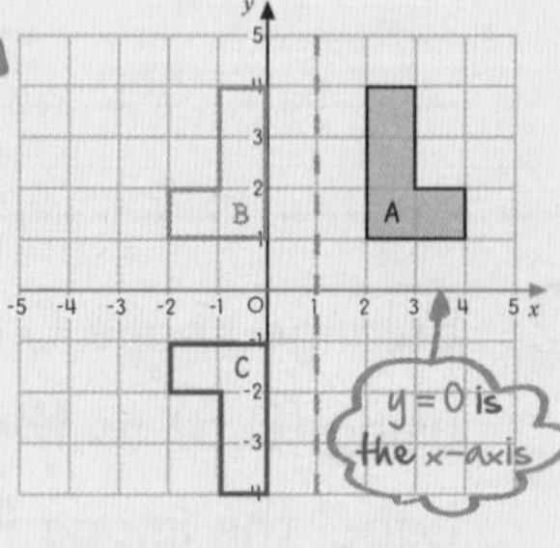

c) Describe fully the single transformation that maps shape A onto shape C.

Look where the two mirror lines cross from parts a) and b)

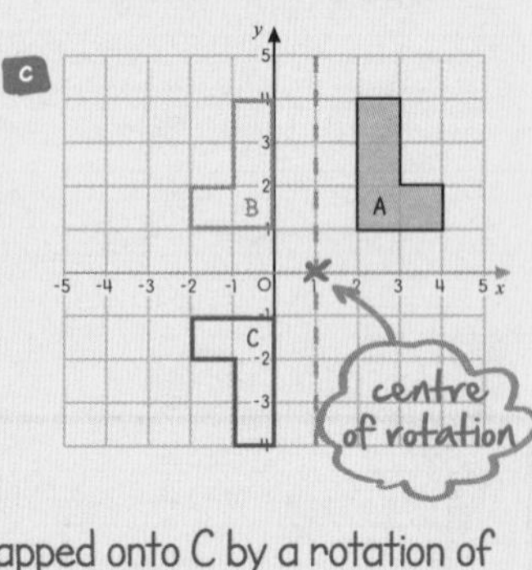

A is mapped onto C by a rotation of 180° with a centre of (1,0)

A. Reflect shape A in the line y = x to give shape B.
Rotate shape B 90° anticlockwise about the point (2,-1) to give shape C.
Describe the single transformation that maps shape A onto shape C.

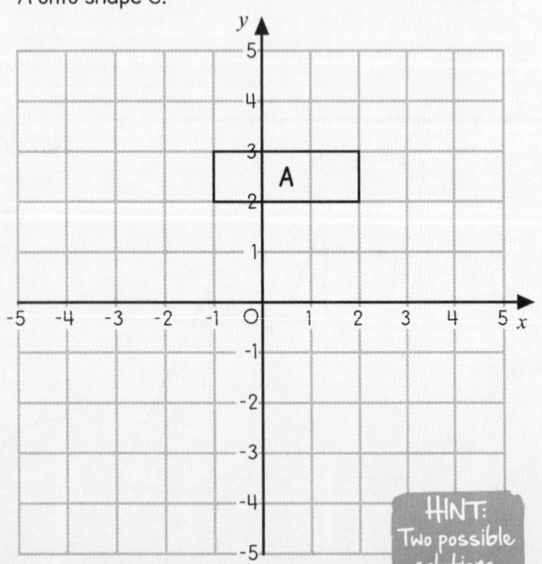

B. Reflect shape A in the line y = -x to give shape B.
Reflect shape B in the y-axis to give shape C.
Describe the single transformation that maps shape A onto shape C.

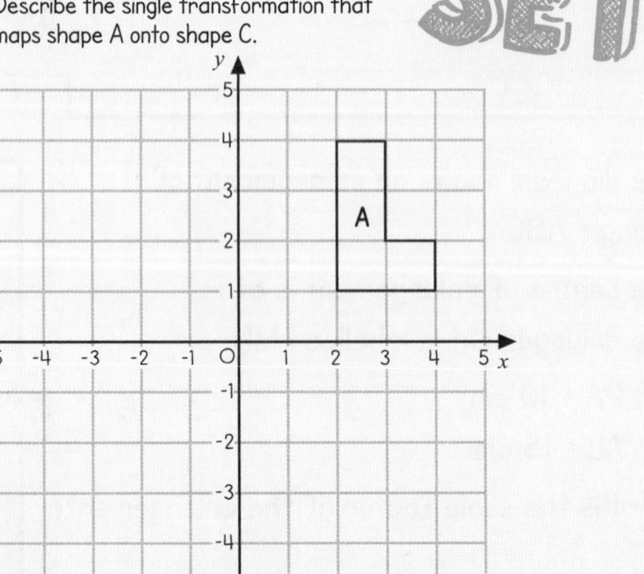

GO! COMBINED TRANSFORMATIONS

Golden!

1. Shape A can be transformed to shape B by:

a reflection in the line x = 2

followed by

a translation $\begin{pmatrix} c \\ d \end{pmatrix}$

Find the values of c and d.

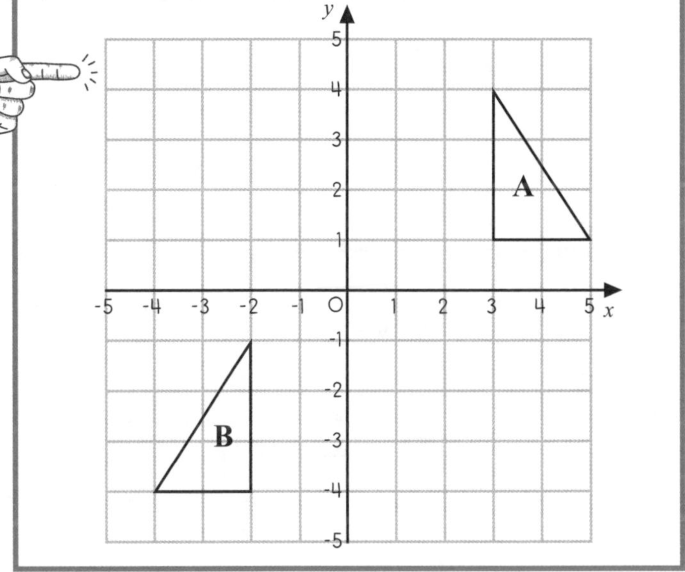

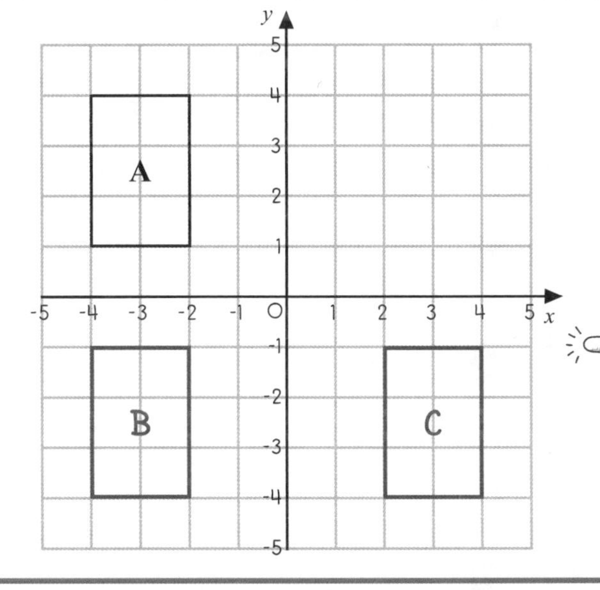

2. Meghan is asked to:

- reflect shape A in the x-axis to get shape B and then to
- reflect shape B in the y-axis to get shape C

Meghan describes the single transformation that maps A onto C:

A is mapped onto C by a reflection and then another reflection

Do you agree with Meghan? Explain why.

3. The diagram shows triangle A.

Jay rotates triangle A 90° clockwise about (1,1) to give triangle B. He then reflects B in the y-axis to give triangle C.

Abbi carries out the same two transformations in a different order. She reflects triangle A in the y-axis to give triangle B. She then rotates B 90° clockwise about (1,1) to give triangle C.

Phil thinks that Jay and Abbi both draw triangle C in the same position.

Do you agree? Use diagrams to support your reasoning.

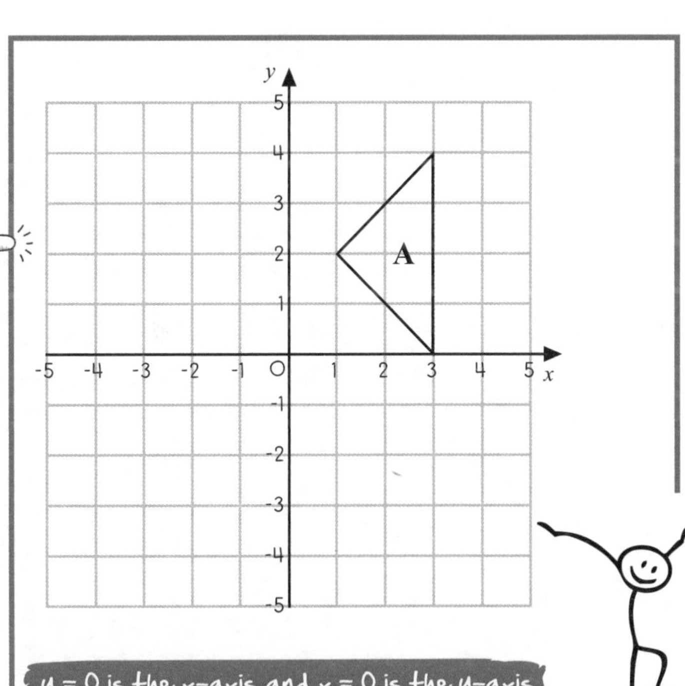

y = 0 is the x-axis and x = 0 is the y-axis

READY?

It's helpful to think of vectors as describing a journey from one place to another. We need to describe these in a way that gives information about the direction and how far to move in that direction. There are several ways to represent vectors. They can be drawn on a grid and/or written as a column vector (like with translations):

Don't get muddled up with fractions $\begin{pmatrix}2\\3\end{pmatrix}$ ✓ $\left(\frac{2}{3}\right)$ ✗

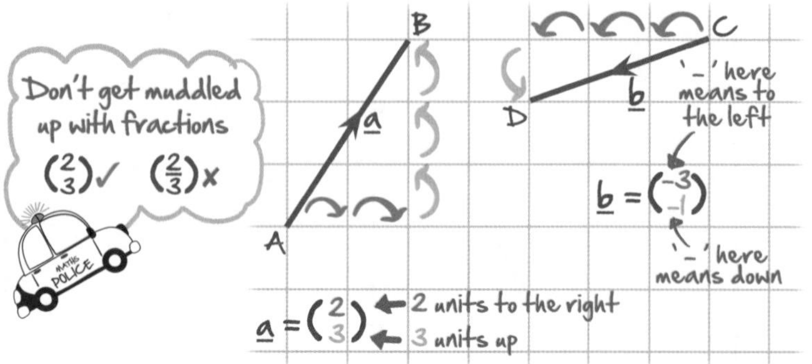

Vectors are labelled in print as a bold letter: e.g. **a**, and handwritten using an underlined letter: e.g. $\underline{a}$

They can also be shown as a movement between two points with an arrow above: e.g. $\overrightarrow{OA}$ (the journey from O to A).

We need to be able to add, subtract and multiply vectors.

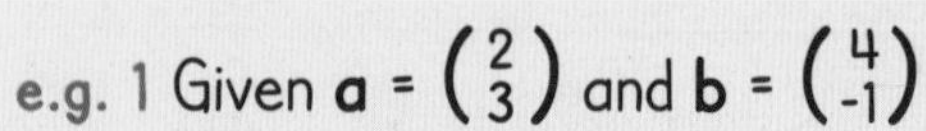

e.g. 1 Given **a** = $\begin{pmatrix}2\\3\end{pmatrix}$ and **b** = $\begin{pmatrix}4\\-1\end{pmatrix}$

Would look like this on a grid:

a) Work out **a** + **b**

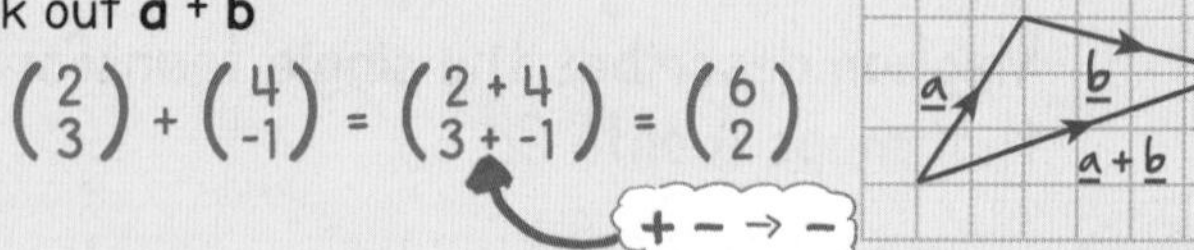

$$\begin{pmatrix}2\\3\end{pmatrix} + \begin{pmatrix}4\\-1\end{pmatrix} = \begin{pmatrix}2+4\\3+-1\end{pmatrix} = \begin{pmatrix}6\\2\end{pmatrix}$$

+ – → –

b) Work out **b** - **a**

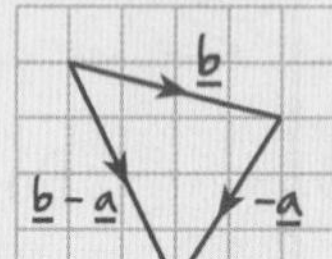

$$\begin{pmatrix}4\\-1\end{pmatrix} - \begin{pmatrix}2\\3\end{pmatrix} = \begin{pmatrix}4-2\\-1-3\end{pmatrix} = \begin{pmatrix}2\\-4\end{pmatrix}$$

c) Work out 2**a** - **b**

$$2\begin{pmatrix}2\\3\end{pmatrix} - \begin{pmatrix}4\\-1\end{pmatrix}$$

Multiply both 2 and 3 by 2

$$= \begin{pmatrix}2\times2\\2\times3\end{pmatrix} - \begin{pmatrix}4\\-1\end{pmatrix} = \begin{pmatrix}4\\6\end{pmatrix} - \begin{pmatrix}4\\-1\end{pmatrix}$$

$$= \begin{pmatrix}4-4\\6--1\end{pmatrix} = \begin{pmatrix}0\\7\end{pmatrix}$$

– – → +

e.g. 2 ABCD is a parallelogram. $\overrightarrow{DA}$ = **p** and $\overrightarrow{AB}$ = **q**.

Find $\overrightarrow{BD}$ in terms of **p** and **q**.

To get from B to D first go from B to A then from A to D

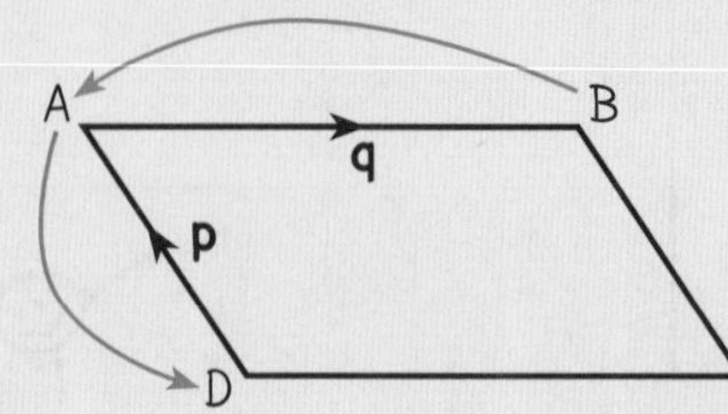

$\overrightarrow{BD} = \overrightarrow{BA} + \overrightarrow{AD}$

$\overrightarrow{BA} = -q$ ← Opposite to $\overrightarrow{AB}$

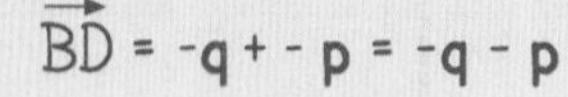

$\overrightarrow{AD} = -p$

$\overrightarrow{BD}$ = -**q** + - **p** = -**q** - **p**

SET?

A. The vectors **a**, **b**, **c** and **d** are shown on the grid:

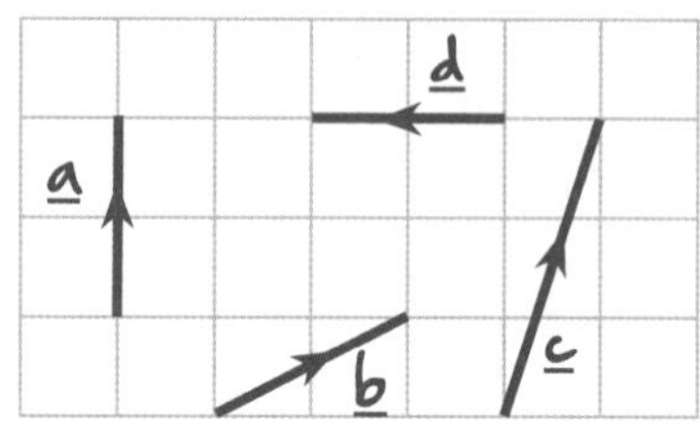

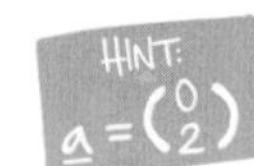

Work out the column vector for:

(i) **a** + **b** (ii) **3d**

(iii) **c** + **b** (iv) **b** + **c** + **d**

(v) **b** + 2**d** (vi) 4**a** - 2**b**

B. Given **p** = $\begin{pmatrix}2\\0\end{pmatrix}$ **q** = $\begin{pmatrix}-1\\3\end{pmatrix}$ and **r** = $\begin{pmatrix}1\\-2\end{pmatrix}$

On the grid, draw and label each of these vectors:

(i) **q** (ii) 3**p**

(iii) **q** + **r** (iv) 2**p** - **r**

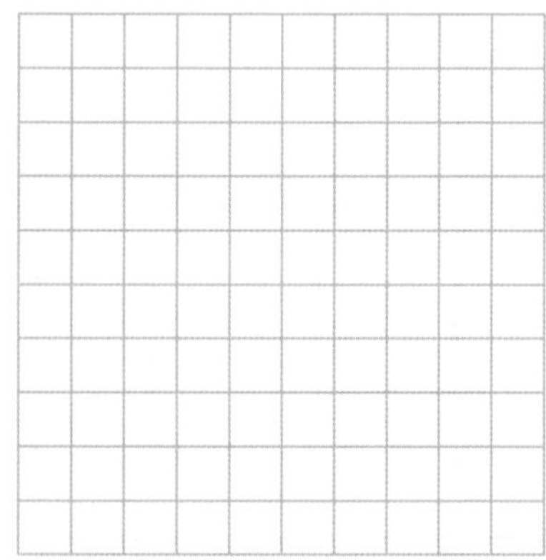

C. Here are some vectors on a grid:

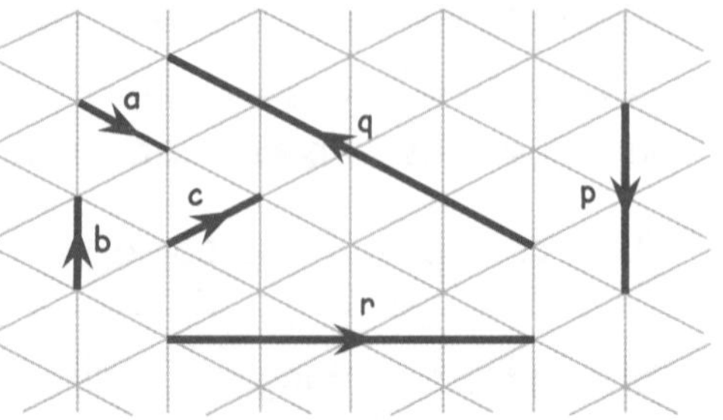

Write each of the following in terms of **a**, **b** and/or **c**. Part (i) has been done for you.

(i) **p** = -2**b**

(ii) **q** =

(iii) **r** =

GO!

Tip-top!

1. Vicky is given the following information:

$\underline{a} = \begin{pmatrix} -2 \\ 3 \end{pmatrix}$ $\quad \underline{b} = \begin{pmatrix} 6 \\ 5 \end{pmatrix}$ $\quad \underline{c} = 3\underline{a} - \underline{b}$

She works out that $\underline{c}$ is $\begin{pmatrix} -12 \\ 4 \end{pmatrix}$

Vicky writes:

$$\begin{pmatrix} -12 \\ 4 \end{pmatrix} = \begin{pmatrix} -3 \\ 1 \end{pmatrix} \quad (\div 4)$$

Do you agree with Vicky?

Give reasons for your answer.

2. Matthew is given:

$\underline{a} = \begin{pmatrix} -5 \\ -2 \end{pmatrix}$ $\quad \underline{b} = \begin{pmatrix} 1 \\ -3 \end{pmatrix}$

He works out $\underline{b} - \underline{a}$. Here is his working:

$$\underline{b} - \underline{a} = \begin{pmatrix} 1 \\ -3 \end{pmatrix} - \begin{pmatrix} -5 \\ -2 \end{pmatrix} = \begin{pmatrix} -4 \\ -5 \end{pmatrix}$$

Is his solution correct?

Justify your conclusion.

3. Here are two vectors:

$\underline{a} = \begin{pmatrix} -3 \\ 1 \end{pmatrix}$ $\quad \underline{b} = \begin{pmatrix} 2 \\ -4 \end{pmatrix}$

Find the values of m and n that make this statement true:

$$4\underline{a} - m\underline{b} = \begin{pmatrix} -16 \\ n \end{pmatrix}$$

4. Look at the diagram:

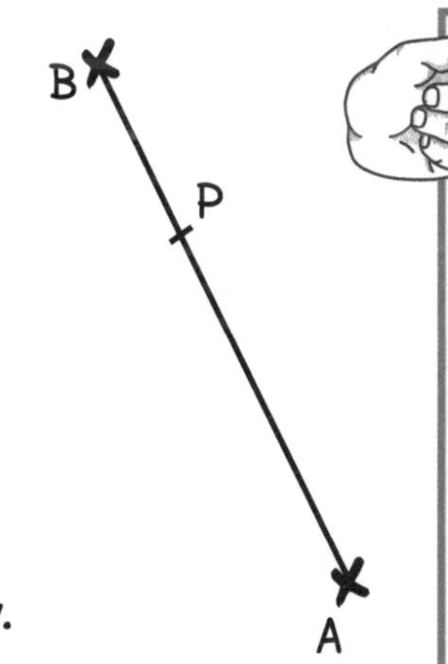

$\overrightarrow{AB} = \underline{a}$

AP : PB = 2 : 1

Max thinks that $\overrightarrow{AP} = \frac{1}{3}\underline{a}$

Max is wrong. Explain why.

READY?

It is **REALLY USEFUL** to remember :

* Probability tells us how likely it is that an event will (or won't) happen
* Probabilities can be written as fractions, percentages or decimals
* Events that are:
  - certain have a probability of 1 (or 100%)
  - impossible have probability of 0 (or 0%)

When calculating the probability of something happening, there is one **GOLDEN** rule:

$$\text{Probability} = \frac{\text{number of required outcomes}}{\text{total number of outcomes}}$$

A probability scale numbered from 0 to 1 can be used to place events on.

e.g. 1 Here is a 6-sided spinner.
Lauren is going to spin the spinner once.

On the probability scale, mark with a cross (x) the probability that it will land on:

a) an even number Required outcomes → 3 (2, 4 and 6)

Total outcomes → 6

Probability of an even number = $\frac{3}{6}$ $(= \frac{1}{2})$

b) a number greater than 4 Required outcomes → 2 (5 and 6)

Total outcomes → 6

Probability of a number greater than 4 = $\frac{2}{6}$ $(= \frac{1}{3})$

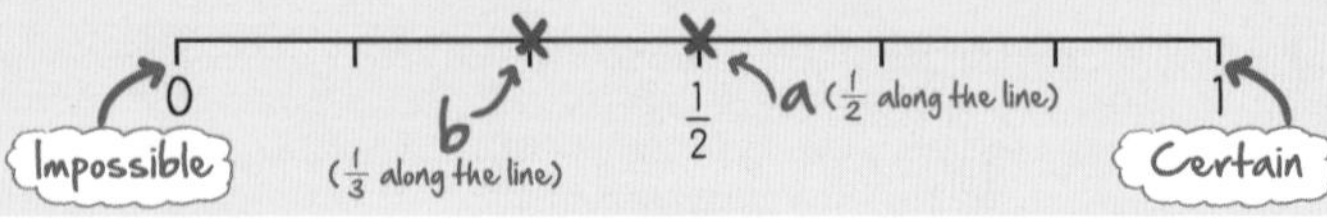

We don't always need a probability scale.

e.g. 2 Gill has a bag of 18 sweets. 5 of the sweets are blue, 4 of the sweets are red and 9 of the sweets are green.

Gill takes a sweet from the bag at random.

Write down the probability that Gill takes a sweet that is:

P(red) means 'probability of picking red'

a) red. P(red) = $\frac{4}{18}$ ← Required outcomes → 4 red sweets; Total outcomes → 18 sweets

b) blue or green. P(blue or green) = $\frac{14}{18}$ ← 5 blue + 9 green

c) purple. P(purple) = $\frac{0}{18}$ = 0 ← No purple sweets

All probabilities for an event add up to 1. This means we can calculate the probability of an event NOT happening.

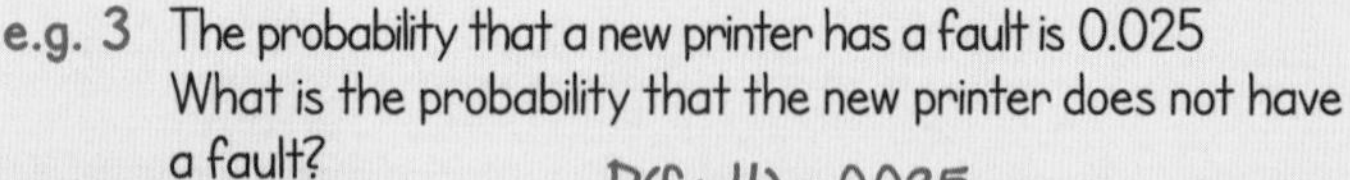

e.g. 3 The probability that a new printer has a fault is 0.025
What is the probability that the new printer does not have a fault?

P(fault) = 0.025

P(not a fault) = 1 - 0.025

= 0.975

P (fault) + P (no fault) = 1

Sometimes probabilities are given in a table.

e.g. 4 A counter is taken from a bag at random. The table shows the probability that the counter will be blue or red.

Colour	Blue	Red	White	Pink
Probability	0.5	0.2		

The number of white counters in the bag is the same as the number of pink counters in the bag.

Work out the probability that the counter is white.

1. P(B or R) = 0.5 + 0.2 = 0.7
2. So ... P(W or P) = 1 – 0.7 = 0.3
3. Since P(W) = P(P) → 0.3 ÷ 2 = 0.15

Colour	Blue	Red	White	Pink
Probability	0.5	0.2	0.15	0.15

white = 0.15

We can also use probability to solve problems.

e.g. 4 *continued* If there are 240 counters in the bag, how many of them are red?

P(red) = 0.2 and 0.2 means 20% ...

0.2 × 240 = 48 OR 20% of 240 = 48

A. A fair seven-sided spinner is numbered from 1 to 7. Tania spins the spinner once.

On the probability scale, label the probability that the spinner lands on:

A: An odd number

B: A multiple of 2

C: A number less than 8

D: A square number

0 ———————————————— 1

B. A letter is chosen at random from the word:

MULTIPLICATION

Find the probability that the letter is:

(i) I (iii) C

(ii) L (iv) X

C. The probability that a randomly chosen student can swim is $\frac{23}{30}$

HINT: $\frac{30}{30} = 1$

What is the probability that a randomly chosen student cannot swim?

D. The probability that a light bulb will last for less than 500 hours is 0.04

What is the probability that the light bulb will last for 500 hours or longer?

E. Zak either wakes up too early, on time, or too late. The probabilities of him waking up early and late are shown in the table.

Outcome	Early	On time	Late
Probability	0.3		0.1

(i) What is the probability that Zak wakes up on time?

(ii) Zak goes to school 20 days in one month. Estimate how many times he wakes up early in this month.

HINT: 0.3 = 30%

PROBABILITY

Unreal!

1. The two-way table shows information about some students and subjects that they study.

a) Complete the table.

b) A student is chosen at random. Find the probability that the student is female.

c) A male is chosen at random. Find the probability that they study art.

	Art	RE	PE	Total
Male		12	18	
Female	15	11		37
Total	28		29	80

2. The table shows the probability of getting different numbers on a biased five-sided spinner:

Number	1	2	3	4	5
Probability		0.3	0.25		0.15

a) The probability the spinner lands on 1 is twice the probability that it lands on 4. Complete the table.

b) The spinner is spun 1000 times. Which of these statements is correct?

A The number of twos will be equal to the number of fives

B The number of twos will be greater than the number of fives

C The number of twos is likely to be greater than the number of fives

D The number of twos is unlikely to be greater than the number of fives

Biased means 'not fair'

3. An orchestra has a string and a wind section.

Of the 28 musicians who play a string instrument, 21 are male,
46 of the musicians are female,
18 male musicians play a wind instrument.

a) Draw a frequency tree to represent this information.

b) A musician is going to be chosen at random. Write down the probability that the musician plays a wind instrument.

c) A female is going to be chosen at random. What is the probability that she plays a string instrument?

4. Rufus is training for a triathlon. He puts some coloured counters in a bag. Rufus will choose one counter at random. The colour of the counter will tell him whether to go for a run, ride a bike, go for a swim or visit the gym.

a) The probability of each colour being chosen is shown in the table. What is the probability of Rufus picking a green counter?

b) Twelve counters are red. How many counters are in the bag in total?

Colour	Red	Blue	Yellow	Green
Activity	Run	Ride	Swim	Gym
Probability	$\frac{3}{10}$	$\frac{1}{4}$	$\frac{1}{5}$	

READY?

Probability tree diagrams are a great way of organising information about two (or more) events. There are three **GOLDEN** rules when using probability trees:

- The probabilities on each set of branches add up to 1
- We multiply probabilities along the branches
- We may need to add probabilities from the outcomes column

e.g. 1 A spinner is spun twice. It can land on green or it can land on red.

a) Complete the diagram.

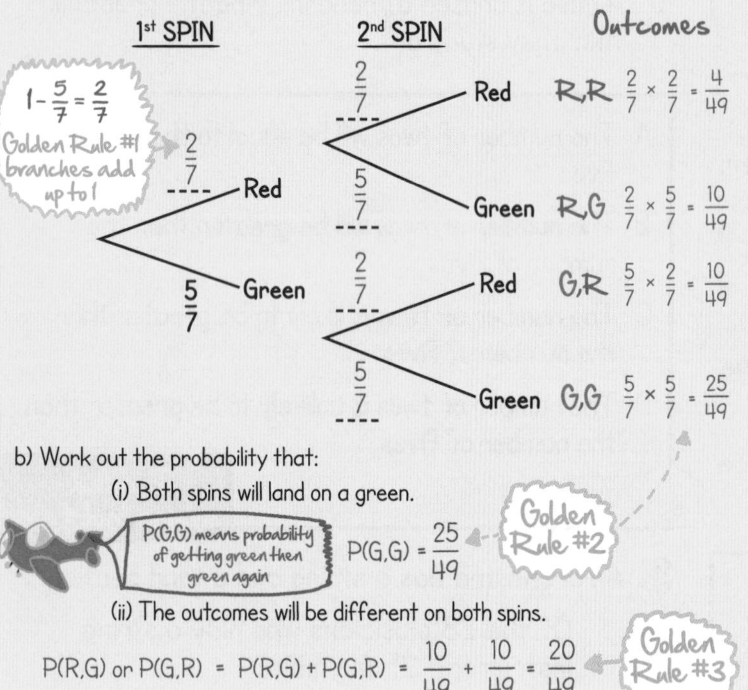

b) Work out the probability that:

(i) Both spins will land on a green.

P(G,G) means probability of getting green then green again

$P(G,G) = \frac{25}{49}$ ← Golden Rule #2

(ii) The outcomes will be different on both spins.

$P(R,G)$ or $P(G,R) = P(R,G) + P(G,R) = \frac{10}{49} + \frac{10}{49} = \frac{20}{49}$ ← Golden Rule #3

When the first event has no effect on the second event, we call them independent events.

e.g. 2 2 students take a test.

The probability that Alex will pass the test is 0.6

The probability that Ben will pass the test is 0.8

a) Draw a probability tree diagram to represent this information.

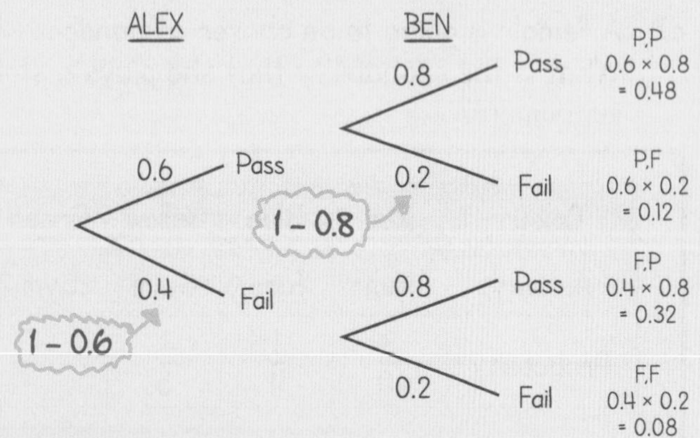

b) Work out the probability that at least one of them passes the test.

At least one of them passing is: PP, PF or FP

P(P,P) = 0.48

P(P,F) = 0.12

P(F,P) = 0.32

0.48 + 0.12 + 0.32 = 0.92

SET?

A. A bag contains 7 red counters and 3 blue counters.
A counter is chosen at random, the colour recorded and then placed back in the bag. A second counter is then chosen.

(i) Complete the tree diagram.

(ii) What is the probability that both counters are blue?

(iii) What is the probability that one counter of each colour is chosen?

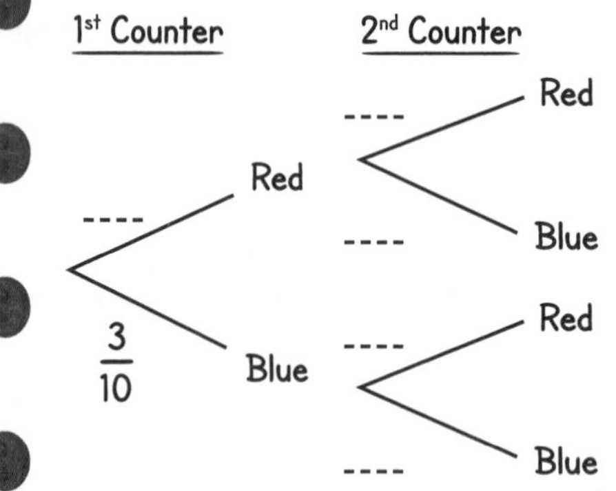

B. The probability that Nick's train is late on Monday is 0.15
The probability that the train is late on Tuesday is 0.25

(i) Complete the diagram.

(ii) What is the probability that the train is late on both days?

(iii) What is the probability that Nick's train is late on at least one of the days?

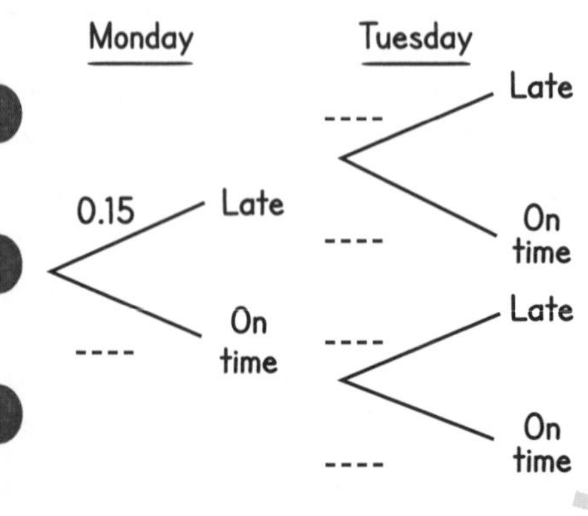

GO! PROBABILITY TREE DIAGRAMS 1

Ingenious!

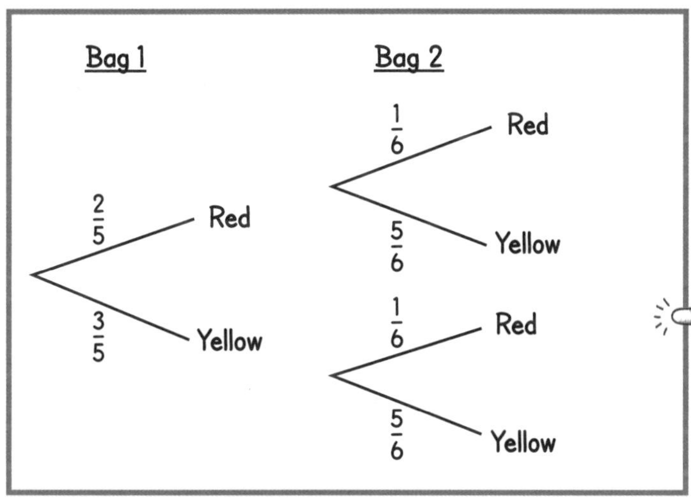

1. Two bags contain some red and some yellow counters. Ben is given a tree diagram that shows information about these two bags.

He works out the probability of choosing two red counters as follows:

$$\frac{2}{5} + \frac{1}{6} = \frac{12}{30} + \frac{5}{30} = \frac{17}{30}$$

Do you agree with Ben? Explain why.

2. Andie lives in London.
Sometimes, she walks to work.
If she doesn't walk, Andie travels on the bus.
The probability that Andie walks to work is 0.3
The probability that Andie walks home from work is 0.6

a) Find the probability that on a given day, Andie walks to work and takes the bus home.

b) What assumption have you made in working out your answer?

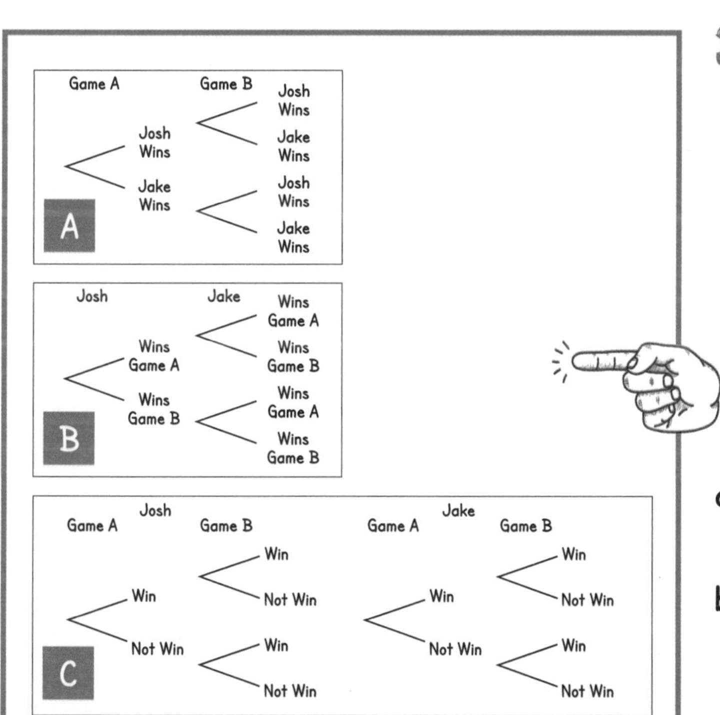

3. Josh and Jake are playing computer games. Information about the probabilities of them winning two different games is shown in the table.

	Probability of winning game A	Probability of winning game B
Josh	0.65	0.4
Jake	0.7	0.25

Oscar wants to work out who is most likely to win both games.

a) Which of these diagrams can be used to solve the problem? Justify your answer.

b) Who is most likely to win both game A and game B?
You must show workings to justify your answer.

READY?

REMEMBER:
- The probabilities on each set of branches add up to 1
- We multiply probabilities along the branches
- We may need to add from the outcomes column

Sometimes, when two (or more) events happen, one event can influence the next event. We call these dependent events. For example, if you take a biscuit from a biscuit tin and eat it, there are now fewer biscuits in the tin for a second pick!

e.g. There are 5 apples and 3 bananas in a bowl. Evelyn picks a piece of fruit at random from the bowl and eats it. She then takes at random a second piece of fruit.

a) Complete the diagram.

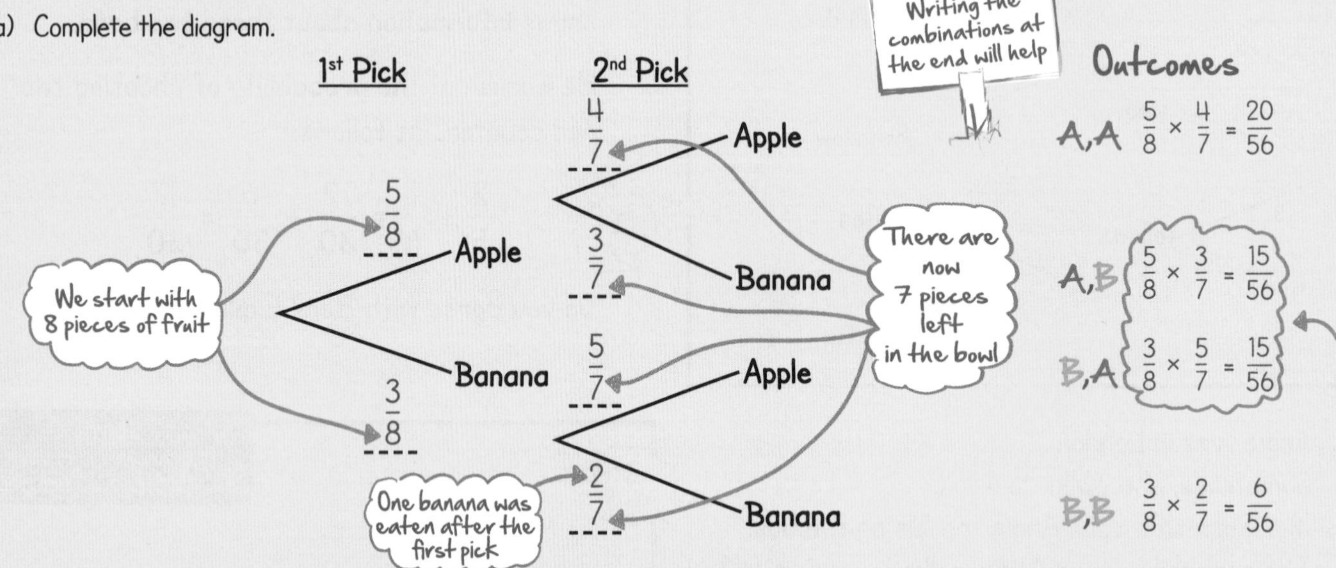

b) Work out the probability that Evelyn takes two apples. $P(A,A) = \frac{20}{56}$

c) Work out the probability that Evelyn takes two different pieces of fruit. $P(A,B) + P(B,A) = \frac{15}{56} + \frac{15}{56} = \frac{30}{56}$

d) Work out the probability that Evelyn takes at least one banana. $P(A,B) + P(B,A) + P(B,B) = \frac{15}{56} + \frac{15}{56} + \frac{6}{56} = \frac{36}{56}$

SET?

A. A box contains 3 blue balls and 9 yellow balls. A ball is picked at random and not replaced. A second ball is then picked.

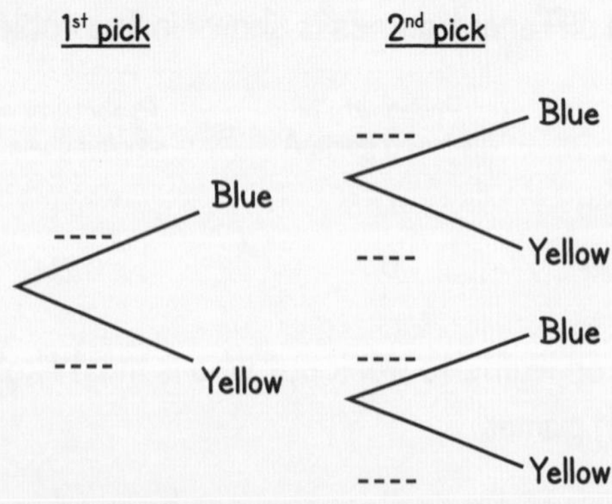

(i) Complete the tree.

(ii) What is the probability that both balls are yellow?

(iii) What is the probability that one ball of each colour is picked?

B. A word game uses letters written on tiles. Players choose tiles from a bag at random. There are 6 vowels and 8 consonants in the bag. Ed chooses two tiles and removes them from the bag.

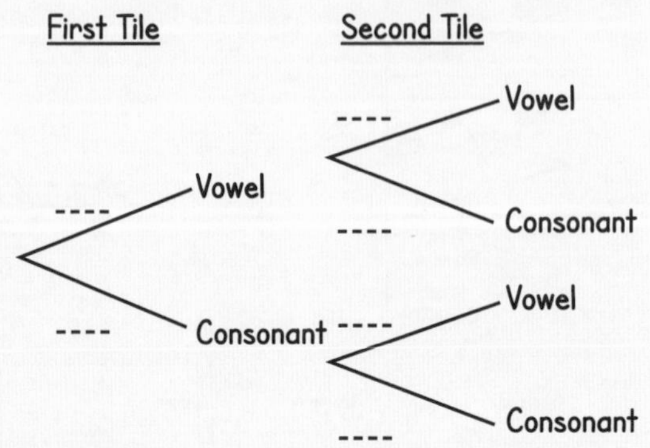

(i) Complete the tree.

(ii) What is the probability that Ed chooses two vowels?

(iii) What is the probability that Ed chooses at least one vowel?

GO! PROBABILITY TREE DIAGRAMS 2

Winner!

1. A bag contains 2 red counters, 3 blue counters and 5 white counters. Two counters are taken from the bag together.

a) What is the probability that both counters are white?

b) What is the probability that one is a red counter and one is a blue counter?

HINT: Draw a tree with 3 branches

2. Jason cycles through two sets of traffic lights on the way to work. The probability that he is stopped at the first set of lights is 0.3

If he is stopped at the first set of lights, the probability that he is stopped at the second set of lights is 0.55

If he is not stopped at the first set of lights, the probability that he is stopped at the second set of lights is 0.35

a) Complete the tree diagram to show this information.

b) What is the probability that Jason is stopped at both sets of lights?

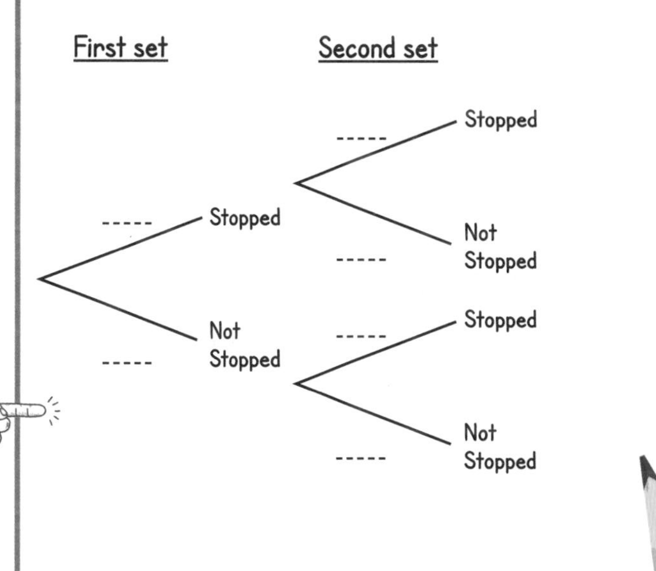

3. A set of ten cards are numbered from 0 to 9
Two of the cards are chosen at random.
Finn draws this tree diagram and works out the probability of choosing two prime numbers as shown.

Finn has made a mistake.

a) Describe the mistake he has made.

b) What is the probability of choosing two prime numbers?

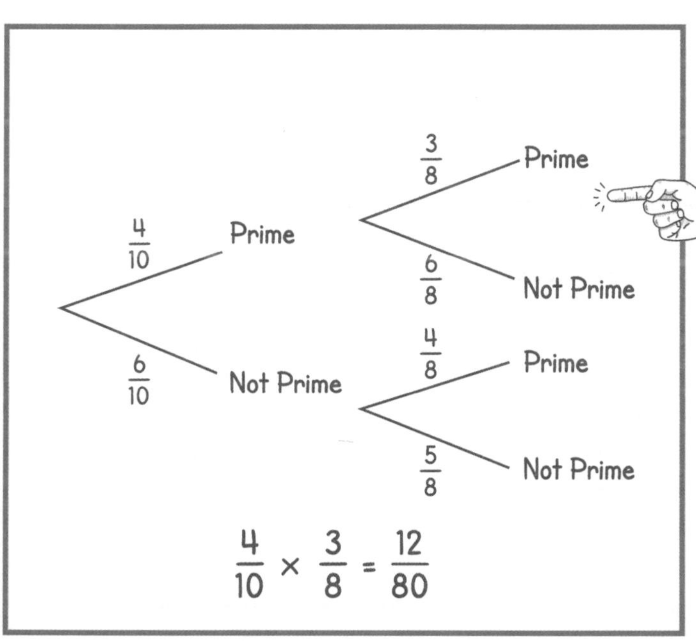

READY?

Venn diagrams are a useful tool for sorting information into sets. They are constructed using overlapping rings (either 2 or 3), each one representing a different set. The rings are enclosed by a rectangle which is the universal set. The intersection and union are two key regions of a Venn diagram:

You REALLY NEED to know some notation:

* A set of items is enclosed in curly brackets like this:

{1, 2, 3, 4, 5, 6, 7, 8, 9, 10, 11} ← Positive numbers less than 12

* The universal set contains everything, and is shown by the Greek letter ξ (pronounced ksi)

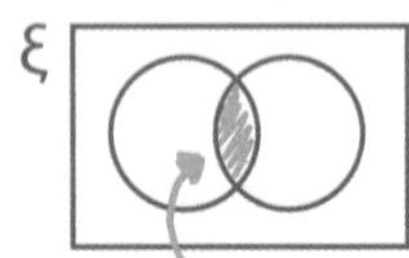

The intersection (the overlap) of two or more sets uses the symbol ∩

The union (the things in all the specified sets) uses the symbol ∪

e.g. 1 30 people were asked whether they like drinking tea or coffee.

14 people like drinking tea.
12 people like drinking coffee.
3 people like drinking both.

The intersection is often a good place to start

Complete the Venn diagram to show this information.

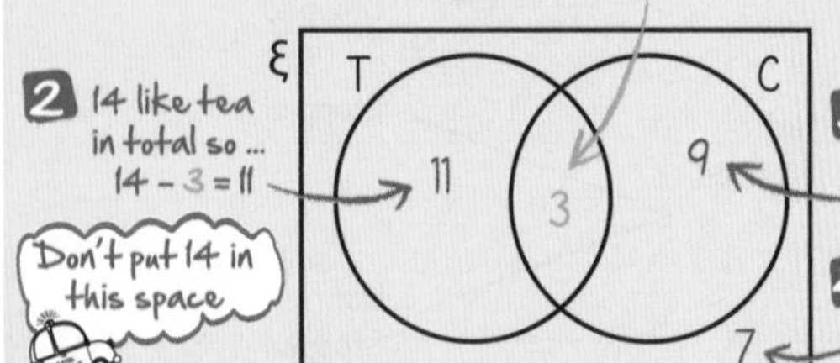

Sometimes a Venn diagram shows the actual items, rather then the number of items.

e.g. 2 Look at this Venn diagram.

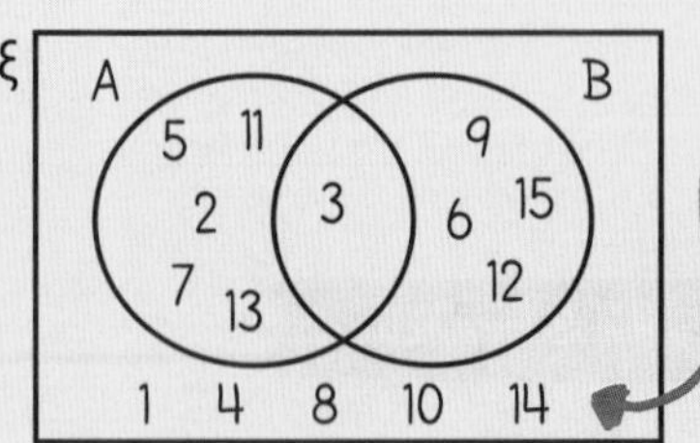

a) Describe ξ What numbers are in the Venn diagram?

Every whole number from 1 to 15

b) What type of numbers are in set A?

Everything in ring A (including the 3)

Prime numbers

c) Write down A ∩ B. The intersection of A and B

3

d) A number is chosen at random from ξ

Write down P (A ∪ B). 'P' means probability

$\frac{10}{15}$

A ∪ B includes: 2, 3, 5, 6, 7, 9, 11, 12, 13 and 15 ... so 10 numbers out of 15

A. 30 students are asked if they can swim (S) and if they can ride a bike (B).

* 5 students can ride a bike but not swim.
* 21 students can ride a bike.
* 7 students can swim but not ride a bike.

(i) Complete the Venn diagram to show this information.

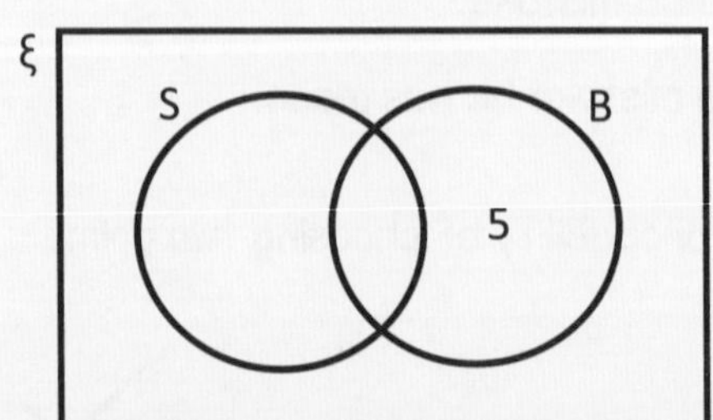

(ii) Work out P(S ∩ B).

B. Flo interviews 40 people at a farmers' market.

* 3 people bought apples, beetroot and cherries
* 4 people bought none of these items
* 1 person bought beetroot and cherries, but no apples
* 18 people bought apples
* 12 people bought beetroot
* 6 people bought just beetroot
* 5 people bought apples and cherries, but no beetroot

Find the probability that a person bought just cherries.

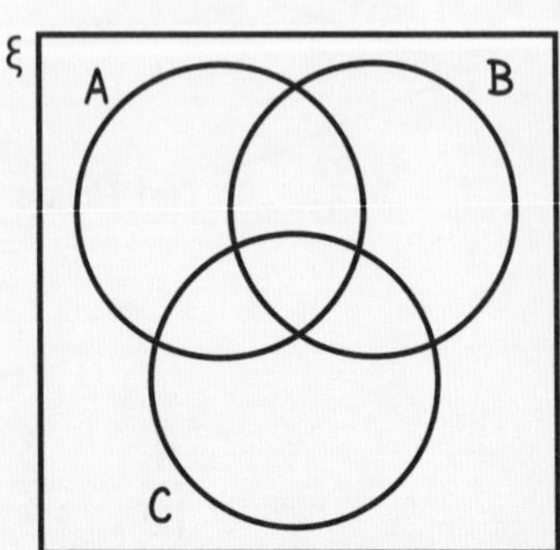

First-rate!

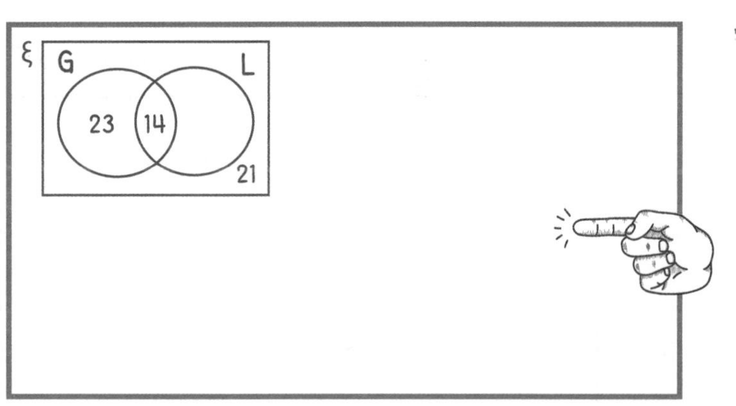

1. 50 people are surveyed to find out if they use glasses (G), contact lenses (L) or both.

   14 people use both contact lenses and glasses.
   21 people use neither glasses nor contact lenses.
   23 people use glasses.

   Jan creates a Venn diagram to show the information.

   Jan is wrong. Draw a correct Venn diagram.

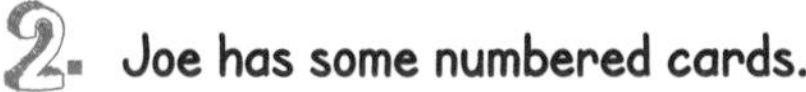

2. Joe has some numbered cards.

   ξ = {integers 1 to 16}
   A = {odd numbers}
   B = {multiples of 3}
   C = {square numbers}

a) Show this information in a Venn diagram.

b) A card is chosen at random. Find $P(A \cap B \cap C)$.

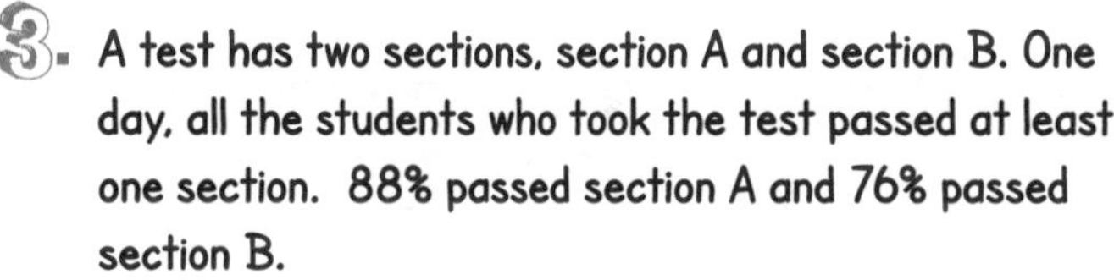

3. A test has two sections, section A and section B. One day, all the students who took the test passed at least one section. 88% passed section A and 76% passed section B.

   One of the students is chosen at random from all the students who took the test that day. What is the probability that this student:

a) Passed both sections?

b) Passed only section A?

4. There are 190 students in Year 9 at a school.

   90 students study French (F).
   119 students study German (G).
   84 students study Spanish (S).
   32 students study all three languages.
   62 students study French and German.
   37 students study French and Spanish.
   40 students study German and Spanish.

a) Show this information in a Venn diagram.

b) A student is chosen at random. Find $P(G \cup S)$.

The equation $5x + 6 = 21$ has one solution (the value of x). An equation such as $2x + y = 10$ has an infinite number of solutions. If we have two equations, we can usually find one solution that fits both equations, such as:

$$2x + y = 10$$
$$6x + y = 26$$

These are called SIMULTANEOUS EQUATIONS!

You **REALLY NEED** to remember:

* A **coefficient** is the number sitting in front of a letter
* How to solve a linear equation
* How to manipulate an algebraic statement

$5x + 6 = 21$ | $-6 \quad -6$ | $5x = 15$ | $\div 5 \quad \div 5$ | $x = 3$

$4x + y = 23$ | $\times 3 \quad \times 3 \quad \times 3$ | $12x + 3y = 69$

e.g. 1 Solve $2x + y = 10$ and $6x + y = 26$

1 Label the equations ① and ②

2 Check, are the coefficients of either x or y the same?

$2x + y = 10$ ①
$6x + y = 26$ ②

YES … both 'y's have a coefficient of 1, so we aim to eliminate the 'y's by subtracting …

② – ① as the values are bigger in ②:

$6x + y = 26$ ②
$-\;2x + y = 10$ ①

3 Solve to find x

$4x = 16$ ($y - y = 0$, y is eliminated)
$\div 4 \quad \div 4$
$x = 4$

4 Substitute $x = 4$ in to ① (or ②) to find the value of y

$2 \times 4 + y = 10$
$8 + y = 10$
$y = 2$

5 Check $x = 4$ and $y = 2$ work in both ① and ②

①: $2 \times 4 + 2 = 10$ ✓ and ②: $6 \times 4 + 2 = 26$ ✓

$x = 4$ and $y = 2$

Sometimes some manipulation is needed first.

e.g. 2 Solve $2x + 7y = 34$ and $3x + 2y = 17$

Label and check if the coefficients of either x or y are the same

$2x + 7y = 34$ ①
$3x + 2y = 17$ ②

NO … so we need to make one of them the same (① × 3 and ② × 2 will make $6x$ in both equations)

① × 3 → $6x + 21y = 102$ ③
② × 2 → $-\;6x + 4y = 34$ ④ (New equations, new numbers)

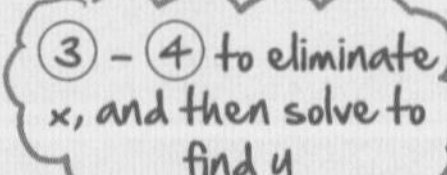

$17y = 68$
$\div 17 \quad \div 17$
$y = 4$

Substitute $y = 4$ in to ① (or ②) to find x and then check

$2x + 7 \times 4 = 34$
$2x + 28 = 34$
$-28 \quad -28$
$2x = 6$
$\div 2 \quad \div 2$
$x = 3$

①: $2 \times 3 + 7 \times 4 = 34$ ✓
and ②: $3 \times 3 + 2 \times 4 = 17$ ✓

$x = 3$ and $y = 4$

SET?

Solve these simultaneous equations:

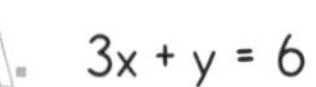

A. $3x + y = 6$
$x + y = 4$

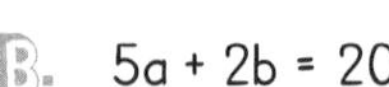

B. $5a + 2b = 20$
$3a + 2b = 16$

C. $7m + 5n = 13$
$7m + n = -3$

D. $10a + b = 52$
$5a + 3b = 31$

E. $3x + 2y = 13$
$5x + 4y = 23$

F. $2b + 5c = 24$
$3b + 7c = 34$

G. $3x + 2y = -8$
$4x + 5y = -13$

GO! SIMULTANEOUS EQUATIONS 1

Result!!

1. Solve the simultaneous equations:

$$3x + 5y = 51$$
$$7x - 61 = -2y$$

2. Jen is solving the simultaneous equations:

$4x + y = 3$ and $8x + 5y = 12$

Her working is shown here.

Jen is wrong. Find her mistake and correct the work.

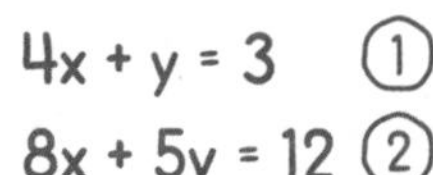

$4x + y = 3$ ①
$8x + 5y = 12$ ②

① × 5: $20x + 5y = 3$ ③
$8x + 5y = 12$ ②

③ - ②: $12x = -9$
$x = -0.75$

Substitute $x = -0.75$ into ①: $4 \times -0.75 + y = 3$
$-3 + y = 3$ so $y = 6$ and $x = -0.75$

3. 4 pens and 5 pencils cost £3.95
3 pens and 8 pencils cost £4.45

a) Write a pair of simultaneous equations to show this information.

b) Find the cost of a pencil.

HINT: Let x = price of 1 pen and y = price of 1 pencil

4. A theatre has different prices for adult tickets and child tickets.

The Gregory family buy four adult tickets and three child tickets. The cost is £108

The Gosling family buy two adult tickets and four child tickets. The cost is £84

The Boughen family are going to buy five adult tickets and four child tickets.

How much will the Boughen family have to pay?

READY?

When solving simultaneous equations involving negatives, we need to think about whether to add OR subtract the equations to eliminate one of the letters.

Once one of the letters have the same coefficient:
* If the coefficients have the same sign, subtract the equations
* If the coefficients have a different sign, add the equations

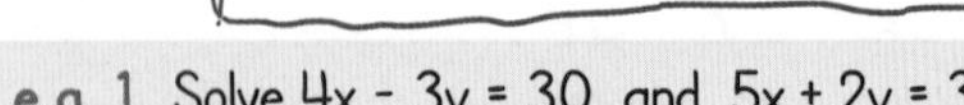

REMEMBER:

How to plot the graphs of linear equations such as $y = 4 - 2x$

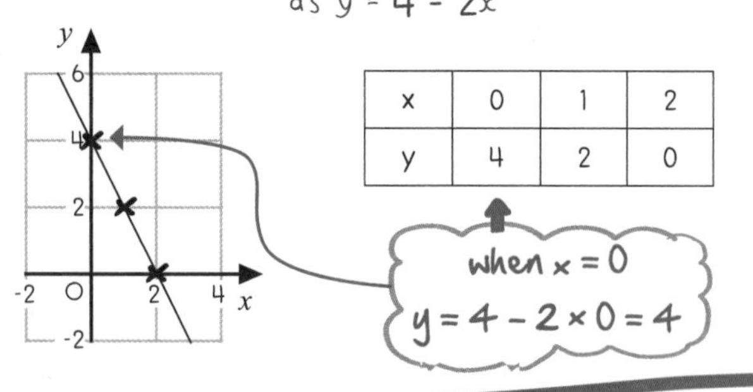

x	0	1	2
y	4	2	0

e.g. 1 Solve $4x - 3y = 30$ and $5x + 2y = 3$

1 Label the equations then check the coefficients

$4x - 3y = 30$ ①
$5x + 2y = 3$ ②

① × 2 → $8x - 6y = 60$ ③
② × 3 → $15x + 6y = 9$ ④
③ + ④ → $23x = 69$
÷23   ÷23
$x = 3$

2 Both 'y's now have a coefficient of 6 but with a different sign (+6 and −6) ... so we add the equations to find x

3 Substitute $x = 3$ in to ① (or ②) to find the value of y and then check

$4 \times 3 - 3y = 30$
$12 - 3y = 30$
−12   −12
$-3y = 18$
÷−3   ÷−3
$y = -6$

①: $4 \times 3 - 3 \times -6 = 30$ ✓
and ②: $5 \times 3 + 2 \times -6 = 3$ ✓

$x = 3$ and $y = -6$

We can also solve simultaneous equations graphically, which means we need to draw graphs. The solution can be found at the point where the graphs cross.

e.g. 3 The graphs of $y = 4 - 2x$ and $y = x + 10$ are shown on the grid. Use the graphs to solve the simultaneous equations $y = 4 - 2x$ and $y = x + 10$

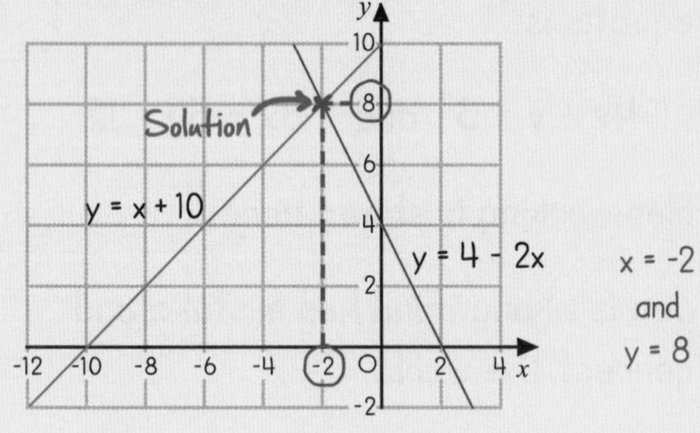

$x = -2$ and $y = 8$

e.g. 2 Solve $2x - y = 13$ and $x - 2y = 11$

$2x - y = 13$ ①
$x - 2y = 11$ ②

① × 2 → $4x - 2y = 26$ ③
② → $x - 2y = 11$
③ − ② → $3x = 15$
$x = 5$

The 'y's now both have a coefficient of −2 (both have same sign) ... so we subtract the equations to find x

Substitute $x = 5$ in to ① (or ②) to find the value of y and then check

$2 \times 5 - y = 13$
$10 - y = 13$
−10   −10
$-y = 3$
÷−1   ÷−1
$y = -3$

①: $2 \times 5 - -3 = 13$ ✓
and ②: $5 - 2 \times -3 = 11$ ✓

So $x = 5$ and $y = -3$

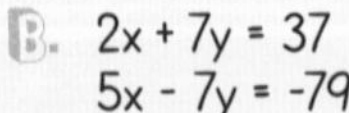

Solve these simultaneous equations:

A. $3x - y = 22$
$5x + y = 50$

B. $2x + 7y = 37$
$5x - 7y = -79$

C. $x + 5y = 22$
$4x - y = 4$

D. $5p - 3q = 22$
$7p + 6q = -10$

E. $8a + 3b = 27$
$18a - 4b = 7$

F. $5x - 3y = 14$
$9x - 4y = 28$

G. Use the graphs to write down the solutions to the equations $y = 3x - 2$ and $x + y = 6$

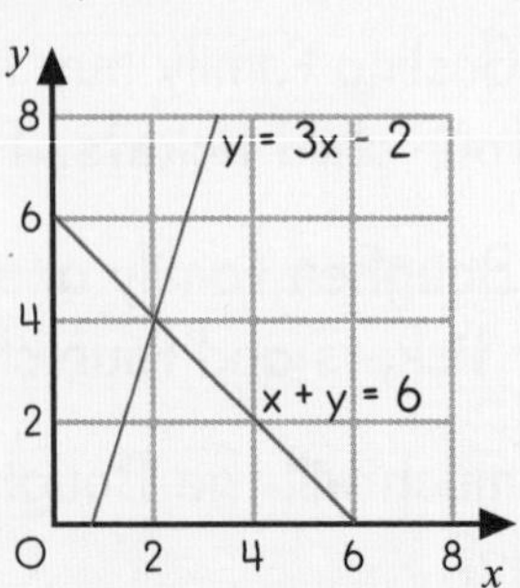

GO! SIMULTANEOUS EQUATIONS 2

Excellent!

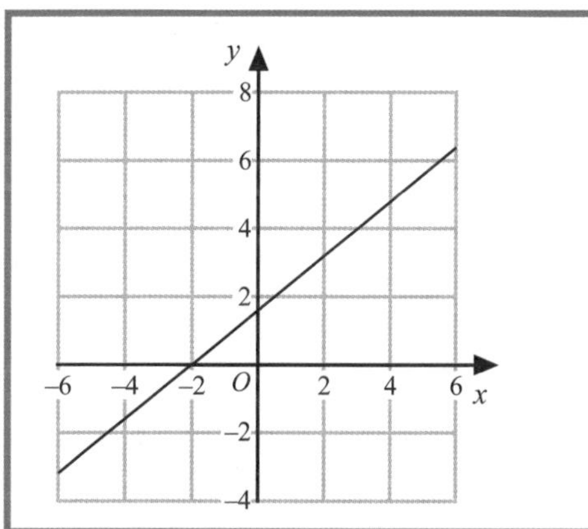

1. The graph of $4x - 5y = -8$ is shown on the grid.

Plot the graph of $y = 2x + 4$ on the same grid.

Use your graphs to solve the simultaneous equations:

$$4x - 5y = -8$$
$$y = 2x + 4$$

2. The graphs of $2x - 7y = 3$ and $3x + 5y = 20$ meet at the point M.

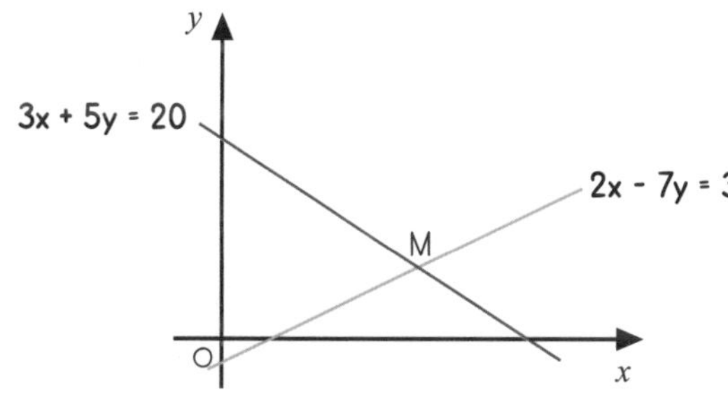

Find the coordinates of the point M.

3. Solve the simultaneous equations:

$$8x - 7 = 4y$$
$$11x - 8y = 4$$

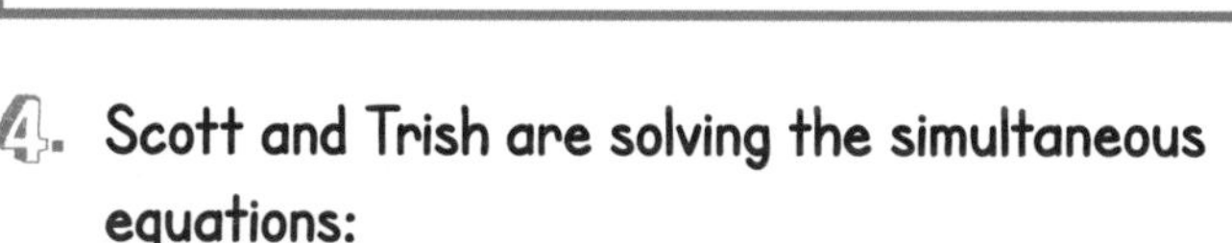

4. Scott and Trish are solving the simultaneous equations:

$$6a + 5b = 23$$
$$10a - 3b = -7$$

Their workings are shown here.

Circle the correct statement:

A Only Scott is correct

B Only Trish is correct

C Scott and Trish are both correct

D Scott and Trish are both incorrect

Scott's method

$6a + 5b = 23$ ①
$10a - 3b = -7$ ②
① × 3: $18a + 15b = 69$
② × 5: $50a - 15b = -35$ (+)
$68a = 34$
$a = 0.5$
Then $3 + 5b = 23$
$5b = 20$
$b = 4$

Trish's method

$6a + 5b = 23$ ①
$10a - 3b = -7$ ②
① × 5: $30a + 25b = 115$
② × 3: $30a - 9b = -21$ (−)
$34b = 136$
$b = 4$
Then $6a + 20 = 23$
$6a = 3$
$a = \frac{1}{2}$

Notes

Solutions this way

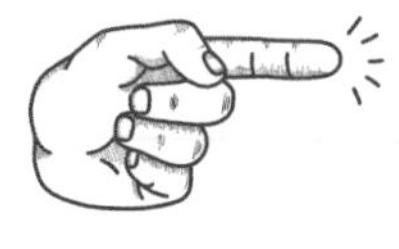

(But only if you have done the question first)

... also available online

Two Way Tables (p.10)

Set?

A

	Finance	Sales	Ops	Total
Male	22	17	7	46
Female	8	11	25	44
Total	30	28	32	90

B	(i) 43 (ii) 30
C	49

Go!

1	No. He has put the number for girls (28) in the wrong place.
2	9
3	41

Frequency Trees (p.12)

Set?

A

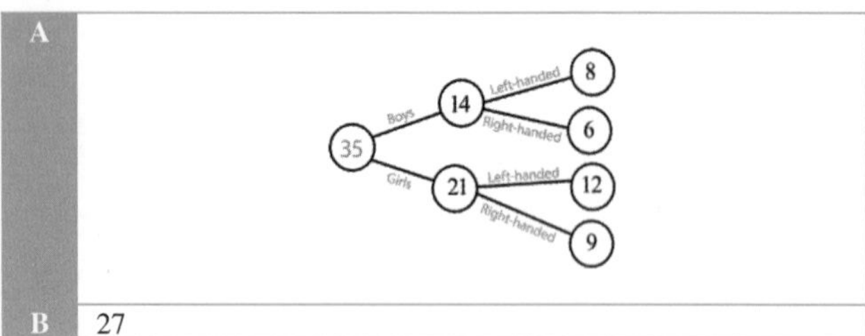

B	27

Go!

1

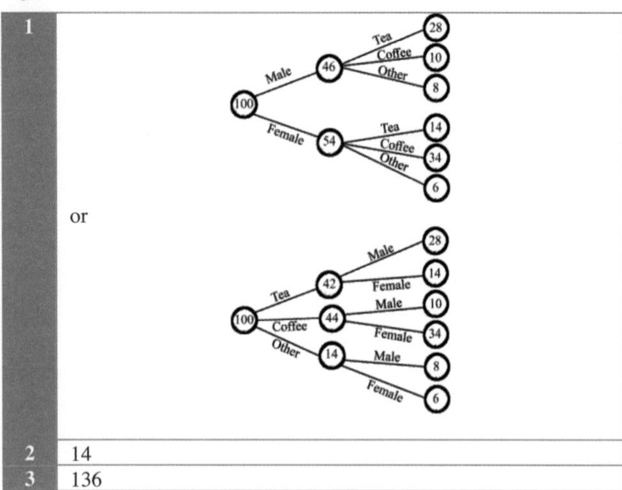

or

100
Tea
Coffee
Other
42
44
14
Male
Female
Male
Female
Male
Female
28
14
10
34
8
6

2	14
3	136

Rounding (p.14)

Set?

(i) 6.6, 6.59, 6.588, 7, 6.6, 6.59
(ii) 78.9, 78.89, 78.889, 80, 79, 78.9
(iii) 0.1, 0.07, 0.072, 0.07, 0.072, 0.0715
(iv) 188.0, 188.05, 188.048, 200, 190, 188

Go!

1	No. She has rounded to 1 decimal place and not 1 significant figure. The correct answer is 2
2	950
3	2.55
4	No. She has not used zeros as place value holders. The correct answer is 130,000
5	81.25 seconds. This is the smallest number (i.e. the fastest time) that rounds to 81.3 seconds.

Error Intervals (p.16)

Set?

A	3450
B	$5.5 \leq$ number < 6.5
C	$5.15 \leq$ length < 5.25
D	$285 \leq n < 295$
E	$4.25 \leq n < 4.35$
F	$12.335 \leq n < 12.345$
G	$7.2 \leq n < 7.3$
H	$9.4 \leq y < 9.5$

Go!

1	No. The length error interval has not been used. The correct answer is $18 \leq$ perimeter < 22
2	$0.515 \leq x < 0.525$
3	Betsy's upper and lower bounds are incorrect for truncation (they are the correct bounds for rounding). The correct answer is $1.5 \leq y < 1.6$
4	Upper bound of length of wood is 4.4 Lower bound of length of metal is 4.35 So, for example, the length of the wood could be 4.39 m and length of the metal could be 4.35 m

Estimation (p.18)

Set?

A	3300 (if values have been rounded to 1 s.f.)
B	140 (if values have been rounded to 1 s.f.)
C	36 (if values have been rounded to 1 s.f.)
D	81 (if values have been rounded to 1 s.f.)
E	$70 \div 2 = 35$ (if values have been rounded to 1 s.f.)
F	$2 \times 120 = 240$
G	$\sqrt{36} = 6$
H	0.2 (if values have been rounded to 1 s.f.)
I	8 (if values have been rounded to 1 s.f.)

Go!

1

Question	Solution
35.2×29	487.6
92×5.3	786.87
$112 \div 12$	120
$\sqrt{72.25}$	9.3
6.3×124.9	1020.8
$60.12 \div 0.501$	8.5

2	It should be less than 4.5 (also $5 \times 0.5 = 2.5$)
3	Beth ($\sqrt[3]{4+2+1} = \sqrt[3]{6}$ which is less than 2)
4	a) Acceptable range: £500 to £636.48 b) It is an underestimate as all values have been rounded down.

Use of Calculator (p.20)

Set?

A	1.029735...
B	0.121088...
C	19.256057...
D	0.66
E	(i) 56.07285305 (ii) 56.1
F	50.4568653

Go!

1	a) −3.088334893 b) −3.1
2	No. The correct answer is 1654.842641
3	a) −114.2960206 b) −114.30
4	3.013605562

Product of Prime Factors (p.22)

Set?

A	$2 \times 3 \times 5$
B	$3^2 \times 7$
C	$2^2 \times 13$
D	$2^2 \times 3 \times 5 \times 7$
E	$2^3 \times 3^3$

Go!

1	Yes. He has found all the prime factors.
2	a = 2, b = 1 and c = 2
3	9 is not a prime number. The correct answer is $5 \times 7 \times 3^2$
4	p = 2 q = 3 r = 11

HCF & LCM (p.24)

Set?

A	36
B	300
C	6
D	16
E	792
F	12

Go!

1	The LCM is 240
2	630 seconds
3	14
4	a) HCF = 20 b) LCM = 11880

Real Life Multiples (p.26)

Set?

A	18:15
B	120 seconds
C	Mathilda: 8 Erin: 5

Go!

1	6
2	The lowest common multiple is 120 so the next time will be 20:00 on Monday.
3	5
4	£25.80

Fractions 1 (p.28)

Set?

A	(i) $\frac{7}{13}$ (ii) $\frac{3}{15} = \frac{1}{5}$ (iii) $\frac{13}{15}$ (iv) $\frac{19}{24}$ (v) $\frac{13}{24}$ (vi) $\frac{9}{40}$
B	(i) $\frac{8}{27}$ (ii) $\frac{5}{30} = \frac{1}{6}$ (iii) $\frac{20}{144} = \frac{5}{36}$
C	(i) $\frac{9}{22}$ (ii) $\frac{63}{2} = 31\frac{1}{2} = 31.5$ (iii) $\frac{7}{60}$
D	$\frac{7}{20}$
E	$\frac{18}{96} = \frac{3}{16}$

Go!

1	He has added both the numerators and denominators together. The correct answer is $\frac{34}{35}$
2	A: False, as $\frac{4}{5}$ does not equal $\frac{2}{5}$ B: True, as $\frac{119}{190}$ does equal $\frac{119}{190}$
3	60
4	37

Fractions 2 (p.30)

Set?

A	(i) $4\frac{27}{28}$ (ii) $1\frac{11}{12}$ (iii) $1\frac{29}{48}$ (iv) $1\frac{11}{25}$
B	(i) $10\frac{2}{5}$ (ii) $3\frac{7}{11}$ (iii) $10\frac{10}{11}$
C	(i) $1\frac{7}{50}$ (ii) $2\frac{2}{5}$

Go!

1	a) $\frac{121}{9}$ or $13\frac{4}{9}$ b) $\frac{21}{4}$ or $5\frac{1}{4}$
2	37
3	No. The subtraction has been done in the wrong order. The correct answer is $1\frac{15}{28}$
4	$46\frac{3}{4}$ inches^2

Ratio 1 (p.32)

Set?

A	(i) £12 and £48 (ii) £18 and £42 (iii) £16 and £44 (iv) £9 and £51 (v) £10, £20 and £30
B	(i) £30 (ii) £17.50
C	£99
D	24
E	(i) $\frac{1}{5}$ (ii) $\frac{4}{5}$
F	Any three of 1, 3, 5, 9 or 21
G	£24

Go!

1	Yes. The angles are 15°, 75° and 90°
2	No. Lucy has 28 sweets (21 MORE sweets).
3	24 or 36
4	2

Ratio 2 (p.34)

Set?

A	4 : 12 : 9
B	25 : 10 : 4
C	4 : 5
D	(i) 8 : 12 : 15 (ii) 105
E	(i) 15 : 22 (ii) 258

Go!

1	10 : 15 : 6 : 30
2	Yes. The ratio of men : women : children is 5 : 4 : 5
3	He has not made the number of parts for the red cars the same numbers. The correct ratio is 35 : 6
4	48

Direct Proportion (p.36)

Set?

A	96
B	15
C	12
D	(i) 60 (ii) 30 (iii) 20 (iv) 14.4
E	see table below
F	10 g

E:

Number of fields	1	2	5
Number of sheep	20	40	100
Number of cows	8	16	40

Go!

1	5
2	If one amount doubles, the other amount doubles.
3	No. He is incorrect. The correct answer is Graph D as it starts at the origin.
4	a) $m = 8.75h$ b) 19

Proportion: Best Value (p.38)

Set?

A	300 teabags (e.g. 1 teabag = 1.6 p)
B	4 pints (e.g. 1 pint = 28.75 p)
C	30 (e.g. 1 plant = 21.7 p)
D	1.5 kg (e.g. 1 g = 13.3 p)

Go!

1	750 g (e.g. 1 g = 0.108 p)
2	Yes. You get more millilitres for £1
3	Garden Centre A (12 trays for the price 8 trays).
4	No. Standard now £1 = 351.6 g whereas Family £1 = 316 g

Proportion: Recipes (p.40)

Set?

A	(i) 1800 g (1.8 kg) Corned Beef 3 onions 9 carrots 900 ml of gravy (ii) 300 g Corned Beef $\frac{1}{2}$ onion $1\frac{1}{2}$ carrots 150 ml of gravy (iii) 900 g Corned Beef $1\frac{1}{2}$ onions $4\frac{1}{2}$ carrots 450 ml of gravy
B	(i) 300 g (ii) 10 eggs (iii) 200 g (iv) 10 (v) 3 eggs, 120 g sugar, 225 g flour, 90 g margarine
C	1600 ml (1.6 litres)

Go!

1	Yes. She has enough eggs and flour to make 60 cakes. She has enough sugar to make 72 cakes and enough margarine to make 48 cakes.
2	No. 100 g of margarine is needed.
3	15 people
4	see table below

4:

People	Ingredient
6	**4.5** ounces pasta
3	100% more onions
1	$1\frac{1}{4}$ pints of tomato soup
10	$\frac{1}{2}$ ounce cheese
8	50% more tuna

Proportion: Exchange Rates (p.42)

Set?

A	4200
B	138
C	700
D	240
E	11

Go!

1	1867 rand or £105.90
2	£1.13
3	Poland In Poland, £1 = 5 zloty which is greater than 4.80 zloty.
4	No because he has used the 10 yen exchange rate. The correct answer is 28571 yen.

Inverse Proportion (p.44)

Set?

A	18 minutes
B	1 day
C	2 hours
D	see table below
E	D

D:

x	3	9	0.75	0.3
y	21	7	84	210

Go!

1	No. If the number of workers increases, the number of days will decrease. She has used direct proportion not inverse proportion. It would take 2.5 days.
2	Only Sadie is correct.
3	72 minutes
4	a) 35 b) They work at the same rate.

Percentages 1 (p.46)

Set?

A	72
B	132
C	63
D	5.95
E	17.5
F	They are the same. They equal 22.
G	£432
H	£76.50

Go!

1	No. He should have typed 0.04 × 435 (the correct answer is $17.40)
2	£9.80
3	She should not divide by 20 to find 20%. The correct answer is 120 kg.
4	£312

Percentages 2 (p.48)

Set?

A	70%
B	80%
C	16.7% (to 1 d.p.)
D	125%
E	90%
F	£194.40
G	£79.90
H	93.6 kg

Go!

1	18.1%
2	She has not used the original amount. The correct answer is 33.3% (to 1 d.p.).
3	No. For example, if she had £100, 1.25 × £100 = £125 and 0.75 × £125 does not equal £100
4	10%
5	34.8% decrease (to 1 d.p.)

Interest and Growth (p.50)

Set?

A	£150
B	£528
C	£99.89
D	£1278.03
E	3960 (to the nearest whole number)

Go!

1	She has used simple interest and not compound interest. The correct answer is £2812.16
2	Bank B £705.44 interest rather than £675 interest at Bank A.
3	Emily Aaron has used simple interest.
4	a) 1,630,000 b) 2024 (at the start of 2025 it is greater than 2,000,000). c) It could reach 2 million sooner than 2024.

Depreciation and Decay (p.52)

Set?

A	£5145
B	£13,182.13
C	£3374.80
D	32,805
E	£4087

Go!

1	£2779.34
2	She has used the wrong multipliers (they should be 0.7 and 0.8). She has also used the original amount each time. The correct answer is £5734.40 (e.g. $16000 \times 0.7 \times 0.8^3$).
3	Andy and Vicki are both correct. She has used the multiplier 0.98 twice. He has taken away 2% twice.
4	18,639,000 square kilometres (to the nearest thousand).

Reverse Percentages (p.54)

Set?

A	£2500
B	£1.20
C	750 g
D	£700
E	£80

Go!

1	He has used £40 as the original amount. It should be £50.
2	150 minutes or 2 hours 30 minutes
3	C The original cost is £160
4	Yes His salary is now £40,393.60

Index Laws (p.56)

Set?

A	4^5
B	p^8
C	7^4
D	m^3
E	m^5
F	5^4
G	m^{20}
H	$\frac{1}{4}$
I	1
J	$\frac{1}{3}$

Go!

1	a) $2a^3$ b) m^{-5} c) m^7 d) p^{-21} e) $12m^2$ f) $8h^9$
2	4^6
3	a) 4 b) 0 c) 3 d) 8
4	She has only cubed the g^2 The correct answer is $64g^6$
5	a) $20m^5r^6$ b) $27x^6y^{12}$ c) $4m^{-2}n^4$ or $\frac{4n^4}{m^2}$ d) 1 e) $\frac{5}{4}$mn or $\frac{5mn}{4}$ f) $3m^{-1}n$ or $\frac{3n}{m}$

Expand and Simplify (p.58)

Set?

A	(i) $8a + 4$ (ii) $7x + 5y$ (iii) $4x^2 + 2x$ (iv) $3a^2 - 5b^2 + 7b$
B	(i) $3a + 6$ (ii) $8x + 12$ (iii) $y^2 - 6y$ (iv) $7h^2 + 3h$ (v) $40k + 4k^2$ (vi) $12m^2 - 6m$
C	(i) $7x + 17$ (ii) $a - 11$ (iii) $-4p + 24$
D	(i) $x^2 + 9x + 20$ (ii) $y^2 + 3y - 18$ (iii) $p^2 - 16p + 60$

Go!

1	$p = 3$
2	She should have written $12x - 8 - 20x - 5$ The correct answer is $-8x - 13$
3	No The correct answer is $y^2 - y - 6$
4	a) $2y^2 + 20y + 48$ b) $x^2 - 36$ c) $12a^2 - 47a + 40$ d) $2p^2 - 5pq - 3q^2$
5	Area of square ABGH = $(x + 2)(x + 2) = x^2 + 4x + 4$ Area of rectangle BCDG = $5(x + 2) = 5x + 10$ Area of square DEGF = $5 \times 5 = 25$ Total area = $x^2 + 9x + 39$

Sequences (p.60)

Set?

A	(i) 3, 11, 19, 27, 35 (ii) 32, 44, 56, 68, 80 (iii) 17, 14, 11, 8, 5 (iv) −5, −3, −1, 1, 3
B	(i) $7n + 4$ (ii) $6n - 4$ (iii) $n + 6$ (iv) $4n - 8$
C	(i) 8, 11, 16, 23, 32 (ii) 107

Go!

1	$22 - 2n$ (or $-2n + 22$)
2	She has confused the *n*th term with the term-to-term rule '+5' The *n*th term should be $5n - 3$
3	No, because when solved n is not a whole number (57.5).
4	$5n + 3$, $30 - 3n$, $n^2 + 9$
5	31

Solving Equations (p.62)

Set?

A	$x = 9$
B	$k = \frac{11}{5}$ (= 2.2)
C	$d = -4$

D	$a = \frac{15}{2} = 7.5$
E	x = 3
F	$y = \frac{1}{3}$
G	$k = \frac{32}{10} = \frac{16}{5} = 3.2$
H	$b = \pm 5$

Go!

1	Yes His method works because he has divided both sides by 6 and then added 2 to both sides. Note: this is an alternative method to solve equations with brackets.
2	Two $x = \pm 4$
3	Equation: 3x+2=8, 3x−2=8, 8=2−3x, -8=2+3x; Solution: x=-2, $x=\frac{10}{3}$, x=2, $x=-\frac{10}{3}$
4	a) m = 6 b) m = 5

Forming and Solving (p.64)

Set?

A	N = 4p + 20b
B	16 cm
C	80°
D	Helen £14.25 Sheena £29.25 James £28.50

Go!

1	110°
2	A: 55 B: 110 C: 52
3	50 cm²
4	Ella's number should be 2n – 5 Correct solutions: Cath: 28 Dave: 56 Ella: 51

Inequalities (p.66)

Set?

A	$-1 < w \leq 3$
B	(i) −3, −2, −1, 0, 1, 2, 3 (ii) 5, 6, 7, 8, 9 (iii) 4, 5, 6
C	$x > 7$
D	$x \leq 7$ 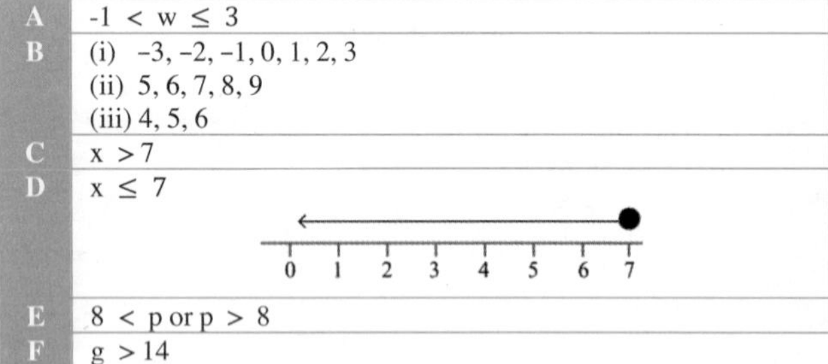
E	$8 < p$ or $p > 8$
F	$g > 14$

Go!

1	One mistake is the first step should be '+10' Second mistake, she has written the solution without an inequality symbol ($x \geq -1$)
2	$y \leq 14$ and $y > 17$ So it is not possible to have a value of y that satisfies both inequalities.
3	a) $-2 < x \leq 5$ b) 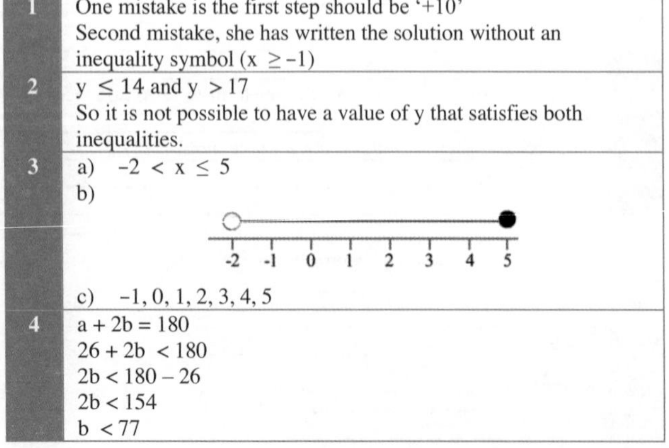 c) −1, 0, 1, 2, 3, 4, 5
4	a + 2b = 180 26 + 2b < 180 2b < 180 – 26 2b < 154 b < 77

Factorising 1 (p.68)

Set?

A	(i) 2(x + 5) (ii) 3(3 + 5y) (iii) 7 (2s – 3) (iv) 11(-a + 2)
B	(i) 4(a + 7b) (ii) 10(2p – q) (iii) 4(5t – 9u) (iv) 15(3a + 4d)
C	(i) x(x – 1) (ii) y(y + 1) (iii) 4a(3a – 1) (iv) $5s(2s^2 - 4s - 3)$
D	(i) 5(3x + y – 8z) (ii) 4(2x – 3y – 5z) (iii) 5a(3 + 5b – 8c)

Go!

1	a) $3x^2y(5xy + 8)$ b) $3pq(4q^2 - 4q + 5r)$
2	No She has not factorised completely. Correct answer is 12(p + 3)
3	Both are correct. 2(x + y) = 2x + 2y
4	Possible solutions: 45x + 27 = 9(5x + 3) 15x + 27 = 3(5x + 9) 5x + 27 = 1(5x + 27) 135x + 27 = 27(5x + 1)

Factorising 2 (p.70)

Set?

A	(i) (x + 6)(x + 2) (ii) (y + 1)(y + 12) (iii) (h – 8)(h + 2) (iv) (p – 5)(p – 10)
B	(i) (x – 10)(x + 10) (ii) (a – 6)(a + 6) (iii) (m – 1)(m + 1) (iv) (a – b)(a + b)
C	(i) a = -3, a = -8 (ii) p = -5, p = -6 (iii) y = 7, y = -4 (iv) x = 1, x = 7
D	(i) x = 0, x = -10 (ii) x = 0, x = 6
E	x = 3, x = -3

Go!

1	(y + 1) and (y + 9)
2	No It can be factorised to (x – 13)(x + 13)
3	No It has not been fully factorised. It should be (x + 3)(x + 7)
4	He has factorised incorrectly. The correct solutions are p = -6 and p = 3
5	8 and 3 or 24 and 1

Changing the Subject (p.72)

Set?

A	$n = \frac{T}{5}$
B	c = a − b
C	$x = y^2$
D	$t = \frac{s+1}{2}$
E	$p = \frac{s-1}{-2}$ (or $p = \frac{1-s}{2}$)
F	$x = \frac{y-6}{\frac{1}{2}} = 2(y - 6)$
G	r = 2A − s
H	$q = (p - 5)^2$

Go!

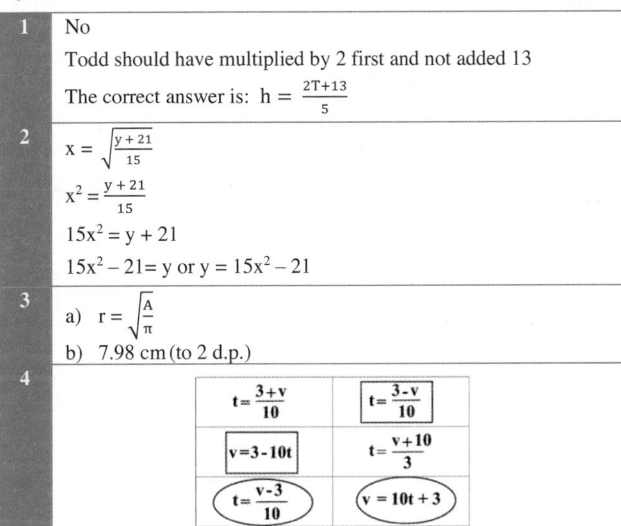

1	No Todd should have multiplied by 2 first and not added 13 The correct answer is: $h = \frac{2T+13}{5}$
2	$x = \sqrt{\frac{y+21}{15}}$ $x^2 = \frac{y+21}{15}$ $15x^2 = y + 21$ $15x^2 - 21 = y$ or $y = 15x^2 - 21$
3	a) $r = \sqrt{\frac{A}{\pi}}$ b) 7.98 cm (to 2 d.p.)
4	$t = \frac{3+v}{10}$; $t = \frac{3-v}{10}$; $v = 3 - 10t$; $t = \frac{v+10}{3}$; $t = \frac{v-3}{10}$; $v = 10t + 3$

Standard Form 1 (p.74)

Set?

A	(i) 8×10^3 (iii) 4.6161×10^5	(ii) 3.14×10^4 (iv) 1.1111×10^4
B	(i) 6×10^{-4} (iii) 7.61×10^{-1}	(ii) 5.43×10^{-3} (iv) 1.0101×10^{-2}
C	(i) 700 000 (iii) 2 230 000 (v) 40 892	(ii) 78 000 (iv) 990.9 (vi) 64
D	(i) 0.00005 (iii) 0.00228 (v) 0.0000009999	(ii) 0.00065 (iv) 0.09842 (vi) 0.1

Go!

1	No. The first number is not between 1 and 10. The correct answer is 2.8×10^4
2	4×10^4
3	9.85×10^6
4	8×10^{-2}
5	a) A: 16×10^2, 160×10^{-3}, 0.16×10^3, 0.016×10^6, 0.16×10^{-3} B: 1.6×10^4, 1.6×10^2, 1.6×10^3, 1.6×10^{-4}, 1.6×10^{-1} b) 1.6×10^3

Standard Form 2 (p.76)

Set?

A	(i) 3.02×10^5 (ii) 6.5×10^6 (iii) 2.97×10^6 (iv) 3.5×10^6
B	(i) 6×10^8 (ii) 6×10^5 (iii) 1.2×10^9 (iv) 3×10^6 (v) 3×10^9 (vi) 3×10^6
C	(i) 6.2×10^7 (ii) 3.5×10^{-2} (iii) 9.5×10^7 (iv) 8.3×10^{-3} (v) 6.7×10^9 (vi) 5.2×10^3 (vii) 4.8×10^{-3} (viii) 2.7×10^{-11}

Go!

1	a) 0.06×10^5, 0.6×10^5, 60×10^4, 6 million b) 46×10^{-6}, 0.46×10^{-3}, 0.046, 4.6×10^{-1}
2	No. He should have added the indices (powers) and not multiplied. The correct answer is 7.5×10^8.

3	a = 5, b = 2, c = –5, d = 3
4	9.3×10^7 seconds
5	Yes The total height of the paper is 4.5 cm which is less than 5 cm.

Alternate/Corresponding Angles (p.78)

Set?

A	61° Possible reasons: Angles on a straight line add up to 180° Corresponding angles are equal
B	m = 155° Possible reason: Corresponding angles are equal n = 105° Possible reasons: Angles on a straight line add up to 180° Alternate angles are equal
C	y = 70° Possible reasons: Alternate angles are equal The sum of the angles in a triangle is 180°
D	x = 73° Possible reasons: The sum of the angles in a triangle is 180° Alternate angles are equal
E	y = 82° Possible reasons: Alternate angles are equal The sum of the angles in a triangle is 180°

Go!

1	No She has not given enough reasons. E.g. Angles on a straight line add up to 180° **and** corresponding angles are equal.
2	x = 40° Possible reasons: The sum of the angles in a triangle is 180° Alternate angles are equal
3	y = 11
4	x = 47.5° Possible reason: Co-interior angles add up to 180°

Interior and Exterior Angles (p.80)

Set?

A	m = 110° The sum of the interior angles in a quadrilateral is 360°
B	a = 125° Possible reasons: The sum of interior angles in a pentagon is 540° 2a = 250°
C	9
D	x = 155°
E	No Exterior angle = 42° and 360° ÷ 42° is not a whole number.

Go!

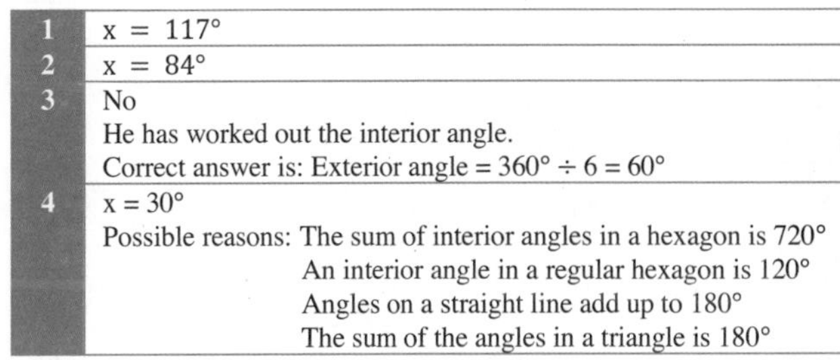

1	x = 117°
2	x = 84°
3	No He has worked out the interior angle. Correct answer is: Exterior angle = 360° ÷ 6 = 60°
4	x = 30° Possible reasons: The sum of interior angles in a hexagon is 720° An interior angle in a regular hexagon is 120° Angles on a straight line add up to 180° The sum of the angles in a triangle is 180°

Plans and Elevations (p.82)

Set?

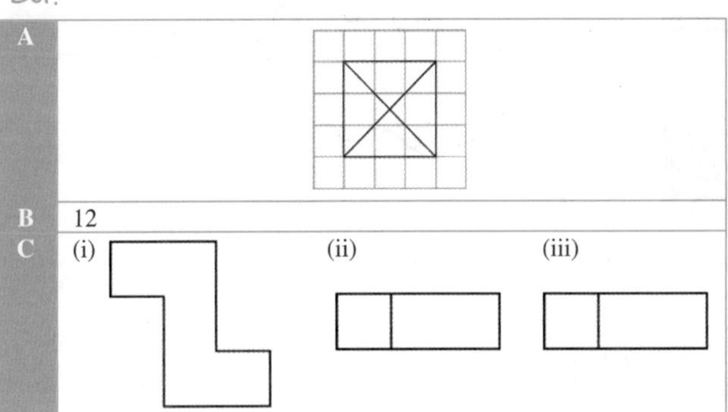

A	
B	12
C	(i) (ii) (iii)

Go!

1	a) A cuboid with dimensions (cm) of $1 \times 1 \times 20$ or $1 \times 2 \times 10$ or $1 \times 4 \times 5$ or $2 \times 2 \times 5$ b) If: $1 \times 1 \times 20$: Three rectangles: 1×1, 1×20, 1×20 $1 \times 2 \times 10$: Three rectangles: 1×2, 1×10, 2×10 $1 \times 4 \times 5$: Three rectangles: 1×4, 1×5, 4×5 $2 \times 2 \times 5$: Three rectangles: 2×2, 2×5, 2×5 Diagrams must be clearly labelled with dimensions of each side length, front elevation, side elevation and plan dependent upon the orientation of the cuboid.
2	a) b) 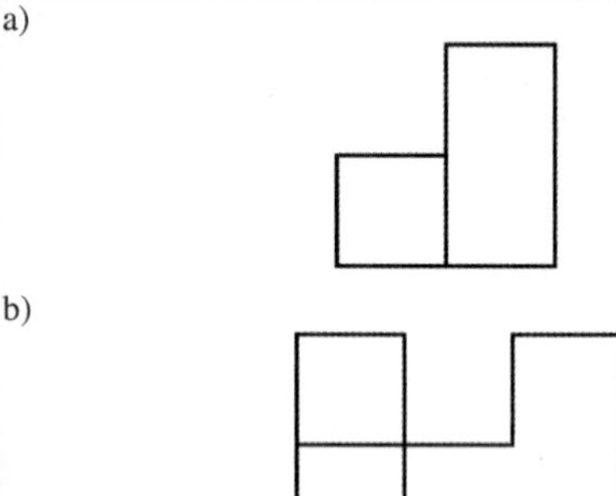
3	She has drawn an elevation not the plan.
4	Correct sketch of a triangular prism; e.g. 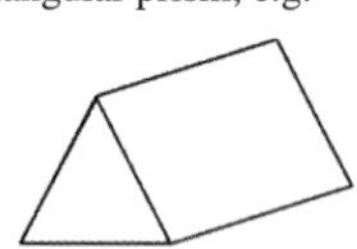

Constructions (p.84)

Set? *See www.justaroo.co.uk/solutions for detailed solutions.*

A	A straight line 10 cm long with a perpendicular bisector constructed. All construction arcs must be shown.
B	A straight line 78 mm long with a perpendicular bisector constructed. All construction arcs must be shown.
C	An angle of 60° drawn with an angle bisector constructed. All construction arcs must be shown.
D	An angle of 110° drawn with an angle bisector constructed. All construction arcs must be shown.
E	Perpendicular line constructed from A to the line. All construction arcs must be shown.

Go!

1	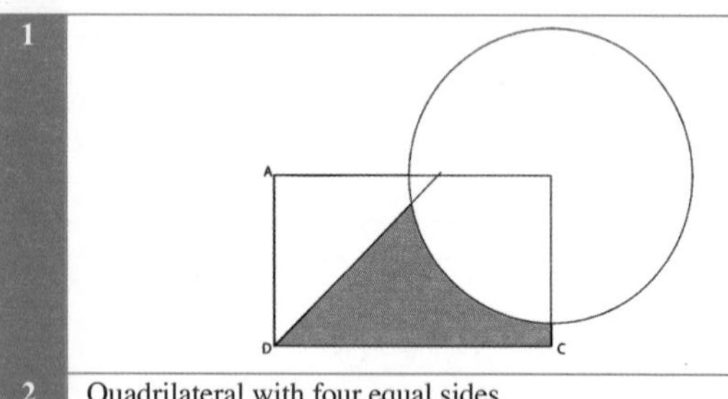
2	Quadrilateral with four equal sides. All construction arcs must be shown. *See www.justaroo.co.uk/solutions for a detailed solution.*
3	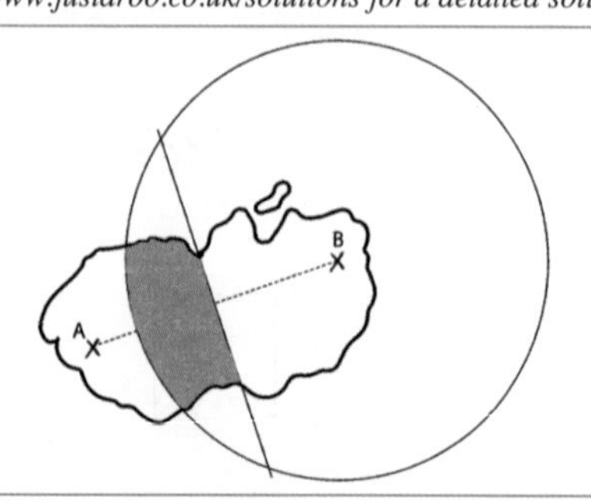

Bearings (p.86)

Set?

A	(i) 143° (± 2°) (ii) 323° (± 2°)
B	No 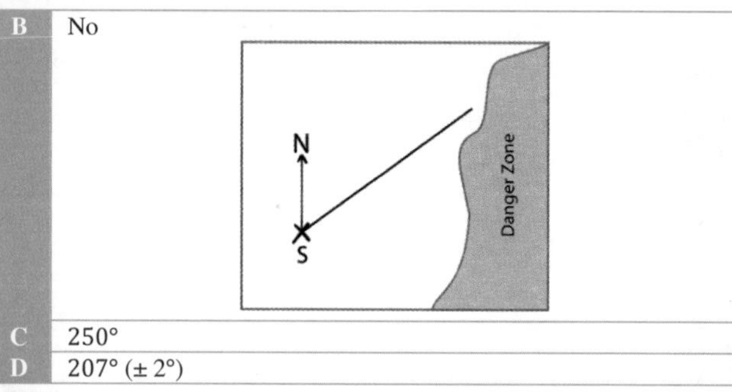
C	250°
D	207° (± 2°)

Go!

1	No He has measured anti-clockwise.
2	see table below
3	015°
4	No 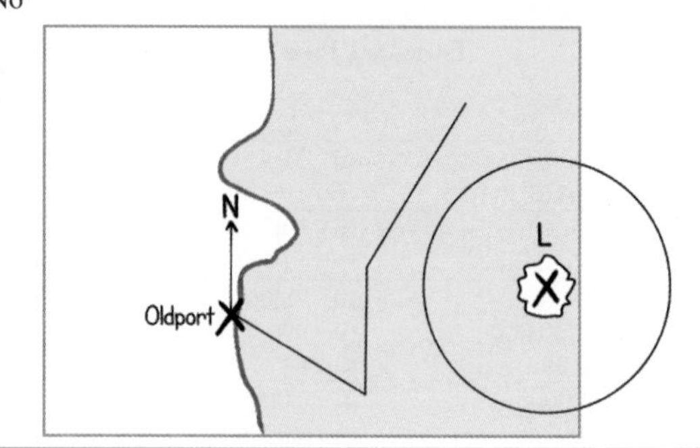

The bearing of …	from …	is …
Bristol	Birmingham	220° (± 5°)
London	Bristol	090°
Southampton	Birmingham	180°

Pythagoras' Theorem 1 (p.88)

Set?

A	15 m
B	9.9 cm (to 1 d.p.)
C	8 cm
D	30 cm
E	Yes The ladder will reach a height of over 5 m (5.2 m to 1 d.p.).

Go!

1	10 cm
2	8.5 cm (to 1 d.p.)
3	53 km
4	No Billy should have written: $12^2 - 5^2 = c^2$ $144 - 25 = c^2$ $c^2 = 119$ $c = 10.9$ cm (to 1 d.p.)

Pythagoras' Theorem 2 (p.90)

Set?

A	Yes $12^2 + 16^2 = 144 + 256 = 400$ $20^2 = 400$ So Pythagoras' Theorem does work.
B	$8^2 + 10^2 = 64 + 100 = 164$ XZ = 12cm; $12^2 = 144$ So Pythagoras' Theorem does not work.
C	8.6 units (to 1 d.p.)
D	7.4 cm (to 2 s.f.)

Go!

1	6.40 units (to 3 s.f.)
2	96 cm^2
3	7 cm (to 1 s.f.) or 6.9 cm (to 1 d.p.)
4	10.9 cm (to 3 s.f.)

Trigonometry 1 (p.92)

Set?

A	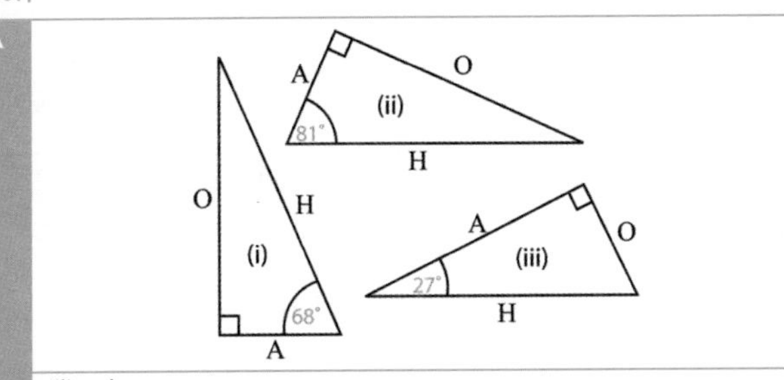
B	(i) sin (ii) tan (iii) cos
C	(i) 19.9 cm (to 1 d.p.) (ii) 7.2 cm (to 1 d.p.) (iii) 12.7 cm (to 1 d.p.)

Go!

1	He has rearranged incorrectly. The correct working is: $k = \frac{8}{\tan 48°} = 7.2$ cm (to 1 d.p.)
2	24.98594771… cm = 25 cm (to nearest whole number)
3	6.53566842… = 6.5 cm (to 1 d.p.)
4	15.5 km (to 3 s.f.)

Trigonometry 2 (p.94)

Set?

A	67.4°
B	23.6°
C	62.2°
D	17.4°
E	38.0°

Go!

1	No He needs to use cos (cosine). Correct answer is 69.5° (to 1 d.p.).
2	67.4° (to 3 s.f.)
3	36.9° and 53.1° (to 1 d.p.)
4	9.3° (to 2 s.f.)

Trigonometry 3 (p.96)

Set?

A	(i) $\frac{1}{2}$ (ii) 1 (iii) 0 (iv) 0 (v) $\frac{\sqrt{2}}{2}$
B	$\cos 60° = \frac{8}{BC}$ $BC = \frac{8}{\cos 60°}$ $BC = \frac{8}{0.5} = 16$ cm
C	9 m
D	$\sin 30° = \frac{1.5}{x}$ $x = \frac{1.5}{\sin 30°}$ $x = \frac{1.5}{0.5} = 3$ m

Go!

1	Length: $\frac{9\sqrt{3}}{2}$ cm Width: $\frac{9}{2}$ cm (or 4.5 cm)
2	$\tan 60° = \frac{h}{2}$ $\sqrt{3} = \frac{h}{2}$ $h = 2\sqrt{3}$ cm
3	No 45° has the same value for sine and cosine.
4	4 cm

Pythagoras with Trigonometry (p.98)

Set?

A	a) (i) 12.3 cm (to 1 d.p.) (ii) 10.3 cm (to 1 d.p.) (iii) 13.2 cm (to 1 d.p.) b) 42.9°
B	24 cm
C	8.2 cm (to 1 d.p.)

Go!

1	18.2 cm (to 1 d.p.)
2	a) The hypotenuse of triangle STW must be longer than 20 cm. b) 27.8 cm (to 1 d.p.)
3	9.89 cm (to 2 d.p.)

Circles 1 (p.100)

Set?

A	C = 56.5 cm A = 254.5 cm^2
B	C = 18.8 m A = 28.3 m^2
C	C = 72.3 cm A = 415.5 cm^2
D	C = 28.3 m A = 63.6 m^2
E	C = 18π cm A = 81π cm^2

Go!

1	He has used the diameter and not the radius. The correct answer is 49π cm^2
2	12
3	763 mm^2 (to 3 s.f.)
4	432

Circles 2 (p.102)

Set?

A	7.96 cm
B	5.41 m
C	3.57 mm
D	16 cm
E	A = 127 cm^2 P = 46.3 cm
F	60.7 cm^2

Go!

1	She should have divided by π first. The correct answer is 5.35 (to 3 s.f.)
2	50.3 cm^2
3	Yes Diameter of the wheel is 134.6 cm
4	A = 50π cm^2 P = 20π cm

Arcs and Sectors (p.104)

Set?

A	7.95 cm^2
B	8.80 cm
C	15π cm^2
D	115 cm^2
E	42.7 cm

Go!

1	He should have used the diameter not the radius. The correct answer is 107.1 cm (to 1 d.p.).
2	2.1 cm
3	a) 169π mm^2 b) $26\pi + 26$ mm
4	a) 36.3 cm^2 b) h = 3 cm (to the nearest whole number)

Surface Area and Volume 1 (p.106)

Set?

A	Volume = 125 m^3 Surface area = 150 m^2
B	Volume = 600 cm^3 Surface area = 660 cm^2
C	Volume = 96 cm^3 Surface area = 152 cm^2
D	Volume = 678.6 cm^3 Surface area = 508.9 cm^2

Go!

1	2 tins. (The surface area is 11.3 m^2).
2	0.5 m
3	Many solutions, e.g. x = 2 cm, y = 6 cm, z = 4 cm $[(x \times y) \div 2] \times z = 24$
4	No He has just multiplied all the numbers together. The correct answer is 42 m^3

Surface Area and Volume 2 (p.108)

Set?

A	(i) Volume = 48 cm^3 (ii) Surface area = 96 cm^2
B	(i) Volume = 37.7 cm^3 (ii) Surface area = 75.4 cm^2
C	Surface area = 144π cm^2 Volume = 288π cm^3

Go!

1	300π cm^2
2	244 cm^3
3	a) 475π cm^3 b) 1490 cm^3
4	301.6 cm^2

Sampling (p.110)

Set?

A	(i) Each student has an equal chance of selection. (ii) E.g. picking student names from a hat. (iii) Every student of the school.
B	(see table below)
C	Yes The pupils do not have an equal chance of being selected.

	Census	Sample
Advantages	3,6	1,2
Disadvantages	5	4,7

Go!

1	It is only true for his sample.
2	a) A sample is part of a population. b) She needs to make sure the sample represents the population; e.g. asking students from other year groups.
3	Possible solutions: Anna (advantage: everyone is represented) Fred (advantage: quicker) Anna (disadvantage: it takes longer) Fred (disadvantage: it could be biased)
4	1. She only asks students who use the canteen. 2. She only asks the first 10 students. 3. She only asks students on a Friday.

Averages (p.112)

Set?

A	M
B	(i) 72 (ii) 73.5
C	22
D	23.29 (to 2 d.p.)
E	Player A Mean: Player A = 42.2 (to 1 d.p.), Player B = 36.7 (to 1 d.p.) or Median: Player A = 31, Player B = 18.5

Go!

1	a) £23,000 b) £23,500 c) £27,812.50 d) No. Six of the eight salaries are less than £27,000. One salary is much more than the other salaries and will affect the mean.
2	Theo did not work out the total before dividing by 5
3	12 and 14
4	64%

Averages from a Table (p.114)

Set?

A	Europe
B	(i) 4 (ii) 4 (iii) 3.4 (to 1 d.p.) (iv) 4
C	(i) 1 (ii) 1.6 (to 1 d.p.) (iii) 1

Go!

1	a) Total number of children = 86, total frequency = 28 so the mean is 86 ÷ 28 = 3.1 (to 1 d.p.). b) Possible reason: This is based on a sample not the UK population (some families have zero, some families have more than 5 children).
2	a) 1.875 b) 1
3	The median number of errors is 3
4	True Mean: 126 ÷ 18 = 7 Median: number between 9th and 10th values = 7 Mode: 7 (it has the highest frequency).

Averages from Grouped Data (p.116)

Set?

A	(i) $10 \le d < 15$ (ii) $5 \le d < 10$ (iii) 9.2 km (to 1 d.p.)
B	(i) $0 \le d < 10$ (ii) $10 \le d < 20$ (iii) 28.6 km (iv) As the data has been grouped, she does not know the highest and lowest values.

Go!

1	She has divided by 4 and she should have divided by 41. The correct answer is: 1875 ÷ 41 = 45.7 (to 1 d.p.).
2	Yes The modal class is $20 \le h < 22$ and median (15th value) lies in the class interval $20 \le h < 22$
3	a) 445 b) 728.2 (to 1 d.p.) c) As the exact values are not known, the midpoints have been used and not the actual values.
4	93

Frequency Diagrams (p.118)

Set?

A	2, 6, 14, 30, 50, 70
B	(i) (table below) (ii) (diagram below)

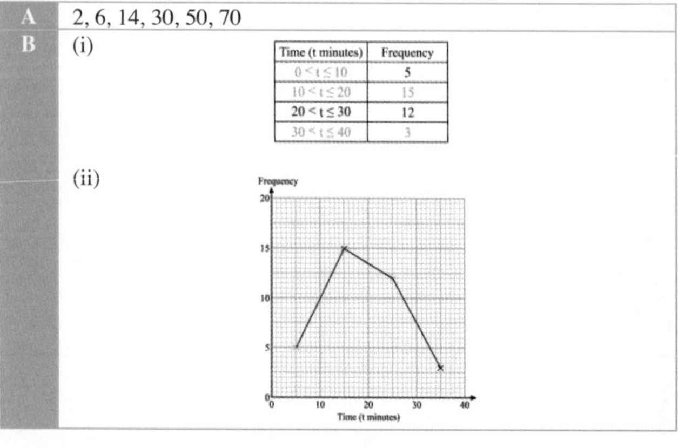

Time (t minutes)	Frequency
$0 < t \le 10$	5
$10 < t \le 20$	15
$20 < t \le 30$	12
$30 < t \le 40$	3

Go!

1	Possible statements: Both classes have scored between 0 to 40 More pupils in Class B scored between 30 and 40 More pupils in Class A scored between 0 and 10

2

Time (minutes)	Frequency
1 - 5	5
6 - 10	12
11 - 15	8
16 - 20	10

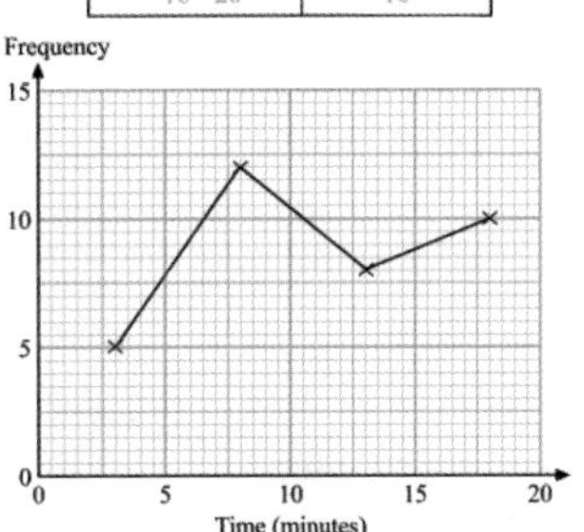

3 Mistake 1: Points are not plotted at the midpoints.
Mistake 2: The frequency polygon has been joined up.
Mistake 3: The horizontal axis is labelled incorrectly.

Scatter Graphs (p.120)

Set?

A a)

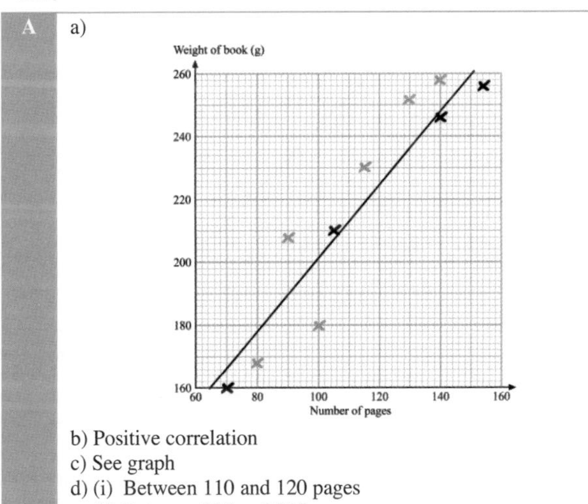

b) Positive correlation
c) See graph
d) (i) Between 110 and 120 pages
(ii) Between 235 and 245 grams

Go!

1 a)

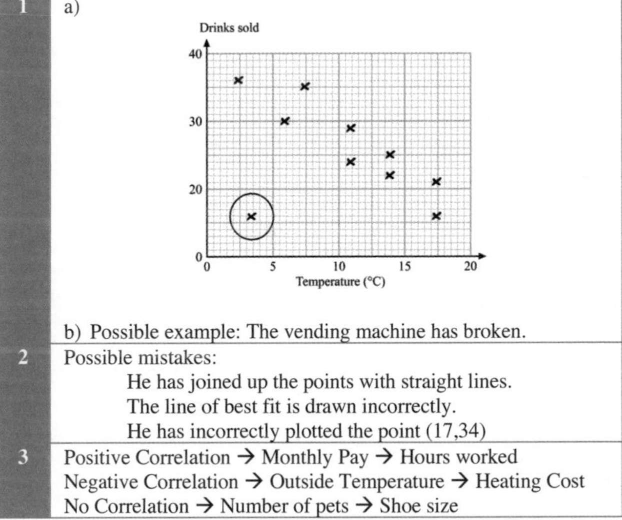

b) Possible example: The vending machine has broken.

2 Possible mistakes:
He has joined up the points with straight lines.
The line of best fit is drawn incorrectly.
He has incorrectly plotted the point (17,34)

3 Positive Correlation → Monthly Pay → Hours worked
Negative Correlation → Outside Temperature → Heating Cost
No Correlation → Number of pets → Shoe size

Time Series (p.122)

Set?

A

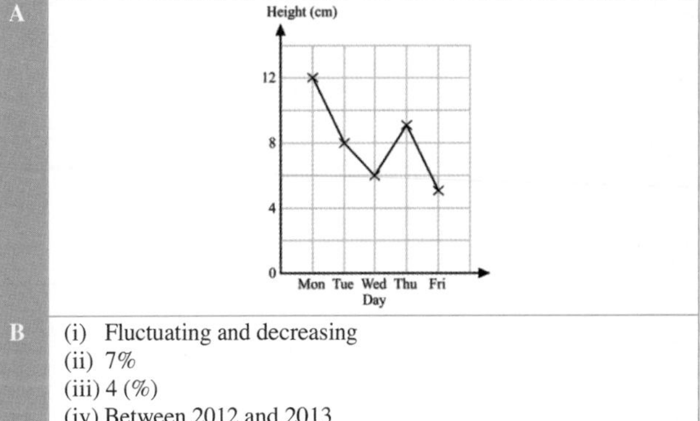

B (i) Fluctuating and decreasing
(ii) 7%
(iii) 4 (%)
(iv) Between 2012 and 2013

Go!

1 a)

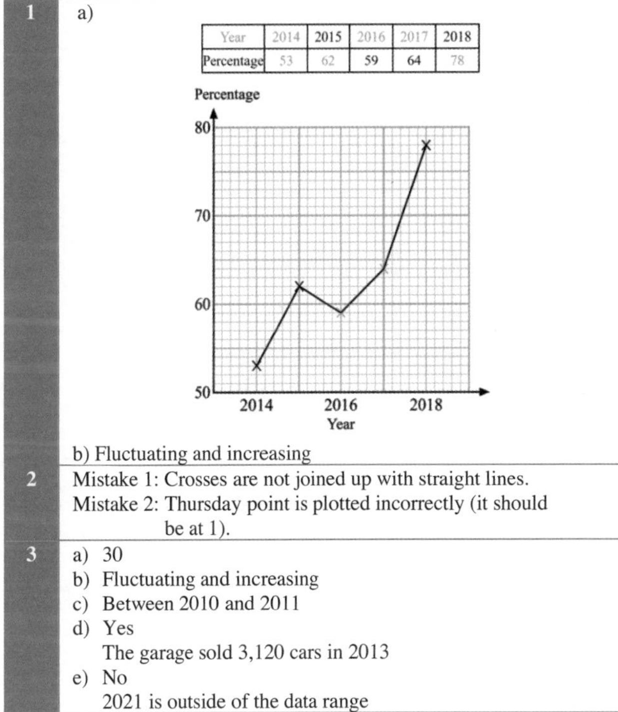

Year	2014	2015	2016	2017	2018
Percentage	53	62	59	64	78

b) Fluctuating and increasing

2 Mistake 1: Crosses are not joined up with straight lines.
Mistake 2: Thursday point is plotted incorrectly (it should be at 1).

3 a) 30
b) Fluctuating and increasing
c) Between 2010 and 2011
d) Yes
The garage sold 3,120 cars in 2013
e) No
2021 is outside of the data range

Pie Charts (p.124)

Set?

A Angles: (18°), 96°, 198°, 48°

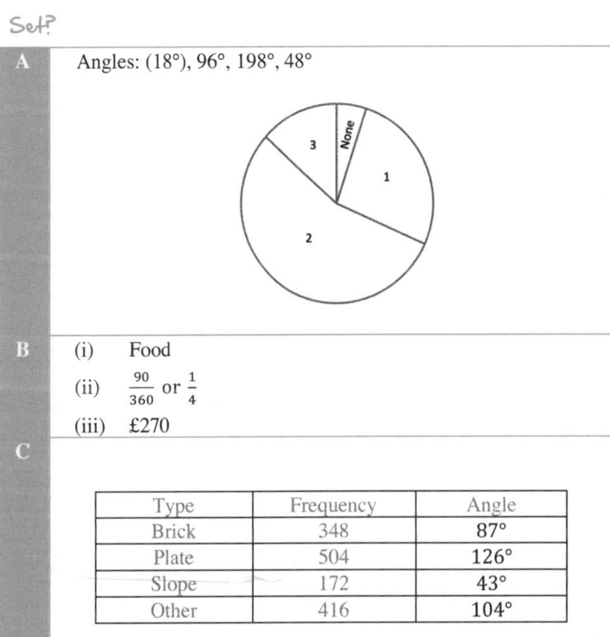

B (i) Food
(ii) $\frac{90}{360}$ or $\frac{1}{4}$
(iii) £270

C

Type	Frequency	Angle
Brick	348	87°
Plate	504	126°
Slope	172	43°
Other	416	104°

Go!

1	a) £13.2 billion b) £3 billion
2	Angles: 24°, 108°, 168°, 60°
3	B (Bronwen is incorrect) The number of bronze medals is represented by a larger proportion of the circle in 2016 so the overall total will be smaller than in 2008
4	189

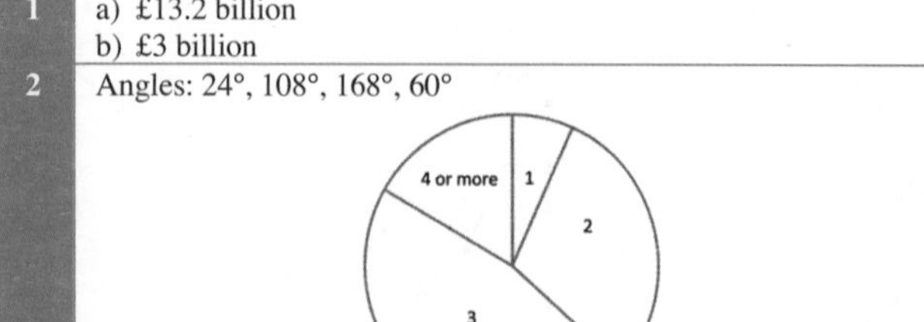

Coordinates (p.126)

Set?

A	(4, 2)
B	(3, 2)
C	(−0.5, 1)
D	(3, 3)

Go!

1	No She has found only one of the possibilities. The other two possible answers are: (−5, 0) and (−5, 4) (−3, 2) and (1, 2)
2	(−4, 2)
3	He has found the midpoint of the given coordinates rather than the location of point Q. The coordinates of point Q should be (6, 2)
4	(3, 20)

Straight Line Graphs 1 (p.128)

Set?

A

x	-2	-1	0	1	2
y	-6	-2	2	6	10

B

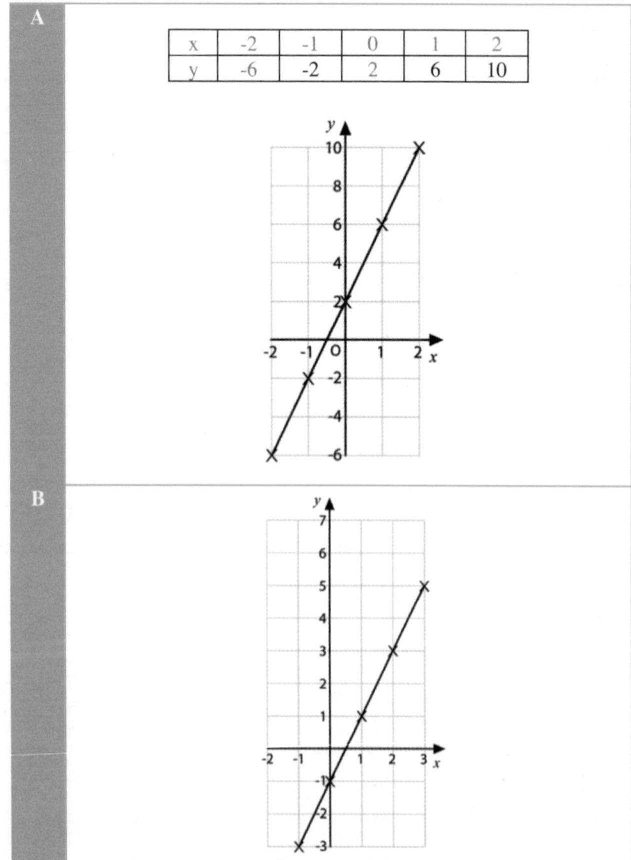

C

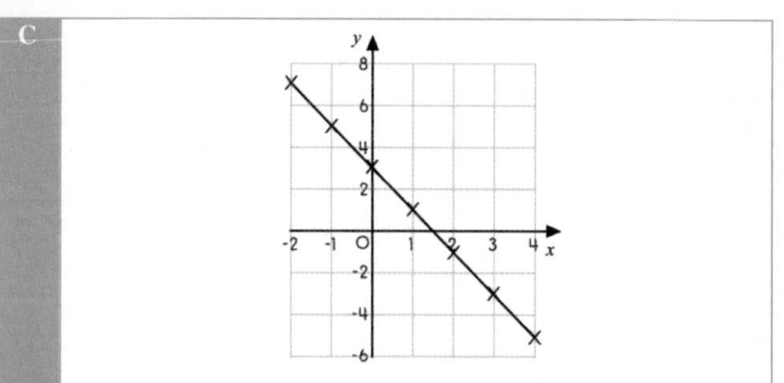

Go!

1

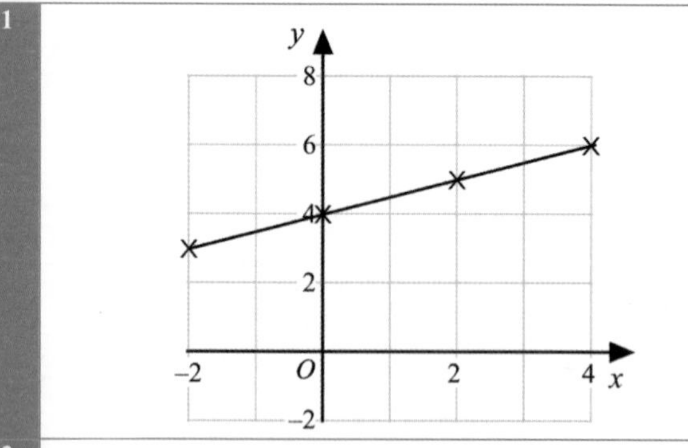

2

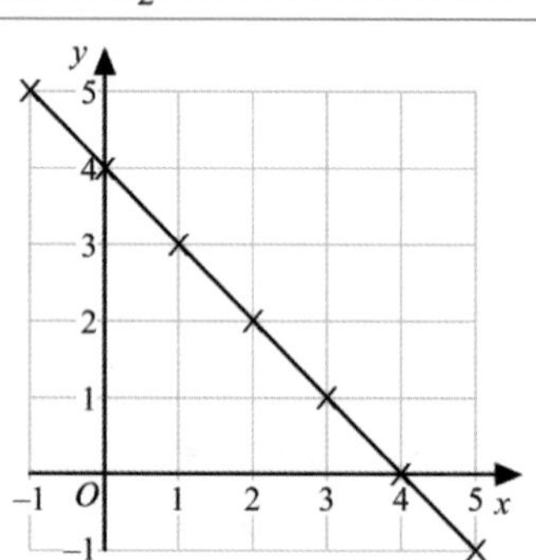

3 a)

Hours worked	0	1	2	3	4
Total cost (£)	40	65	90	115	140

b)

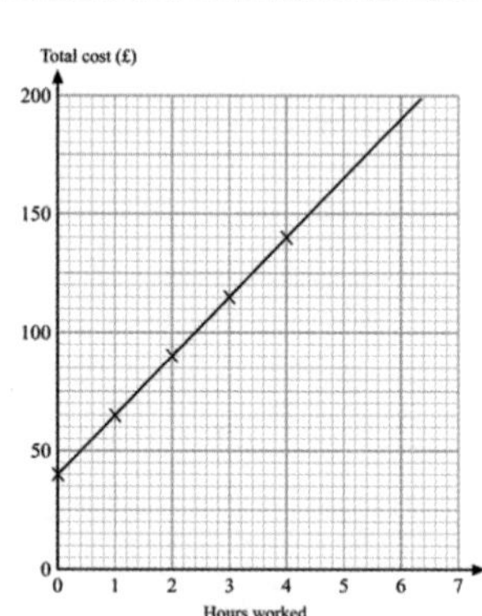

c) 5.4 hours

4 Irfan
Every coordinate on Irfan's graph has an x value and y value which add up to 8 (e.g. when x = 0, y = 8 and when x = 8, y = 0 and when x = 4, y = 4).

Straight Line Graphs 2 (p.130)

Set?

A	(i) 1 (ii) −2
B	3
C	−2
D	$-\frac{4}{8}\left(=-\frac{1}{2}\right)$

Go!

1	a) 2 b) 2 c) They are parallel lines.
2	a) He should have divided the change in y by the change in x. b) $\frac{2}{3}$
3	−2
4	d = 22

Straight Line Graphs 3 (p.132)

Set?

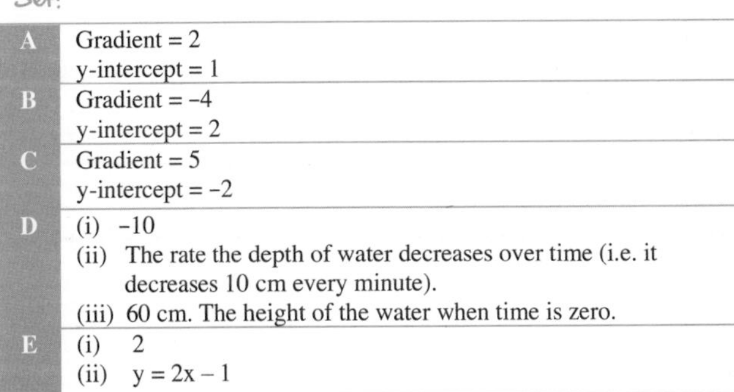

A	Gradient = 2 y-intercept = 1
B	Gradient = −4 y-intercept = 2
C	Gradient = 5 y-intercept = −2
D	(i) −10 (ii) The rate the depth of water decreases over time (i.e. it decreases 10 cm every minute). (iii) 60 cm. The height of the water when time is zero.
E	(i) 2 (ii) y = 2x − 1

Go!

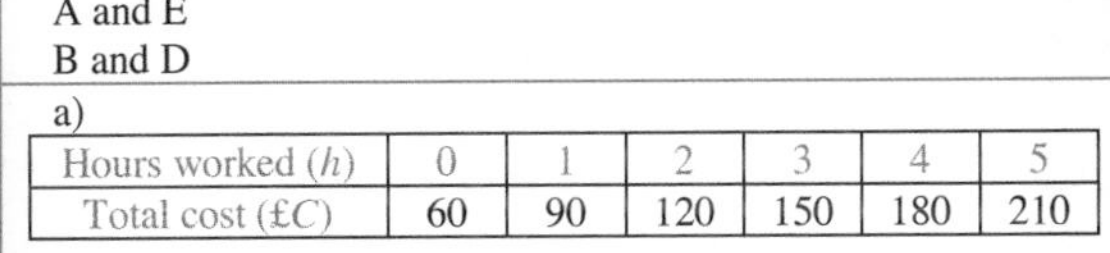

1. A and E
   B and D

2. a)

Hours worked (h)	0	1	2	3	4	5
Total cost (£C)	60	90	120	150	180	210

b)

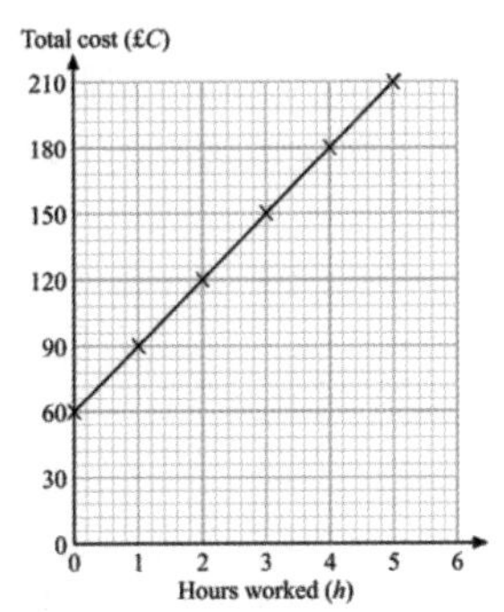

c) The cost per hour.
d) The callout fee.
e) C = 30h + 60

3. a) Both lines have a gradient of 3 (the second equation can be rearranged to y = 3x − 1)
   b)

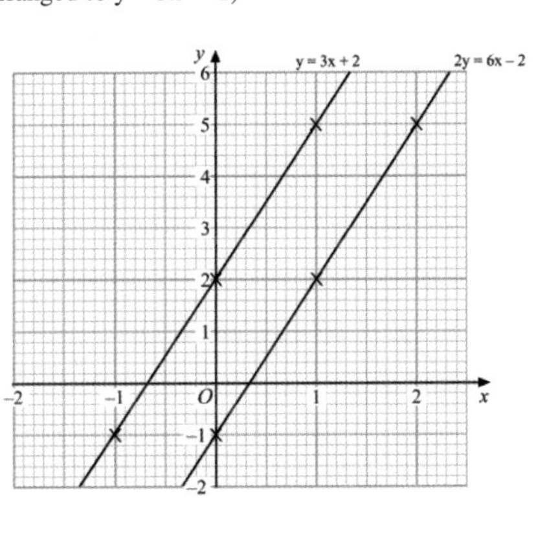

Non-Linear Graphs (p.134)

Set?

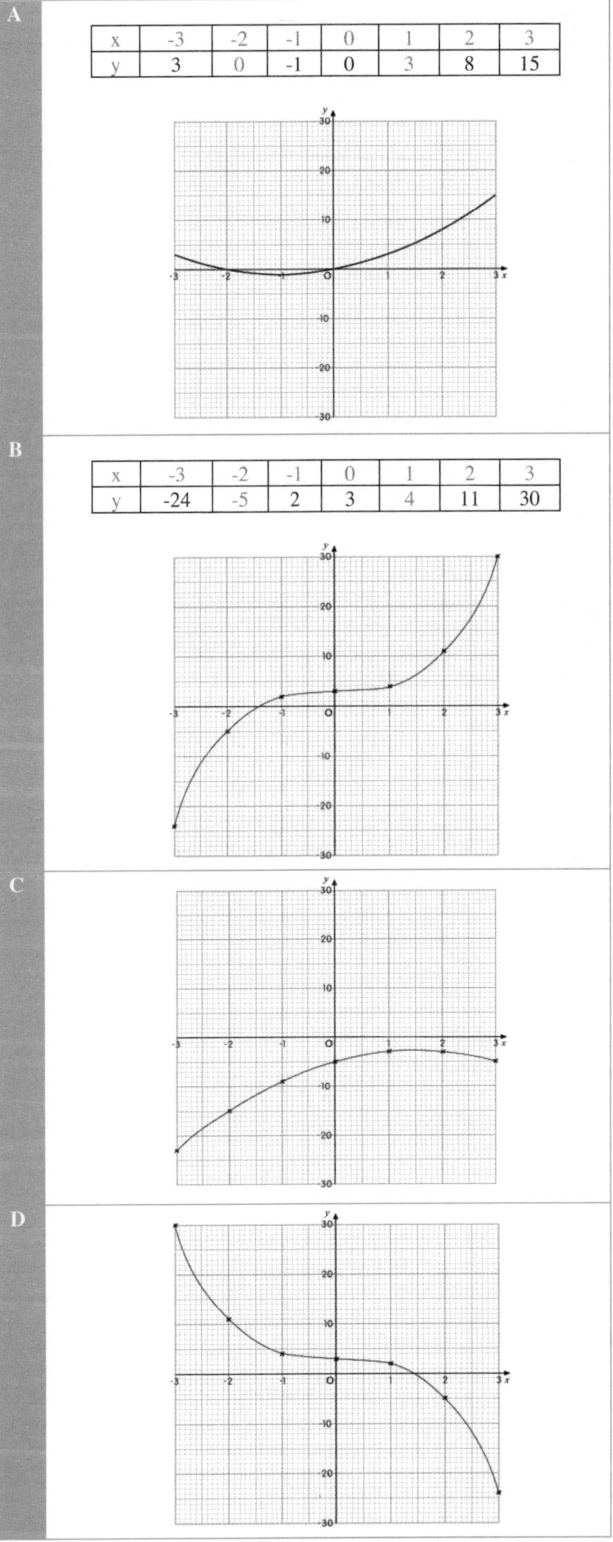

A

x	-3	-2	-1	0	1	2	3
y	3	0	-1	0	3	8	15

B

x	-3	-2	-1	0	1	2	3
y	-24	-5	2	3	4	11	30

C

D

Go!

1

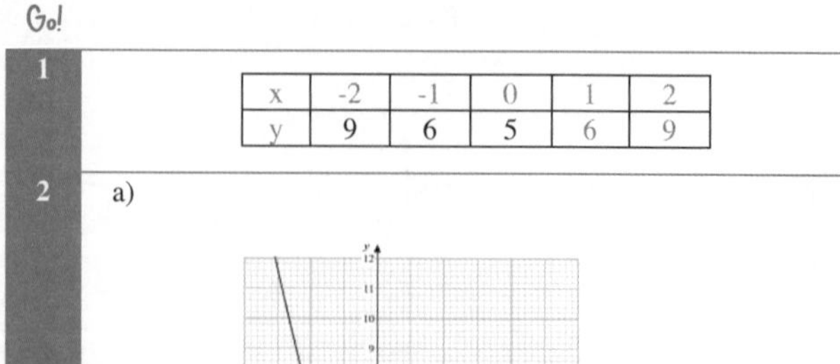

x	-2	-1	0	1	2
y	9	6	5	6	9

2 a)

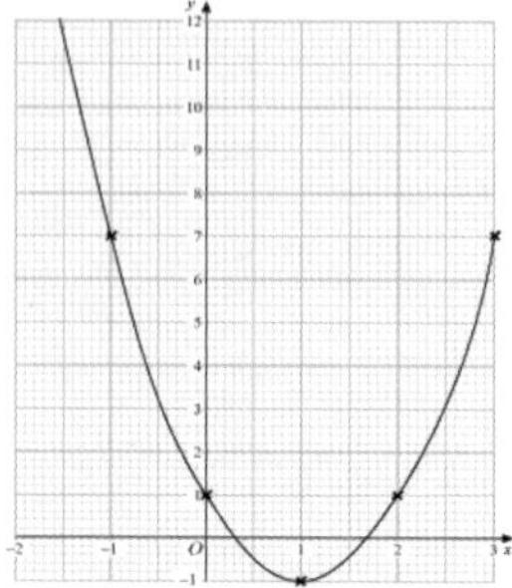

b) (1, -1)

c) One root between 0.2 and 0.4
One root between 1.6 and 1.8

3

x	0.5	1	2	3	4	5	6
y	12	6	3	2	1.5	1.2	1

Speed, Distance, Time (p.136)

Set?

A	(i) 6 mph (ii) 8 km/h (iii) 3 hours (iv) 135 km
B	64 mph
C	10 km/h

Go!

1	0.25 hours is $\frac{1}{4}$ of an hour = 15 minutes
2	3 km/h
3	18:11
4	54 mph

Compound Measures (p.138)

Set?

A	992.3 g
B	0.23 cm^3 (to 2 s.f.)
C	4.2 kg
D	Hong Kong Number of people: 7 UK Population Density: 255 (rounded from 254.5051517…)
E	2.5 N/cm^2

Go!

1	Louis should have done 8 ÷ 19.3 The correct answer is 0.4145 cm^3 (to 4 d.p.).
2	No If you want to half the pressure, you need to double the area.
3	National Park A It has the larger density of elephants/km^2 (3.06 elephants/km^2 compared to 1.6 elephants/km^2 in Park B)
4	8.14 g/cm^3 (to 2 d.p.)

Real Life Graphs (p.140)

Set?

A	(i) 250 m (ii) 25 minutes (iii) 50 metres per minute (iv) 1.2 km/h
B	A → 2 B → 3 C → 1

Go!

1

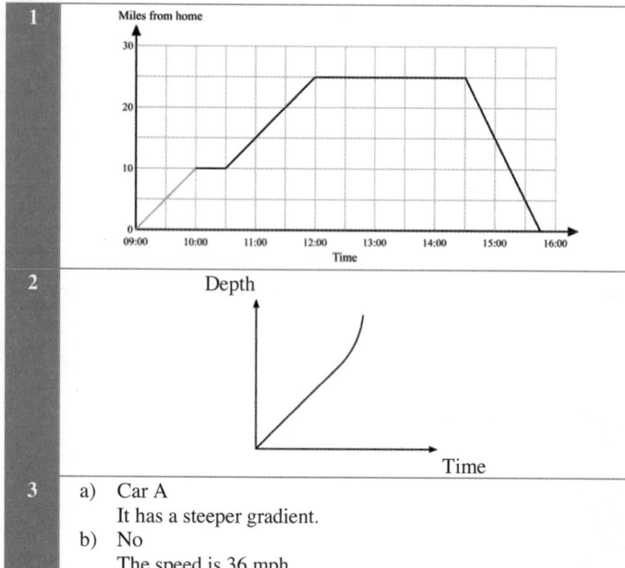

2

3 a) Car A
It has a steeper gradient.
b) No
The speed is 36 mph.
c) 100 minutes
Possible assumption: Both cars continue at the same speed.

Congruence (p.142)

Set?

A

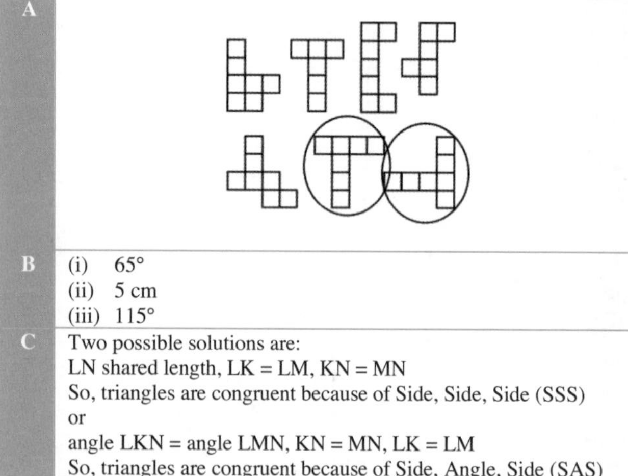

B	(i) 65° (ii) 5 cm (iii) 115°
C	Two possible solutions are: LN shared length, LK = LM, KN = MN So, triangles are congruent because of Side, Side, Side (SSS) or angle LKN = angle LMN, KN = MN, LK = LM So, triangles are congruent because of Side, Angle, Side (SAS)

Go!

1	Yes Shapes A, B and F are congruent.
2	a = 1.5, b = 3.5
3	Two possible ways: 1) PR shared length, PQ = PS, QR = SR So, triangles are congruent because of Side, Side, Side (SSS) 2) angle PQR = angle PSR, PQ = PS, QR = SR So, triangles are congruent because of Side, Angle, Side (SAS)

Similar Shapes (p.144)

Set?

A	A and B
B	(i) 8 cm (ii) 3 cm
C	9 cm
D	(i) 4.8 cm (ii) 1.25 cm

Go!

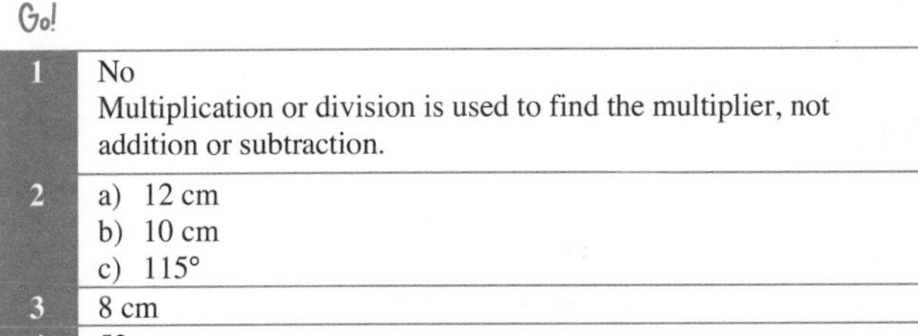

1	No Multiplication or division is used to find the multiplier, not addition or subtraction.
2	a) 12 cm b) 10 cm c) 115°
3	8 cm
4	52 m

Reflections (p.146)

Set?

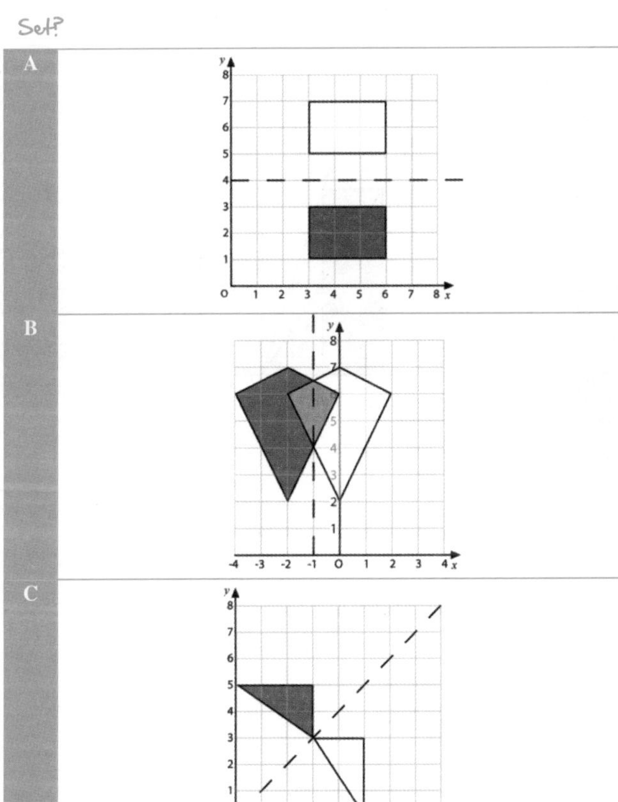

Go!

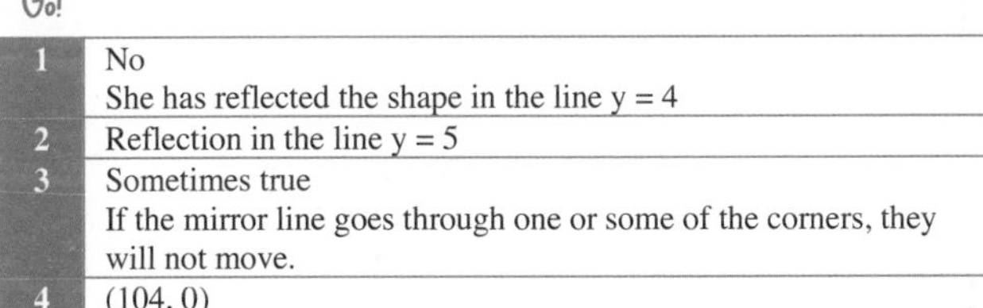

1	No She has reflected the shape in the line y = 4
2	Reflection in the line y = 5
3	Sometimes true If the mirror line goes through one or some of the corners, they will not move.
4	(104, 0)

Rotations (p.148)

Set?

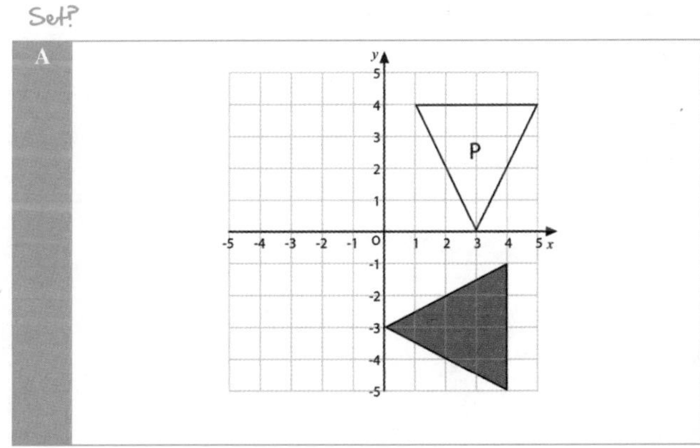

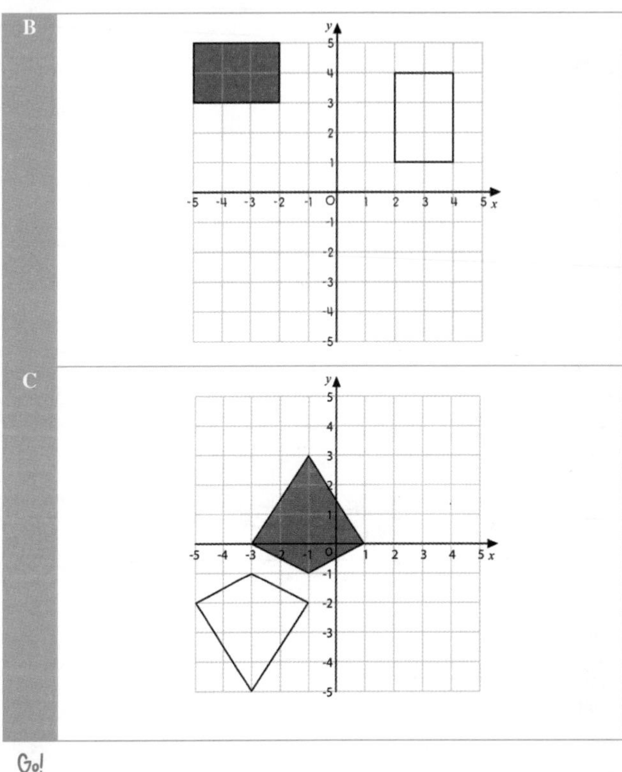

Go!

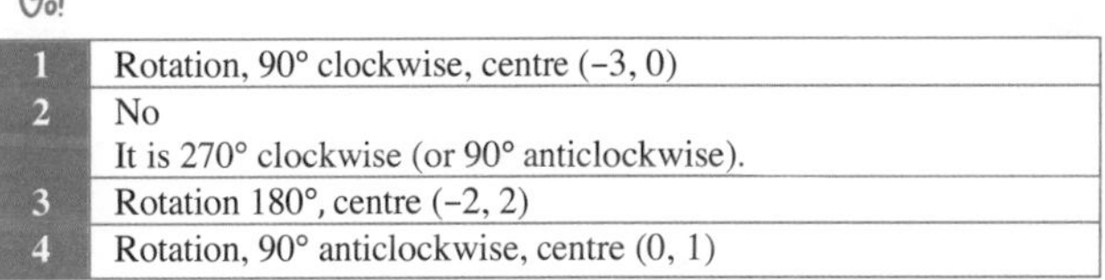

1	Rotation, 90° clockwise, centre (−3, 0)
2	No It is 270° clockwise (or 90° anticlockwise).
3	Rotation 180°, centre (−2, 2)
4	Rotation, 90° anticlockwise, centre (0, 1)

Translations (p.150)

Set?

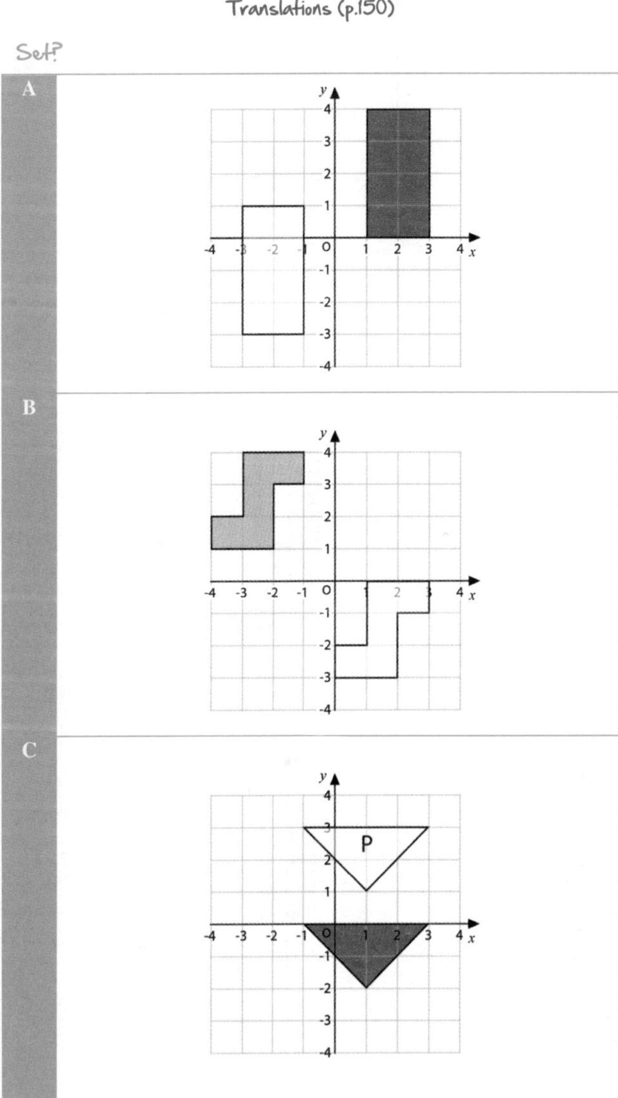

Go!

1

a) $\begin{pmatrix} 5 \\ 0 \end{pmatrix}$

b) $\begin{pmatrix} -2 \\ 3 \end{pmatrix}$

c) $\begin{pmatrix} -3 \\ -5 \end{pmatrix}$

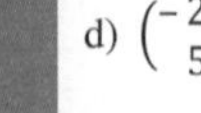

d) $\begin{pmatrix} -2 \\ 5 \end{pmatrix}$

2

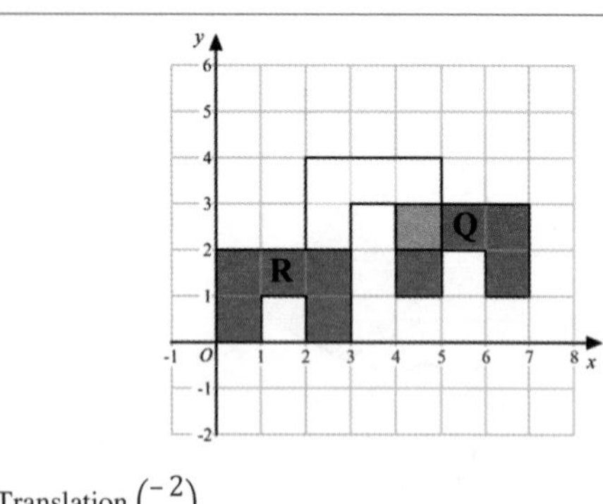

Translation $\begin{pmatrix} -2 \\ -2 \end{pmatrix}$

3 No

The correct answer is: translate P using the vector $\begin{pmatrix} -6 \\ -5 \end{pmatrix}$

4 (44, 8)

Enlargements (p.152)

Set?

A

B

C

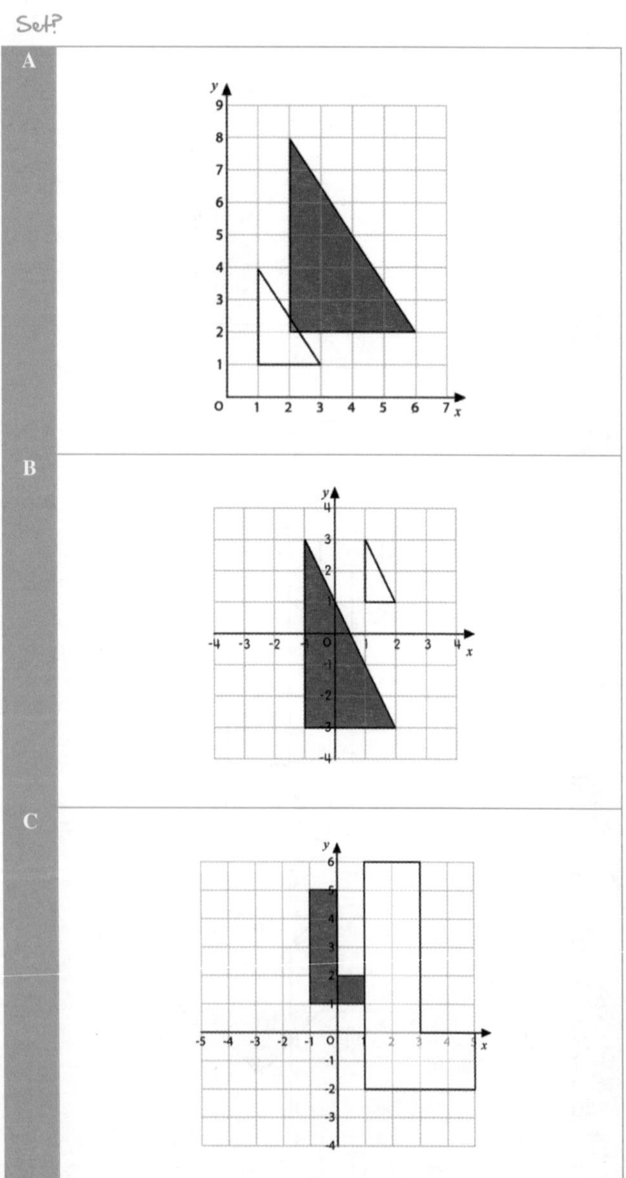

Go!

1 Enlargement, centre (0, 3), scale factor $\frac{1}{2}$

2

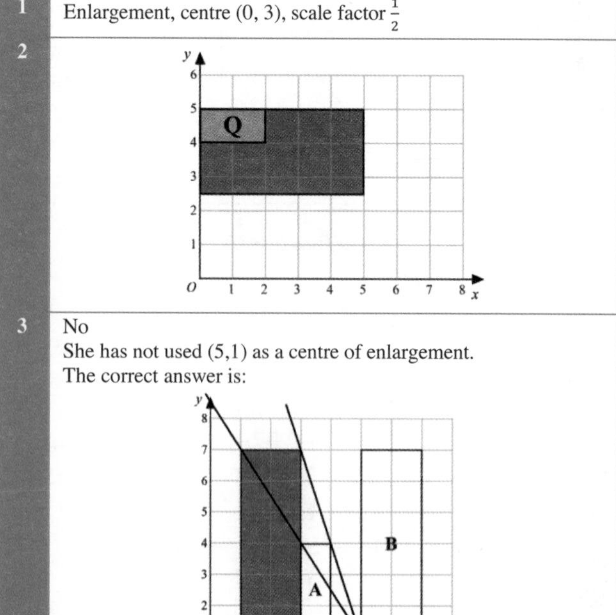

3 No

She has not used (5,1) as a centre of enlargement.

The correct answer is:

4 2.5

Combined Transformations (p.154)

Set?

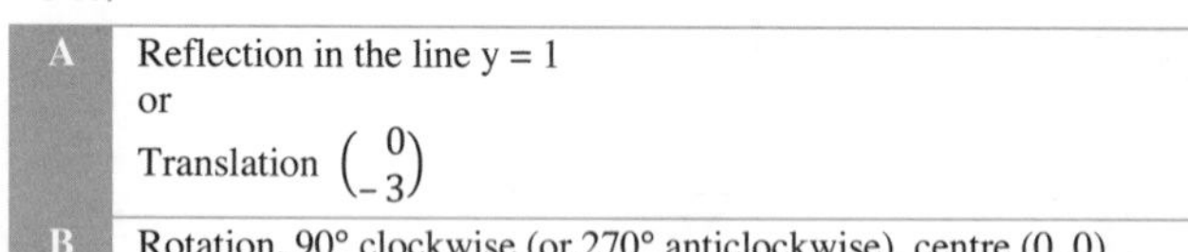

A Reflection in the line y = 1

or

Translation $\begin{pmatrix} 0 \\ -3 \end{pmatrix}$

B Rotation, 90° clockwise (or 270° anticlockwise), centre (0, 0)

Go!

1 $c = -3$

$d = -5$

2 No

She has described it using more than one transformation.

The correct answer is: Rotation of 180° with centre (0,0).

3 No

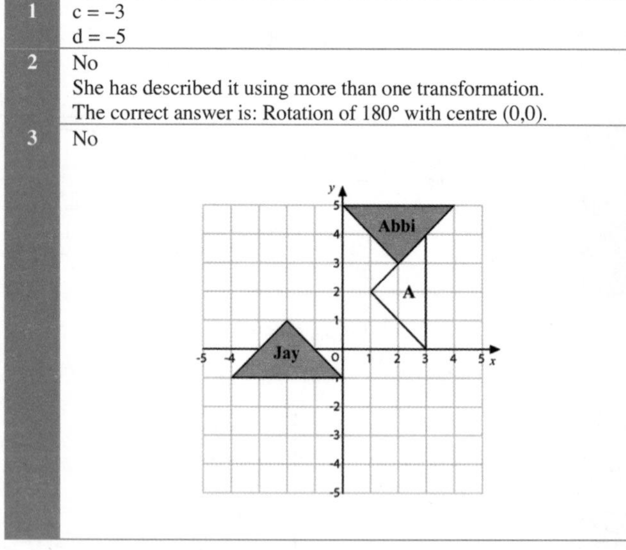

Vectors (p.156)

Set?

A

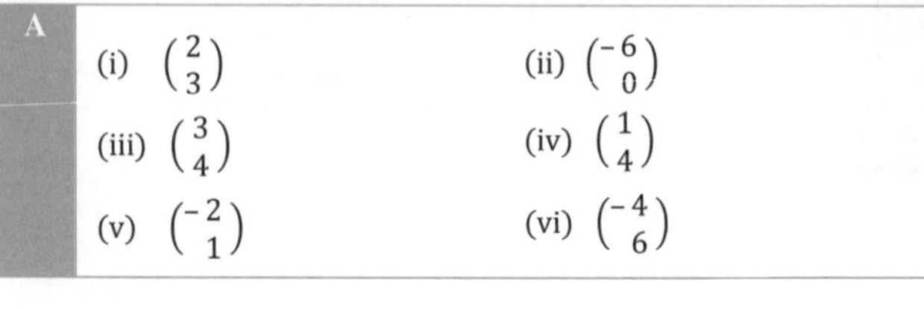

(i) $\begin{pmatrix} 2 \\ 3 \end{pmatrix}$	(ii) $\begin{pmatrix} -6 \\ 0 \end{pmatrix}$
(iii) $\begin{pmatrix} 3 \\ 4 \end{pmatrix}$	(iv) $\begin{pmatrix} 1 \\ 4 \end{pmatrix}$
(v) $\begin{pmatrix} -2 \\ 1 \end{pmatrix}$	(vi) $\begin{pmatrix} -4 \\ 6 \end{pmatrix}$

B	(i) $\underline{q}$ (ii) $3\underline{p}$ (iii) $\underline{q}+\underline{r}$ (iv) $2\underline{p}-\underline{r}$
C	Possible answers are: (i) $\underline{p} = -2\underline{b}$ (ii) $\underline{q} = -4\underline{a}$ (iii) $\underline{r} = 2\underline{a} + 2\underline{c}$

Go!

1	No She should not simplify the vector.
2	No The correct answer is $\begin{pmatrix} 6 \\ -1 \end{pmatrix}$
3	m = 2 n = 12
4	AP is two thirds of the length of AB . $\overrightarrow{AP} = \frac{2}{3}\underline{a}$

Probability (p.158)

Set?

A	D B A C (on a scale from 0 to 1)
B	(i) $\frac{3}{14}$ (iii) $\frac{1}{14}$ (ii) $\frac{2}{14}$ (iv) 0
C	$\frac{7}{30}$
D	0.96
E	(i) 0.6 (ii) 6

Go!

1 a)

Type	Art	RE	PE	Total
Male	13	12	18	43
Female	15	11	11	37
Total	28	23	29	80

b) $\frac{37}{80}$

c) $\frac{13}{43}$

2 a) P(1) → 0.2
P(4) → 0.1
b) C

3 a) Two possible solutions are:

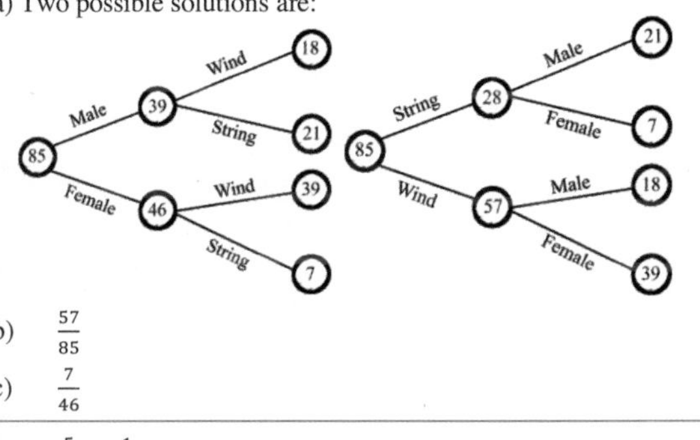

b) $\frac{57}{85}$

c) $\frac{7}{46}$

4 a) $\frac{5}{20}$ $(=\frac{1}{4})$
b) 40

Probability Tree Diagrams 1 (p.160)

Set?

A (i)

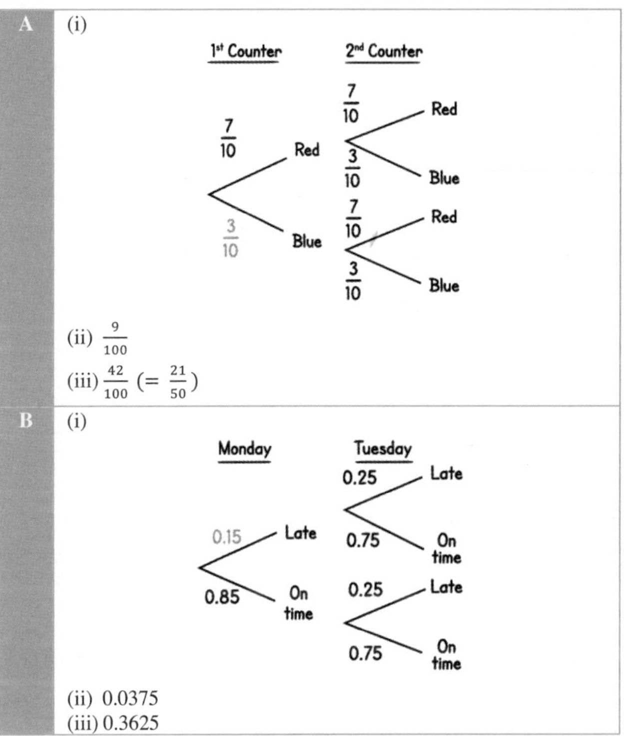

(ii) $\frac{9}{100}$

(iii) $\frac{42}{100}$ $(=\frac{21}{50})$

B (i) (see tree above)

(ii) 0.0375
(iii) 0.3625

Go!

1	No He should multiply the probabilities (correct answer: $\frac{2}{30} = \frac{1}{15}$)
2	a) 0.12 b) The events are independent.
3	a) C b) Josh ($0.65 \times 0.4 = 0.26$, Jake is 0.175)

Probability Tree Diagrams 2 (p.162)

Set?

A (i)

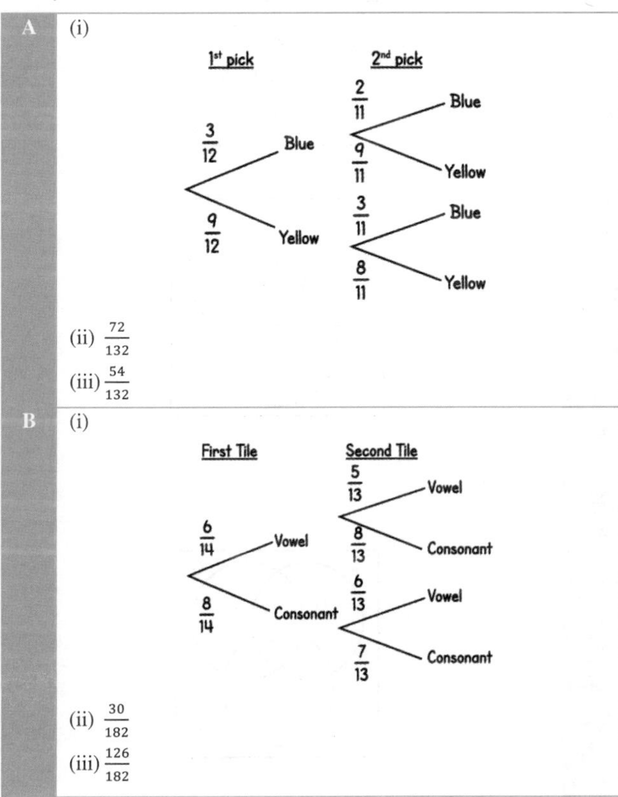

(ii) $\frac{72}{132}$

(iii) $\frac{54}{132}$

B (i) (see tree above)

(ii) $\frac{30}{182}$

(iii) $\frac{126}{182}$

Go!

1	a) $\frac{20}{90}$ b) $\frac{12}{90}$
2	a) 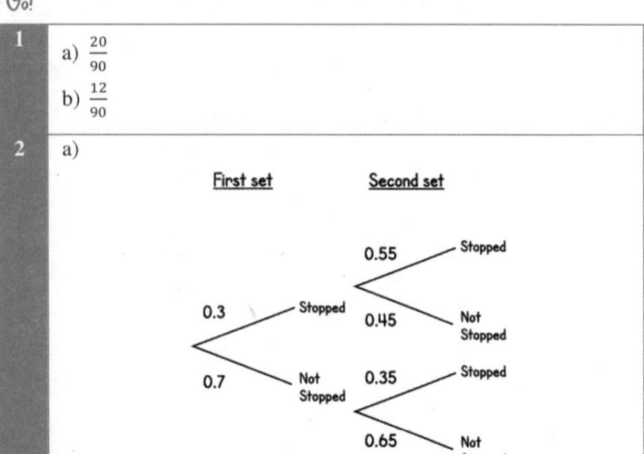 b) 0.165
3	a) The denominators of the fractions on the second branches are incorrect. They should be 9 not 8. b) $\frac{12}{90}$

Venn Diagrams (p.164)

Set?

A	(i) 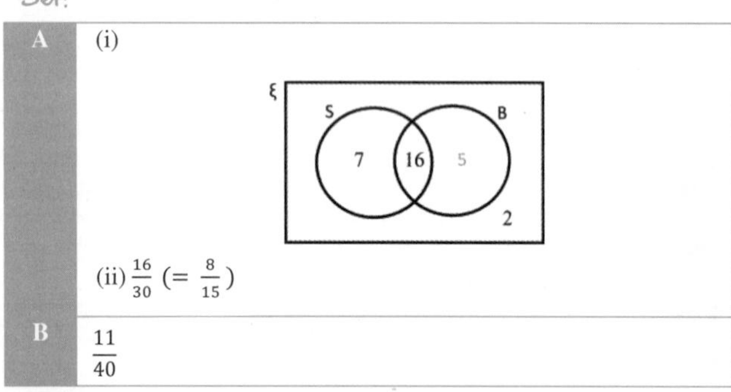 (ii) $\frac{16}{30}$ $(= \frac{8}{15})$
B	$\frac{11}{40}$

Go!

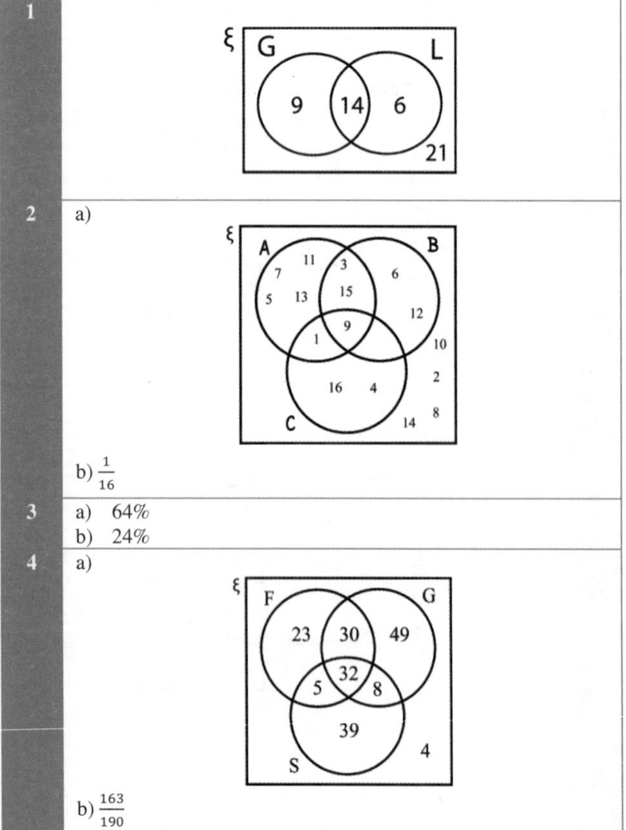

1	
2	a) b) $\frac{1}{16}$
3	a) 64% b) 24%
4	a) b) $\frac{163}{190}$

Simultaneous Equations 1 (p.166)

Set?

A	$x = 1,\ y = 3$
B	$a = 2,\ b = 5$
C	$m = -1,\ n = 4$
D	$a = 5,\ b = 2$
E	$x = 3,\ y = 2$
F	$b = 2,\ c = 4$
G	$x = -2,\ y = -1$

Go!

1	$x = 7,\ y = 6$
2	She has not multiplied all the terms of equation 1 by 5 The correct answer is $x = 0.25,\ y = 2$
3	a) $4x + 5y = 3.95$ or $4x + 5y = 395$ $3x + 8y = 4.45$ $3x + 8y = 445$ b) £0.35 (or 35p)
4	£138

Simultaneous Equations 2 (p.168)

Set?

A	$x = 9,\ y = 5$
B	$x = -6,\ y = 7$
C	$x = 2,\ y = 4$
D	$p = 2,\ q = -4$
E	$a = 1.5\ (= \frac{3}{2}),\ b = 5$
F	$x = 4,\ y = 2$
G	$x = 2,\ y = 4$

Go!

1	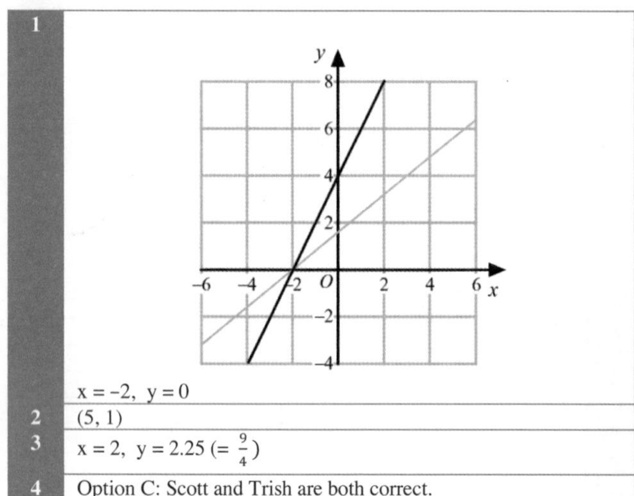 $x = -2,\ y = 0$
2	(5, 1)
3	$x = 2,\ y = 2.25\ (= \frac{9}{4})$
4	Option C: Scott and Trish are both correct.